ARITHMETICAL ALGEBRAIC GEOMETRY

Contributors

André Weil, The Institute for Advanced Study
Walter L. Baily, Jr., The University of Chicago
Tsuneo Tamagawa, Yale University
Bernard M. Dwork, Princeton University
David Mumford, Harvard University
Jean-Pierre Serre, Collège de France
John T. Tate, Harvard University
Shreeram S. Abhyankar, Purdue University
Heisuke Hironaka, Columbia University

Harper's Series in Modern Mathematics

I. N. Herstein and Gian-Carlo Rota,
Editors

Arithmetical Algebraic Geometry

Proceedings of a Conference
Held at Purdue University,
December 5–7, 1963

Organized by the
Division of Mathematical Sciences
Purdue University

Edited by O. F. G. Schilling
Professor of Mathematics,
Purdue University

Harper & Row, Publishers New York

Arithmetical Algebraic Geometry:
Proceedings of a Conference Held at Purdue University,
December 5–7, 1963

 For information address Harper & Row, Publishers, Incorporated, 49 East 33rd Street, New York, N. Y. 10016.

Library of Congress Catalog Card Number: 65-24467

Contents

Preface vii

On the Arithmetical Theory of the Classical Groups 1
ANDRÉ WEIL

On the Orbit Spaces of Arithmetic Groups 4
WALTER L. BAILY, JR.

On Discrete Subgroups of p-Adic Algebraic Groups 11
TSUNEO TAMAGAWA

Analytic Theory of the Zeta Function of Algebraic Varieties 18
BERNARD M. DWORK

Picard Groups of Moduli Problems 33
DAVID MUMFORD

Zeta and *L* Functions 82
JEAN-PIERRE SERRE

Algebraic Cycles and Poles of Zeta Functions 93
JOHN T. TATE

Resolution of Singularities of Arithmetical Surfaces 111
SHREERAM S. ABHYANKAR

On the Equivalence of Singularities, I 153
HEISUKE HIRONAKA

Preface

A Conference on Arithmetical Algebraic Geometry was held at Purdue University, Lafayette, Indiana on December 5–7, 1963. Invited speakers were André Weil, Walter L. Baily, Jr., Tsuneo Tamagawa, Bernard M. Dwork, David Mumford, Jean-Pierre Serre, John T. Tate, Shreeram S. Abhyankar, and Heisuke Hironaka. Abstracts or amplifications of their lectures are collected in this volume.

This conference was made possible through the material support given by Purdue's new School of Science and the constant encouragement of its Dean, Dr. Felix Haas. Thanks are due to Professors H. Flanders, W. Fuller, D. Hertzig, and E. Schenkman of the Division of Mathematical Sciences who were largely responsible for the detailed organization of the meetings.

Harper & Row and its consulting editors in mathematics, Professor I. N. Herstein of the University of Chicago and Gian-Carlo Rota of the Rockefeller University, agreed to publish these Proceedings at self-cost; special acknowledgment is made to them for this valuable service to the mathematical community.

OTTO F. G. SCHILLING

Lafayette, Indiana

On the Arithmetical Theory of the Classical Groups

André Weil

Since Jacobi, it has been known that we can use theta series in order to define modular forms. For instance, the function

$$\theta(z) = \sum_{n=-\infty}^{+\infty} \exp(\pi i z n^2)$$

satisfies the equation

$$\theta(-1/z) = (-iz)^{1/2}\theta(z) \qquad (*)$$

(a fact which was already known to Gauss, and which is an immediate consequence of Poisson's formula applied to the function $u \to \exp(\pi i z u^2)$. At the same time, it is obviously periodic of period 2. Its behavior under the group generated by the two substitutions $z \to -1/z$, $z \to z + 2$ is fully determined by these two facts, although it is not quite easy, because of the square root $(-iz)^{1/2}$, to express it by an explicit formula. This problem was solved by Hermite; deeper results were obtained by Dedekind in connection with Riemann's fragments on modular functions. There is no such difficulty, however, in expressing the behavior of $\theta(z)^4$ under the modular group; this was done by Jacobi, who deduced from it many important identities concerning this function. In particular, $\theta(z)^4$ must coincide with a certain modular form defined by a series of a different type (a so-called Eisenstein series), and this is equivalent to the determination of the number of solutions of $n = x^2 + y^2 + z^2 + t^2$ in integers x, y, z, t, for each integer n. This famous result has been generalized in many ways, particularly by Siegel. His work, and more specifically his 1952 paper on indefinite quadratic forms (*Math. Ann.*, **124**(1952), 17–54 and 364–387), has been the starting point of the investigation described here; a full account will be published in the *Acta Mathematica*.†

The first part has, roughly speaking, the same relationship to Poisson's formula (in an arbitrary locally compact abelian group) as the formula of Hermite, describing the behavior of $\theta(z)$ under the modular group, has to equation (*). For instance, in the case of the space $\mathbf{R}^n$, this leads to the definition of a unitary group of operators on $L^2(\mathbf{R}^n)$, isomorphic to the two-sheeted covering of the symplectic group in $2n$ variables, and such that the Fourier transform is an element of that group; a similar result holds for the n-dimensional vector space over any p-adic field. The two-sheeted covering in question can be defined by a factor set, expressed in terms of Gaussian sums, which turns out to be the same as appears in Hermite's formula. By applying the same method to the n-dimensional space over the adèle ring of an algebraic number field, we obtain as an incidental result a proof of the quadratic reciprocity law, which is not substantially different from Hecke's proof (or, in the case of the rational number field, from Kronecker's proof) but is liberated from the accidental features arising from the use of special functions.

The group of unitary operators obtained in this manner is called the "metaplectic group"; instead of the modular forms of the classical theory, it is found advantageous to consider functions of that group, invariant with respect to "natural" discrete subgroups. Within this

† This work appeared since: Sur certains groupes d'opérateurs unitaires, *Acta Math.* **111**(1964), 143–211. Sur la formule de Siegel dans la théorie des groupes classiques, *Acta Math.* **113**(1965), 1–87.

framework, one can then generalize the two modes of definition of modular forms which occur in the classical theory, namely, the theta series and the Eisenstein series. The recent work of Borel, Harishchandra, and Godement makes it possible to find out when those series converge. Because of the invariance properties of the functions defined in this manner, one may, in comparing them with each other, confine oneself to a fundamental domain, as given by the work of the same authors; one obtains a very wide generalization of the fact that the theta series defined by a quadratic form, while not necessarily equal to the corresponding Eisenstein series, is always at any rate asymptotically equal to it in a suitable sense. Finally, integration over the fundamental domain (corresponding to the summation over all the classes in a genus, in Siegel's theory of positive quadratic forms) always gives equality with an Eisenstein series, whenever the conditions for convergence are satisfied.

Just as in the case of Jacobi's original result, the formula obtained in this manner has arithmetical consequences; in particular, it gives the most complete results presently known concerning the so-called Tamagawa numbers of the classical groups or, what amounts to the same, the volumes of their fundamental domains. More precisely, it shows that within each class of "classical groups" (determined by a given division algebra with involution over the rational number field) all groups have the same Tamagawa number. Thus whenever there is a "canonical isomorphism" which can be used to determine the Tamagawa number of one particular group within a given class, the problem is solved; this happens to be so for all the classes except the "unitary" groups belonging to Hermitian forms over a non-commutative division algebra with an involution of the second kind.

On the Orbit Spaces of Arithmetic Groups

Walter L. Baily, Jr.

In an earlier presentation [4] we have discussed the relationship between the problem of moduli for certain algebraic-geometrical objects and the theory of automorphic functions for certain arithmetically defined discontinuous groups acting on bounded symmetric domains. At that time we explained the desirability of being able to construct compactifications of the orbit spaces of such groups. Our purpose now is to discuss a little more general situation and to indicate at the same time some results of A. Borel and the present author which will be discussed more fully elsewhere [5].

The simplest problem of this nature arises in the case of the (integral) unimodular group $SL(2, \mathbf{Z})$ operating by fractional linear trans-

SUPPORT FOR THIS WORK WAS PROVIDED IN PART BY NATIONAL SCIENCE FOUNDATION GRANT GP-91.

formations on the upper half $\mathfrak{H} = \{\text{Im } z > 0\}$ of the plane of one complex variable. In this case, by a well-known procedure, we may compactify the orbit space $\mathfrak{B} = \mathfrak{H}/SL(2, \mathbf{Z})$ by adjoining to $\mathfrak{H}$ the point at infinity (on the Riemann sphere) and all rational points of the real axis, supplying the union $\mathfrak{H}^*$ of $\mathfrak{H}$ and of all these points with a suitable topology in which all elements of $SL(2, \mathbf{Q})$ act continuously; we can then take the compactification of $\mathfrak{B}$ to be $\mathfrak{H}^*/SL(2, \mathbf{Z})$, which we denote more briefly with $\mathfrak{B}^*$. $\mathfrak{B}$ has a natural complex structure (it may be identified with the complex plane), and $\mathfrak{B}^*$ may be supplied with a complex structure compatible with that on $\mathfrak{B}$ "by introducing a suitable uniformizing parameter at infinity" in the well-known manner. In the more general situations discussed elsewhere in the literature [6, 11, 12, 15], the rational points of the real axis plus the point at infinity are replaced by the so-called rational boundary components.

The first generalization of the above compactification procedure to cases of higher dimension (to our knowledge) was given by Satake [14], who considered the orbit space of the group $Sp(n, \mathbf{Z})$ of $2n \times 2n$ symplectic integral matrices operating on the space $\mathfrak{H}_n$ of $n \times n$ symmetric complex matrices $Z = X + iY$ such that Y is positive definite. The compactification of $\mathfrak{B}_n = \mathfrak{H}_n/Sp(n, \mathbf{Z})$ was taken as the union $\mathfrak{B}_n^* = \mathfrak{B}_n \cup \mathfrak{B}_{n-1} \cup \ldots \cup \mathfrak{B}_0$ supplied with a certain topology in which $\mathfrak{B}_n^*$ becomes a compact Hausdorff space. The topology is described by using certain features of Minkowski's reduction theory. However, being given a suitable topology on $\mathfrak{B}_n^*$ leaves unanswered the question of whether $\mathfrak{B}_n^*$ carries a natural complex analytic structure compatible with the complex structures on $\mathfrak{B}_n, \mathfrak{B}_{n-1}, \ldots$. This question was answered in the affirmative by us [2], using a theorem of Remmert and Stein [13] on the removable singularities of complex analytic sets. Roughly speaking, if we know the existence of a ringed structure on $\mathfrak{B}_n^*$ compatible with the analytic structure on $\mathfrak{B}_n$, whose functions locally separate "most" pairs of points and whose stalk at each point is integrally closed, then using some local relative connectedness property of $\mathfrak{B}_n^*$ and, most importantly, the theorem of Remmert and Stein, we can show that with this ringed structure $\mathfrak{B}_n^*$ is a normal analytic space. At the same time, and much more easily, using existence theorems on automorphic forms with respect to $Sp(n, \mathbf{Z})$, we were able to prove that $\mathfrak{B}_n^*$ is, in fact, imbeddable as a projective algebraic variety in some complex projective space. Subsequently, these results were generalized in the 1957–1958 seminar of H. Cartan, where the corresponding result was obtained for the orbit space of any subgroup of $Sp(n, \mathbf{R})$ commensurable with $Sp(n, \mathbf{Z})$ and, furthermore, where Cartan [8] succeeded in removing a superfluous hypothesis in our prolongation theorem proved in [2] thereby obtaining a more easily applied prolongation criterion.

After these developments, the above results were extended to include orbit spaces of groups commensurable with the Hilbert-Siegel modular group [3], and in a note [11] and subsequently appearing book [12] Pyateckii-Shapiro made an attack on a rather broad class of related compactification problems. Moreover, Satake [14] has obtained results of a rather general nature concerning the compactifications of the orbit spaces of arithmetic groups acting on symmetric spaces (which may or may not be bounded domains). In the work of Satake, one begins by considering some compactification $\bar{\mathfrak{S}}$ of the symmetric space $\mathfrak{S}$ of a semi-simple real Lie group $G_{\mathbf{R}}$, defined by means of some representation ρ. One assumes that G (the complexification of $G_{\mathbf{R}}$) is a certain kind of algebraic group defined over $\mathbf{Q}$ and that the representation ρ satisfies a certain condition of rationality [condition (Q)]; one then forms the union $\mathfrak{S}^*$ of $\mathfrak{S}$ and of certain boundary components of $\mathfrak{S}$ in $\bar{\mathfrak{S}}$ called "rational boundary components"† and supplies $\mathfrak{S}^*$ with a certain topology in which all elements of $G_{\mathbf{Q}}$ operate continuously, such that $\mathfrak{V}^* = \mathfrak{S}^*/G_{\mathbf{Z}}$ is a compact Hausdorff space. $\mathfrak{V}^*$ contains $\mathfrak{V} = \mathfrak{S}/G_{\mathbf{Z}}$ in a natural way, and $\mathfrak{V}^*$ is called the Satake compactification of $\mathfrak{V}$. In [12], the emphasis is on a different aspect of the problem: one considers only the case for which $\mathfrak{S}$ is a bounded symmetric domain; one takes the natural compactification $\bar{\mathfrak{S}}$ of $\mathfrak{S}$, and then under the *assumption* that a procedure very similar to that just outlined above yields a compact Hausdorff space containing $\mathfrak{V}$, one seeks to prove that $\mathfrak{V}^*$ is, with a certain natural ringed structure, a complex analytic space realizable as a complex projec-

† As for the meaning of "rational boundary component," there are several definitions to be found in the cited references. The definition formulated in [12] is stated in terms of certain properties which must be satisfied by some subgroups of the stabilizer of the boundary component; the definition given in [15] for a rational boundary component requires its orbit under $G_{\mathbf{Q}}$ to meet the closure of a fundamental open set; while the definition given in [5] requires the normalizer of the boundary component to be defined over $\mathbf{Q}$.

tive variety. In fact, in [12], this is carried out in detail only for groups commensurable with $Sp(n, \mathbf{Z})$. Of course, it is easy to see that in the above considerations $G_{\mathbf{Z}}$ may be replaced by any subgroup Γ of $G^0_{\mathbf{R}}$ commensurable with $G_{\mathbf{Z}}$.

In order to present and explain some results related to this compactification procedure, we let G be a semisimple, linear, algebraic group defined over $\mathbf{Q}$. Let $\mathfrak{S}$ be a symmetric space such that the component of the identity in $G_{\mathbf{R}}$ is isogenous to the component of the identity in the group of all isometries of $\mathfrak{S}$. We assume that $\mathfrak{S}$ is Hermitian. $\mathfrak{S}$ will then be the same if we replace G by its component of the identity G^0, and if we then replace G by G/C, where C is the finite center of G. Moreover, if Γ is any subgroup of $G_{\mathbf{R}}$ commensurable with $G_{\mathbf{Z}}$, its image in G/C will be a subgroup of $(G/C)_{\mathbf{R}}$—or actually of $(G/C)_{\mathbf{Q}}$, by the results of [6; Remarque, p. 24] and of [7; §6.11]—commensurable with $(G/C)_{\mathbf{Z}}$ (q.v., infra). Hence we may assume to begin with that G is connected, centerless, and therefore the direct product of its absolutely irreducible factors. We say that G is $\mathbf{Q}$-simple if it has no proper normal divisors defined over $\mathbf{Q}$. If G is the direct product of its absolutely simple factors, as we have assumed, then the product of the set of conjugates over $\mathbf{Q}$ of one of these factors is defined over $\mathbf{Q}$ and is $\mathbf{Q}$-simple. Hence G is the direct product of $\mathbf{Q}$-simple factors, $G = G_1 \times \cdots \times G_r$, and if $\mathfrak{S}_i$ is a Hermitian symmetric space associated to $G_{i\mathbf{R}}$ as above, $\mathfrak{S} = \mathfrak{S}_1 \times \cdots \times \mathfrak{S}_r$, and $G_{\mathbf{Z}}$ is commensurable with $G_{1\mathbf{Z}} \times \cdots \times G_{r\mathbf{Z}}$. We want to prove that $\mathfrak{S}/(G_{\mathbf{Z}} \cap G^0_{\mathbf{R}})$ has a compactification (if it is not already compact) which may be realized as a projective algebraic variety. From what we have just observed, it is sufficient to consider the case where G is $\mathbf{Q}$-simple. There are three subcases to consider: (1) all simple factors of $G_{\mathbf{R}}$ are compact; (2) all simple factors of $G_{\mathbf{R}}$ are noncompact; and (3) some simple factors of $G_{\mathbf{R}}$ are compact and some are noncompact. Case (1) is trivial, since here $\mathfrak{S}$ is already a projective variety, and $G_{\mathbf{Z}}$ is obviously finite (we may even assume, though it is not necessary, that $G_{\mathbf{Z}}$ consists of projective transformations; see also [1]). The problem in case (2) has already been given an affirmative answer in results obtained by A. Borel and myself. These results have been explained in [5].

We now consider case (3). First, it follows that $\mathfrak{S} = \mathfrak{D} \times \mathfrak{V}$, where $\mathfrak{D}$ is a bounded domain and $\mathfrak{V}$ is a projective variety. Here $\mathfrak{D} = K_1\backslash G_{1\mathbf{R}}$ and $\mathfrak{V} = K_2\backslash G_{2\mathbf{R}}$, where $G_{1\mathbf{R}}$ is the product of the noncompact simple factors of $(G_{\mathbf{R}})^0$, and $G_{2\mathbf{R}}$ is the product of the compact ones. Let Γ be a group of transformations of $\mathfrak{S}$ commensurable with $G_{\mathbf{Z}}$. It follows from [7, §12.4] that $\mathfrak{W} = \mathfrak{S}/\Gamma$ is already compact, so that it remains only to find a projective imbedding for $\mathfrak{W}$. $\mathfrak{W}$ is a complex analytic V-manifold. We shall construct a positive complex line bundle over $\mathfrak{W}$, and by the result of [1, p. 427] this will complete our proof. (The observation that a proof of our result can be obtained using the criterion of Kodaira [10] is due to A. Borel, and the present proof is based on a straightforward generalization of Kodaira's criterion, to be found in our paper [1]. This fact may also be proved using Poincaré series on $\mathfrak{D}$ with values in the module of homogeneous polynomials of some degree in the coordinates of the ambient projective space containing $\mathfrak{V}$.)

In the first place, we begin by observing that we may assume the group $G_{2\mathbf{R}}$ to act by projective linear transformations on $\mathfrak{V}$; this is easily seen from the usual construction of a projective imbedding for $\mathfrak{V} = K_2\backslash G_{2\mathbf{R}}$. If $x = (z, \zeta) \in \mathfrak{S}$, let $\Gamma_x = \{\gamma \in \Gamma \mid x\gamma = x\}$ (right action by $G_{\mathbf{R}}$), let $m_x = \operatorname{ord}\Gamma_x$, and put $m_0 = \underset{x \in \mathfrak{S}}{\text{l.c.m.}}\, m_x$; m_0 is finite (and $\neq 0$) since $\mathfrak{W}$ is compact. Let m be an even integer divisible by m_0. Denote by pr_i the projection homomorphism of $G_{1\mathbf{R}} \times G_{2\mathbf{R}}$ onto $G_{i\mathbf{R}}$, $i = 1, 2$; put $\Gamma_i = pr_i\Gamma$, $\Gamma_{xi} = pr_i\Gamma_x$, $i = 1, 2$. Then there exists a homogeneous polynomial P of degree m invariant under Γ_{x2} such that $P(\zeta) \neq 0$. Moreover, from the theory of Poincaré series (with respect to a *finite* group), we may easily prove that there exists a holomorphic function g in a neighborhood of z on $\mathfrak{D}$ such that $g(z'\gamma_1)j_{\gamma_1}(z')^m = g(z')$ for all z' in a neighborhood of z and for all $\gamma_1 \in \Gamma_{x1}$, and such that $g(z) \neq 0$. Let N be a neighborhood of x such that Pg does not vanish anywhere on N.† Let $\pi : \mathfrak{S} \to \mathfrak{W} = \mathfrak{S}/\Gamma$ be the canonical mapping. We choose a finite number of points $x_l \in \mathfrak{S}$ and neighborhoods N_l as above with g_l and P_l constructed correspondingly such that $\{\pi(N_l)\}$ is a covering of $\mathfrak{W}$. Let $\bar{N}_l = \pi(N_l)$. When $\bar{N}_l \cap \bar{N}_k \neq \emptyset$, we define a nonzero holomorphic function f_{lk} on $\bar{N}_l \cap \bar{N}_k$ by: if $(z, \zeta) \in N_l$, $(z', \zeta') \in N_k$ are such that $\pi(z, \zeta) = \pi(z', \zeta')$, then there exists $\gamma = (\gamma_1, \gamma_2) \in \Gamma$ such that $(z, \zeta)\gamma = (z', \zeta')$, and we define

$$f_{lk}(\pi(z, \zeta)) = \frac{P_l(\zeta) \cdot g_k(z')}{P_k(\zeta') \cdot g_l(z)} j_{\gamma_1}(z)^m.$$

† We assume N chosen such that $N\Gamma_x = N$ and such that $\{\gamma \in \Gamma \mid N\gamma \cap N \neq \phi\} = \Gamma_x$.

We first observe that if $(z^*, \zeta^*) \in N_l$, $(z^{*\prime}, \zeta^{*\prime}) \in N_k$ are such that $\pi(z^*, \zeta^*) = \pi(z, \zeta) = \pi(z^{*\prime}, \zeta^{*\prime})$, and if $(z^*, \zeta^*)\gamma^* = (z^{*\prime}, \zeta^{*\prime})$, then $\gamma^* = \gamma_\alpha \gamma \gamma_\delta$, where $\gamma_\alpha \in \Gamma_{x_l}$ and $\gamma_\delta \in \Gamma_{x_k}$. Straightforward calculation shows that the definition of f_{lk} is unambiguous. But then it is trivial to verify the condition $f_{lk} f_{k\lambda} = f_{l\lambda}$, and so these functions define a complex line bundle $\mathfrak{B}$ over $\mathfrak{W}$. Now we let K be the Bergman kernel function on $\mathfrak{D}$, we let H be a positive definite Hermitian form (in the projective coordinates ζ) invariant under the compact group $G_{2\mathrm{R}}$, and define

$$\omega = \frac{m}{2\pi i} \partial \bar{\partial} \log(H(\zeta, \zeta) \cdot K(z))$$

on $\mathfrak{W}$; by [1] it is easy to see that ω is a positive definite form in the characteristic class of $\mathfrak{B}$, so that $\mathfrak{B}$ is the desired positive complex line bundle over $\mathfrak{W}$, and our proof is complete.

Taking the above into account, together with the substantially less trivial results of [5], we have the following:

Theorem. Let G be a semisimple, linear algebraic group defined over Q. Assume that a Riemannian symmetric space $\mathfrak{S}$ associated to the identity component of G_{R} is Hermitian symmetric. Write $\mathfrak{S} = K\backslash(G_{\mathrm{R}})^0$, for some compact group K. Let Γ be any subgroup of G^0_{R} commensurable with G_{Z} (defined with respect to some lattice). Then the double coset space $K\backslash G^0_{\mathrm{R}}/\Gamma$ has a natural compactification (if not already compact) which may be realized as a complex projective variety on which $K\backslash G^0_{\mathrm{R}}/\Gamma$ is a Zariski-open set.

REFERENCES

1. Baily, W. L., Jr., On the imbedding of V-manifolds in projective space, *Amer. Jour. Math.*, **79**(1957), 403–430.
2. ———, Satake's compactification of V_n, *Amer. Jour. Math.*, **80**(1958), 348–364.
3. ———, On the Hilbert-Siegel modular space, *Amer. Jour. Math.*, **81**(1959), 846–874.
4. ———, On the theory of automorphic functions and the problem of moduli, *Bull. A.M.S.*, **69**(1963), 727–732.
5. ———, and A. Borel, On the compactification of arithmetically defined

quotients of bounded symmetric domains, *Bull. A.M.S.*, **70**(1964), 588–593.

6. Borel, A., Ensembles fondamentaux pour les groupes arithmétiques, *Colloque sur la théorie des groupes algébriques*, *CBRM*, Bruxelles, (1962), 23–40.
7. ———, and Harish-Chandra, Arithmetic subgroups of algebraic groups, *Annals Math.*, **75**(1962), 485–535.
8. Cartan, H., Prolongement des espaces analytiques normaux, *Math. Annalen*, **136**(1958), 97–110.
9. Seminar of H. Cartan, 1957–1958, Mimeographed notes.
10. Kodaira, K., On Kähler varieties of restricted type (An intrinsic characterization of algebraic varieties), *Annals Math.*, **60**(1954), 28–48.
11. Pyateckii-Shapiro, I. I., Discrete subgroups of the group of analytic automorphisms of a polycylinder and automorphic forms (Russian), *Doklady Akademii Nauk USSR*, **124**(1959), 760–763.
12. ———, The geometry of the classical domains and the theory of automorphic functions (Russian), Gosizdat, Moscow (1961).
13. Remmert, R., and K. Stein, Ueber die wesentlichen Singularitäten analytischer Mengen, *Math. Annalen*, **126**(1953), 263–306.
14. Satake, I., On the compactification of the Siegel space, *Jour. Ind. Math. Soc.*, **XX**(1956), 259–281.
15. ———, On compactifications of the quotient spaces for arithmetically defined discontinuous groups, *Annals Math.*, **72**(1960), 555–580.

On Discrete Subgroups of p-Adic Algebraic Groups

Tsuneo Tamagawa

Throughout this article p denotes a fixed prime number, and Q_p denotes the field of all p-adic numbers. A p-adic algebraic group G is the group of all Q_p-rational points on an algebraic group defined over Q_p. Since Q_p is a locally compact field, G is a locally compact group with respect to its natural topology. If k is an extension of finite degree over Q_p and G is a k-algebraic group, then the operation Rk/Q_p "restriction of the ground field k to Q_p" (cf. A. Weil [3], p. 4–10) maps G isomorphically on a p-adic algebraic group. For this reason, we will consider only Q_p-algebraic groups.

I MUST APOLOGIZE FOR PRESENTING MATERIAL WHICH IS DIFFERENT FROM THE LECTURE I PRESENTED AT THE TIME OF THE SYMPOSIUM. THE REASON IS THAT I CAME TO KNOW T. ONO'S RESULT ON RELATIVE T-NUMBERS, A FAR MORE GENERAL AND BETTER RESULT THAN MINE; SO I FEEL IT ALMOST IMPOSSIBLE TO PRESENT MY SPECIAL RESULTS ON THIS MATTER.

It is easy to see that the additive group of Q_p has no discrete subgroup other than $\{0\}$, but the multiplicative group Q_p^* of nonzero elements has nontrivial discrete subgroups whose quotient groups are compact. In §1 of this chapter we will prove that if there exists a discrete subgroup Γ of a p-adic algebraic group G such that G/Γ is compact, then G is reductive. In §2 we will discuss general properties of discrete subgroups of p-adic algebraic groups. In §3 we will show the existence of discrete subgroups with compact factor spaces for some semisimple algebraic groups.

§1

Let Z_p denote the integral domain of all p-adic integers and $GL(n, Z_p)$ denote the group of all $n \otimes n$ p-adic unimodular matrices. It is well known that $GL(n, Z_p)$ is an open compact subgroup of $GL(n, Q_p)$, and that the order of a finite subgroup of $GL(n, Q_p)$ is bounded by a limitation depending only on n and p. Let ρ be a rational faithful representation of a p-adic algebraic group G into $GL(n, Q_p)$ with a suitable n, then $\rho(G)$ is an algebraic subgroup of $GL(n, Q_p)$ and $\rho^{-1}(GL(n, Z_p)) = U$ is an open compact subgroup of G. The orders of finite subgroups of G are bounded by the same rule applied to finite subgroups of $GL(n, Q_p)$.

Theorem 1. Let G be a p-adic algebraic group. If Γ is a discrete subgroup of G such that G/Γ is of finite volume, G/Γ is compact.

Remark. A homogeneous space G/Γ is said to be of finite volume if there exists a measurable set F such that $F\Gamma = G$ and $\mu(F) < \infty$, where μ is a right invariant Haar measure on G.

Proof. Since G/Γ is of finite volume, a right invariant Haar measure μ on G is also left invariant (cf. C. L. Siegel [2], p. 680, Lemma 5). Let U be an open compact subgroup of G and normalize μ so that the total volume of U is equal to 1. Then we have a unique invariant measure $\bar{\mu}$ on G/Γ such that

$$\int_G f(g)\, d\mu(g) = \int_{G/\Gamma} \Big(\sum_{\xi \in \Gamma} f(g\xi)\Big)\, d\bar{\mu}(\bar{\xi}) \tag{1}$$

for any continuous function f on G with a compact support. Let $Ug\Gamma$ be a double coset of U and Γ. We have

$$\bar{\mu}(Ug\Gamma/\Gamma) = \bar{\mu}\,(g^{-1}Ug \cdot \Gamma/\Gamma) = 1/(g^{-1}Ug \cap \Gamma : 1)$$

where $g^{-1}Ug \cap \Gamma$ is a finite group whose order is bounded. Hence there exists a positive number m such that $\bar{\mu}(Ug\Gamma/\Gamma) > m$ for an arbitrary double coset $Ug\Gamma$. Now $\bar{\mu}(G/\Gamma)$ is finite, so there exist almost $[m^{-1}\bar{\mu}(G/\Gamma)]$ double cosets of U and Γ, hence G/Γ is compact.

Theorem 2. If there exists a discrete subgroup Γ of a p-adic algebraic group G such that G/Γ is compact, then there exists a maximally compact subgroup of G.

Proof. Let Ω be the set of all open compact subgroups of G. For $U \subset \Omega$, $U \cap \Gamma$ is finite, hence $(U \cap \Gamma : 1)$ is bounded. Consequently, there exists an open compact subgroup U_0 such that $U \cap \Gamma = U_0 \cap \Gamma$ for all $U \supset U_0$. Now we have

$$\bar{\mu}(U\Gamma/\Gamma) = \bar{\mu}(U)/(U \cap \Gamma : 1)$$

if the invariant measures μ on G and $\bar{\mu}$ on G/Γ are related by the formula (1); therefore, we have $\bar{\mu}(U\Gamma/\Gamma) = (U : U_0)\bar{\mu}(U_0\Gamma/\Gamma)$ for $U \supset U_0$. Since $\bar{\mu}(G/\Gamma)$ is finite, $(U : U_0)$ is bounded, so there exists a $U_1 \in \Omega$ which gives the maximal $(U_1 : U_0)$. Obviously, U_1 is a maximally compact subgroup of G.

It is known that if a p-adic algebraic group G has a maximally compact subgroup, G is reductive (cf. I. Satake [1], p. 11, Prop. 12). Hence we have the following theorem.

Theorem 3. If G is a p-adic algebraic group with a discrete subgroup such that G/Γ is compact, G is reductive.

§2

First we offer this lemma and proof.

Lemma 1. Let G be a locally compact group and Γ a discrete subgroup of G such that G/Γ is compact. Let $S = \{\xi_1, \ldots, \xi_l\}$ be a finite subset of Γ and $Z(\xi_1, \ldots, \xi_l)$ denote the group of all $g \in G$ with $g\xi_i g^{-1} = \xi_i (i = 1, \ldots, l)$. Then $Z(\xi_1, \ldots, \xi_l)$ is a closed subgroup of G and $Z(\xi_1, \ldots, \xi_l)/Z(\xi_1, \ldots, \xi_l) \cap \Gamma$ is compact.

Proof. Let φ be a mapping of G into the product $G \otimes \cdots \otimes G$ of l copies of G defined by $\varphi(y) = (g\xi_1 g^{-1}, \ldots, g\xi_l \xi^{-1})$. Now $\varphi(\Gamma)$ is a subset of $\Gamma \otimes \cdots \otimes \Gamma$, so is closed. Since φ is continuous,

$\varphi^{-1}(\xi_1, \ldots, \xi_l) = Z(\xi_1, \ldots, \xi_l)$ is closed. We have $\varphi^{-1}(\varphi(\Gamma)) = \Gamma Z(\xi_1, \ldots, \xi_l)$, so $\Gamma Z(\xi_1, \ldots, \xi_l)$ is closed in G. Hence $Z(\xi, \ldots, \xi_l)/Z(\xi, \ldots, \xi_l) \cap \Gamma$ is identified with a closed subset of G/Γ, hence is compact.

Corollary. Let G be a p-adic algebraic group and Γ a discrete subgroup of G such that G/Γ is compact. For an arbitrary subset S of Γ, let $Z(S)$ denote the centralizer of S. Then $Z(S)/Z(S) \cap \Gamma$ is compact.

Proof. For a finite subset S' of S, $Z(S')$ is an algebraic subgroup of G, and if S'' is a finite subset of S such that $S' \subset S''$, then $Z(S'')$ is contained in $Z(S')$. Hence there exists a finite subset S_0 of S such that $Z(S_0) \subset Z(S')$ for all finite subsets S' of S. Obviously, we have $Z(S_0) = Z(S)$, and $Z(S_0)/Z(S_0) \cap \Gamma$ is compact.

The following theorem is a simple application of the lemma.

Theorem 4. If Γ is a discrete subgroup of a p-adic algebraic group G such that G/Γ is compact, every element of Γ is semisimple.

Proof. If $\xi \in G$ is not semisimple, $Z(\xi)$ contains the unipotent factor ξ_N in its center, hence $Z(\xi)$ is not reductive. Now for every $\xi \in \Gamma$, $Z(\xi)/Z(\xi) \cap \Gamma$ is compact, so from Theorem 3, $Z(\xi)$ is reductive. Hence ξ is semisimple.

Let G be a connected reductive p-adic algebraic group and A a maximal trivial torus contained in G. Let $\mathfrak{g}$ be the Lie algebra of G and $\mathfrak{a}$ the subalgebra of $\mathfrak{g}$ corresponding to A. Then we have a decomposition

$$\mathfrak{g} = \mathfrak{g}_0 + \sum_{\alpha>0} \mathfrak{g}_\alpha + \sum_{\alpha<0} \mathfrak{g}_\alpha$$

where $\mathfrak{g}_0$ is the centralizer of $\mathfrak{a}$ and the $\mathfrak{g}_\alpha$'s are the root spaces relative to $\mathfrak{a}$ with a suitable ordering. Put $\mathfrak{n}^+ = \Sigma_{\alpha>0} \mathfrak{g}_\alpha$ and $\mathfrak{n}^- = \Sigma_{\alpha<0} \mathfrak{g}_\alpha$. The subalgebra of $\mathfrak{g}$ generated by $\mathfrak{a}$, $\mathfrak{n}^+$, and $\mathfrak{n}^-$ is an ideal $\mathfrak{g}^*$ of $\mathfrak{g}$ which is uniquely determined. Let N^+ and N^- be unipotent subgroups of G corresponding to $\mathfrak{n}^+$ and $\mathfrak{n}^-$, respectively. The minimal algebraic subgroup G^* of G containing A, N^+ and N^- is the subgroup of G corresponding to $\mathfrak{g}^*$, so is a normal subgroup of G. We will call G^* the noncompact factor of G. Let $\mathfrak{c}$ be the ideal of $\mathfrak{g}$ such that $\mathfrak{g} = \mathfrak{c} + \mathfrak{g}^*$ and $\mathrm{Tr}(XY) = 0$ for all $X \in \mathfrak{c}$ and $Y \in \mathfrak{g}^*$ (trace is taken with respect to a suitable faithful rational representation of G). Then $\mathfrak{c}$ is an algebraic ideal of $\mathfrak{g}$ and the corresponding algebraic subgroup C of G is a compact normal subgroup such that $C \cap G^*$ is finite and G^*C is a dense subgroup of G with respect to the Zariski topology. The natural mapping $G^* \times C \to G$ is an isogeny, so the index $(G : G^*C)$ is finite. C will be called the compact factor of G.

Lemma 2. Let H be a reductive algebraic subgroup of G such that G/H is compact; then H contains the noncompact part G^* of G.

Proof. It is known that if H is an algebraic subgroup of G such that G/H is compact, H contains a maximal trivial torus A and a maximal unipotent subgroup N^+ corresponding to the nilpotent subalgebra of $\mathfrak{g}$ spanned by the positive root spaces with respect to a suitable ordering. Let $\mathfrak{h}$ be the subalgebra of $\mathfrak{g}$ corresponding to H. Since $\mathfrak{h}$ is reductive subalgebra of $\mathfrak{g}$ and

$$\mathfrak{h} \supset \mathfrak{a} + \sum_{\alpha>0} \mathfrak{g}_\alpha,$$

$\mathfrak{h}$ contains $\Sigma_{\alpha<0}\, \mathfrak{g}_\alpha$. Hence we have $\mathfrak{g}^* \subset \mathfrak{h}$ and $G^* \subset H$.

Theorem 5. Let Γ be a discrete subgroup of a p-adic algebraic group G such that G/Γ is compact. Then the minimal algebraic subgroup containing Γ contains G^*.

Proof. Let H be the minimal algebraic subgroup of G containing Γ. Then H is a closed subgroup of G and H/Γ is compact. Hence H is reductive and G/H is compact. From Lemma 3, we have $H \supset G^*$.

From Theorem 5 we see that if $G = G^*$, a discrete subgroup Γ of G (such that G/Γ is compact) is dense with respect to the Zariski topology.

From the Corollary of Lemma 1 we see that if Γ is a discrete subgroup of G such that G/Γ is compact, then $Z(\Gamma)/Z(\Gamma) \cap \Gamma$ is compact. Hence if Γ is dense with respect to the Zariski topology, $Z(\Gamma)$ is equal to the center of G. So we have the following:

Theorem 6. Assume that $G = G^*$. Then for a discrete subgroup Γ with compact G/Γ, the factor group $Z/Z \cap \Gamma$ is compact where Z is the center of G.

Let G_0 be the maximal semisimple normal subgroup of G. Then ZG_0 is a subgroup of finite index of G, so $ZG_0/ZG_0 \cap \Gamma$ is compact if G/Γ is compact. Let Γ' be the group of all $\xi' \in G_0$ such that $\xi' Z \cap \Gamma = \emptyset$. If $Z/Z \cap \Gamma$ is compact, $Z\Gamma/Z$ is a discrete subgroup of G/Z, and Γ' is the inverse image of $Z\Gamma/\Gamma$ by the natural homomorphism φ of G_0 into G/Z. Obviously, the kernel of φ is a finite group contained in the center of G_0, so Γ' is a discrete subgroup of G_0.

Theorem 7. If $(\Gamma' : [\Gamma', \Gamma']) < \infty$, then $G_0/G_0 \cap \Gamma$ is compact.

Proof. We see that G_0/Γ' is compact. For every $\xi' \in \Gamma$ we have $\zeta \in Z$ such that $\xi'\zeta \in \Gamma$. The mapping $\xi' \to \zeta(Z \cap \Gamma)$ is a homomorphism of Γ' into $Z/Z \cap \Gamma$, so we have $[\Gamma', \Gamma'] \subset \Gamma$. Hence if $(\Gamma' : [\Gamma'; \Gamma']) < \infty$, $G_0/G_0 \cap \Gamma$ is compact.

In the case of real semisimple groups of a certain type, we know that $(\Gamma' : [\Gamma'; \Gamma']) < \infty$ is true for any discrete subgroup with compact factor space. So we might expect similar result for p-adic algebraic groups, for example, groups of type $SL(n, Q_p)$ with $n > 2$.

§3

In this section, we will discuss a construction of discrete subgroups of p-adic algebraic group with compact factor spaces. Let k be a totally real algebraic number field, and $\mathfrak{p}$ a prime ideal of k. Let G be an algebraic group defined over k. Let G_A denote the adèle group attached to G and G_∞ the "∞-part" of G_A or the connected component of G_A. If $\mathfrak{p}_{\infty,1}, \ldots, \mathfrak{p}_{\infty,n}$ are the archimedian places of k, then G_∞ is equal to $G_{k\mathfrak{p}_{\infty,1}} \otimes \cdots \otimes G_{k\mathfrak{p}_{\infty,n}}$. Assume that G_∞ is compact. Then the group G_k of all k-rational points on G has no unipotent element, and there is no rational character defined over k. Hence G_A/G_k is compact. Let $G_{Z\mathfrak{q}}$ denote the group of all integral elements on $G_{k\mathfrak{q}}$ with respect to a suitable representation ρ of G where $\mathfrak{q}$ denotes a nonarchimedian prime. Put

$$G' = G_{k\mathfrak{p}} \otimes \prod_{\mathfrak{q} \neq \mathfrak{p}} G_{Z\mathfrak{q}} \otimes G_\infty.$$

Then G' is an open subgroup of G_A, so $G'/G \cap G_k$ is compact. Let Γ be the image of $G' \cap G_k$ by the natural projection π of G' onto $G_{k\mathfrak{p}}$. The kernel of π is compact by the assumption, we see that $G_{k\mathfrak{p}}/\Gamma$ is compact. If the absolute degree of $\mathfrak{p}$ is equal to 1, and $\mathfrak{p}$ is unramified over the rational field Q, then $k_\mathfrak{p}$ is isomorphic to Q_p and $G_{k\mathfrak{p}_2}$ is a p-adic algebraic group. By using this construction, we can prove the existence of discrete subgroups with compact factor spaces for many simple p-adic algebraic groups, for example, any classical groups and groups of type F_4 and G_2.

REFERENCES

1. Satake, I., Theory of spherical functions on reductive algebraic groups over p-adic fields, *Inst. hautes études sci. publ. math.*, **18**(1964).
2. Siegel, C. L., Discontinuous groups, *Amer. Math.*, **44**(1943), 674–689.
3. Weil, A., *Adèles and algebraic groups*, Princeton, N.J. Institute for Advanced Study, 1961.

Analytic Theory of the Zeta Function of Algebraic Varieties

Bernard M. Dwork

Introduction. In these lectures we hope to explain the main ideas in the application of p-adic analysis to the zeta function of a variety defined over a finite field. Although detailed reports of this material are available in the literature, it may be useful to give a shorter account which may clarify the connection between the various parts of the theory.

Let $\mathfrak{H}$ be a nonsingular hypersurface of degree d in n dimensional projective space of characteristic p and let $\mathfrak{H}$ be defined over the field of $q(=p^a)$ elements. For each interger $s \geq 1$ let N_s be the number of points of H which have coordinates in the field of q^s elements. The zeta function of $\mathfrak{H}$ is defined to be the power series in one variable,

$$z(\mathfrak{H}, t) = \exp\left(\sum_{s=1}^{\infty} \frac{N_s t^s}{s}\right).$$

The main results of the theory is that this power series is rational of the form

$$z(\mathfrak{H}, t) = \frac{P(t)^{(-1)^n}}{[(1-t)(1-qt)\cdots(1-q^{n-1}t)]},$$

where $P(t)$ is a polynomial of degree $N = d^{-1}\{(d-1)^{n+1} + (-1)^{n+1}(d-1)\}$ and that $w \to q^{n-1}/w$ is a permutation of reciprocals of the roots of P. These results form part of the Weil conjectures for complete nonsingular varieties defined over a finite field. In the case of hypersurfaces, the Riemann conjecture asserts that the roots of P have equal absolute valves, but this conjecture remains open.

In this exposition we shall assume that p is odd, that d is not divisible by p, and that the coordinate axes may be chosen so that for each nonempty subset A of $S = \{1, 2, \ldots, n+1\}$, the intersection $\mathfrak{H}_A$ of $\mathfrak{H}$, with the linear subspace defined by $x_i = 0$ for each $i \in S - A$, forms a nonsingular hypersurface in that subspace. None of these conditions are needed and many of our statements will remain valid without these conditions.

§1. GENERALITIES

We recall that associated with the prime p, the field $\mathbf{Q}$ of rational numbers has a valuation which may be defined by writing each nonzero element b of $\mathbf{Q}$ in the form mp^ν/m_0 where m_1, m_2, and ν are integers, and both m_1 and m_2 are relatively prime to p. We write

$$\begin{aligned} \operatorname{ord} b &= \nu \\ \operatorname{ord} 0 &= +\infty. \end{aligned}$$

If x and y are elements of $\mathbf{Q}$ then

$$\begin{aligned} \operatorname{ord} xy &= \operatorname{ord} x + \operatorname{ord} y \\ \operatorname{ord}(x+y) &\geq \operatorname{Min}(\operatorname{ord} x, \operatorname{ord} y). \end{aligned}$$

Associated with this valuation of $\mathbf{Q}$ we have the p-adic topology of Q (briefly: $\operatorname{ord} x \to +\infty$ implies $x \to 0$) and, in fact, a uniform structure. The ord function has a unique extension to the completion $\mathbf{Q}'$ of $\mathbf{Q}$ under this uniform structure and this extension has a unique extension to the algebraic closure of $\mathbf{Q}'$. The completion Ω of the algebraic closure is itself algebraically closed, and most of our analysis involves this field. In Ω we have the ring of integers $\mathfrak{O} = \{x \mid \operatorname{ord} x \geq 0\}$ and this ring has a unique maximal ideal $\mathfrak{P} = \{x \mid \operatorname{ord} x > 0\}$. The field $\mathfrak{O}/\mathfrak{P}$ is the algebraic closure of the field of p elements. Each power series in one variable t with coefficients in Ω has associated with it a radius of convergence. A series which converges everywhere in Ω is said to be entire, and by a theorem of Schnirelmann such a series can be represented uniquely as a product,

$$At^{\nu} \prod_{i=1}^{\infty} (1 - \lambda_i t)$$

where $\operatorname{ord}\lambda_i \to +\infty$. The notion of meromorphic function as ratio of entire functions is clear. The logarithmic function

$$\log(1 - t) = - \sum_{s=1}^{\infty} \frac{t^s}{s}$$

converges for $t \in \mathfrak{P}$ and vanishes only when $1 - t$ is a pth power root of unity. The exponential function

$$\exp t = \sum_{s=0}^{\infty} \frac{t^s}{s!}$$

converges for $\operatorname{ord} t > 1/(p - 1)$ and the Artin-Hasse exponential function,

$$E(t) = \exp\{ \sum_{s=0}^{\infty} t^{p^s}/p^s \},$$

has coefficients in $\mathfrak{O}$ and hence converges everywhere in $\mathfrak{P}$. Of particular interest in our theory is the power series

$$\theta_1(t) = \exp(\pi t - \pi t^p),$$

where π is chosen such that $\pi^{p-1} = -p$. This series converges for $\operatorname{ord} t > -(p - 1)/p$ and $\theta_1(1)$ is a primitive pth root of unity.

If s is an integer $s \geq 1$, then the roots in Ω of the equation $x^{p^s} - x = 0$ form a multiplicative system of representatives of the field k of p^s roots of unity. Thus for each element $\bar{x}$ of k there exists a unique representative $\tilde{x}$ which satisfies this equation, and the most important fact is that

$$\bar{x} \to \theta_1(\tilde{x})\theta_1(\tilde{x}^p) \cdots \theta_1(\tilde{x}^{p^{s-1}})$$

is a nontrivial additive character of k. We now define $\theta(t) = \exp(\pi t - \pi t^q)$ and note that

$$\bar{x} \longrightarrow \prod_{j=0}^{s-1} \theta(\tilde{x}^{q^j})$$

is a nontrivial additive character of the field of q^s elements.

§2. TRACE FORMULA

Let K be a field of characteristic zero containing all roots of unity of order prime to q where q is an integer greater than unity. Let H be a polynomial in $K[X] = K[X_1, \ldots, X_n]$. For $u = (u_1, \ldots, u_n)$ an n tuple with nonnegative integral coefficients, let

$$X^u = \prod_{i=1}^{n} X_i^{u_i}$$

and we define an endomorphism ψ of $K[X]$ (as linear K space) by setting

$$\psi(X^u) = \begin{matrix} X^{u/q} \text{ if } q \text{ divides } u, \\ 0 \text{ otherwise.} \end{matrix}$$

The endomorphism $\alpha : \xi \longrightarrow \psi(H\xi)$ of $K[X]$ as linear K space has the property that for each integer $s \geq 1$, the trace of α^s is well defined and the basic trace formula is

$$(q^s - 1)^n \operatorname{Tr}\alpha^s = \Sigma H(x)H(x^q) \cdots H(x^{q^{s-1}}),$$

the sum being over all $(x_1, \ldots, x_n)$ such that $x_i^{q^s-1} = 1$, $i = 1, \ldots, n$.

This idea can be expanded in the following way. Let Ω be as in the previous section and let $H(X) = \Sigma A_w X^w$ be a power series in $X_1, X_2, \ldots, X_n$ with coefficients in Ω such that for some real number $b > 0$, we have

$$\operatorname{ord} A_w \geq b(w_1 + \cdots + w_n)$$

for all $(w_1, \ldots, w_n) \in Z_+^n$. Let α now be the endomorphism $\xi \longrightarrow \psi(H\xi)$ of $\Omega[[X_1, \ldots, X_n]]$ as Ω space. Relative to a monomial basis of $\Omega[[X]]$, α may be represented by an infinite matrix, $\det(\mathrm{I} - t\alpha)$ is an entire function on Ω, well defined as limit of determinants of finite submatrices and the trace of α^s is well defined for each integer $s \geq 1$. The trace formula remains valid.

§3. REPRESENTATION OF THE ZETA FUNCTION

Since the trace formula refers to sums over roots of unity, it is more convenient to first represent the zeta function of

$$\mathfrak{H}' = \{(x_1, \ldots, x_{n+1}) \in \mathfrak{H} \mid \prod_{i=1}^{n+1} x_i \neq 0\}.$$

Let $f(X)$ be a homogeneous irreducible polynomial of degree d in $\mathfrak{O}[X]$ such that $\mathfrak{H}$ is given by the congruence

$$f(X) \equiv 0 \bmod \mathfrak{P}.$$

We further assume that the coefficients of f are roots of the polynomial $t^q - t$. The number of points of $\mathfrak{H}'$ rational over a finite field can be expressed as an additive character summed over a suitable set of points in characteristic zero. By using the result of §1 this can be expressed as a sum over a set of points in characteristic zero and by §2, this can be expressed in terms of the trace of a suitable endomorphism. The final result is that

$$z(\mathfrak{H}', t) = (1 - t)^{(-\delta)^n} \det(I - t\alpha)^{(-\delta)^{n+1}}$$

where α is the endomorphism, $\psi \circ F$ of $\Omega[[X_0, X_1, \ldots, X_{n+1}]]$ as Ω space, $\hat{F}(X) = \exp(\pi X_0 f(X))$, $F = \hat{F}(X)/\hat{F}(X^q)$ and δ is the endomorphism

$$g(t) \to g^\delta = g(t)/g(qt)$$

of the group $1 + t\Omega[[t]]$.

This shows that $z(\mathfrak{H}', t)$ is meromorphic as p-adic function, is represented by a power series with rational integral coefficients, and has a nonzero radius of convergence in the classical sense. The rationality of $z(\mathfrak{H}', t)$—and hence of $z(\mathfrak{H}, t)$—follows from this with the aid of a generalization of a late nineteenth century result of E. Borel.

We note that the zeta function of any algebraic set defined over a finite field is rational and is represented by a power series with integral coefficients and constant term 1. It follows from a theorem of Fatou, (*Acta Math.*, **30**(1906), 364) that the zero and poles of the zeta function are reciprocals of algebraic integers.

§4. PRECISE FORM OF ZETA FUNCTION

For each nonempty subset A of S, let $1 + m(A)$ be the number of elements of A, and with $\mathfrak{H}_A$ as defined in the introduction we write

$$z(\mathfrak{H}_A, t) = \frac{P_A(t)^{(-1)^{m(A)}}}{\prod_{i=0}^{m(A)-1} (1 - q^i t)},$$

the product being 1 if $m(A) = 0$. This defines a rational function $P_A(t)$ and by formal computations,

$$\det(I - t\alpha)^{\delta^{1+n}} = (1 - t)\Pi P_A(qt),$$

the product being over all nonempty subsets A of S.

We now make use of the condition that each $\mathfrak{H}_A$ is nonsingular. This is equivalent to the condition that if we set $f_i = E_i f$, $E_i = \partial/\partial X_i$ for each $i \in S$, the polynomials $f_1, \ldots, f_{n+1}$ have no common zero mod $\mathfrak{P}$. From this we can analyze the differential operators

$$D_i = 1/\hat{F} \circ E_i \circ \hat{F} = E_i + \pi X_0 f_i \qquad i = 1, 2, \ldots, n+1$$

on

$$L(b) = \{ \sum_{dw_0 = w_1 + \cdots + w_{n+1}} B_w X^w \mid B_w \in \Omega, \operatorname{Inf}(\operatorname{ord} B_w - bw_0) > -\infty \},$$

a subspace of $\Omega[[X_0, X_1, \ldots, X_{n+1}]]$.

The homogeneous form of the Macaulay unmixedness theorem leads to the result that if $1/(p-1) < b \leq p/(p-1)$, then

1. $\mathfrak{W}(b) = L(b)/\Sigma_{i=1}^{n+1} D_i L(b)$ has dimension d^n (this can be extended to $b = 1/(p-1)$ if Ω is replaced by Ω_0, a complete, locally compact subfield, in the definition of $L(b)$.
2. If $\xi_1, \ldots, \xi_r$ are elements of $L(b)$, $r \leq n+1$ and $\Sigma_{i=1}^{r} D_i \xi_i = 0$, then there exists an $r \otimes r$ skew symmetric matrix (η_{ij}) with coefficients in $L(b)$ such that

$$\xi_i = \sum_{j=1}^{r} D_j \eta_{ij}, \qquad i = 1, 2, \ldots, r.$$

It follows that if $1/(p-1) < b \leq p/(p-1)$, the sequence

$$0 \leftarrow \mathfrak{W}(b) \overset{i}{\leftarrow} L(b) \overset{\delta_1}{\leftarrow} (L(b))^{n+1} \overset{\delta_2}{\leftarrow} L(b)^{\binom{n+1}{2}} \leftarrow \cdots$$

is exact, where i is the natural map, δ_1 is the mapping $(\xi_1, \ldots, \xi_{n+1}) \to \sum_{i=1}^{n+1} D_i \xi_i$, and $\delta_2, \delta_3, \ldots$ are defined in the well-known manner in terms of the operators $D_1, \ldots, D_{n+1}$.

Now let $b = (p-1)/p$. It is verified that $F(X) \in L(b/q)$, that $\alpha = \psi \circ F$ is an endomorphism of $L(b)$ and trivially for each $i \in S$,

$$\alpha \circ D_i = q D_i \circ \alpha.$$

From this we deduce that α is stable on $\sum_{i=1}^{n+1} D_i L(b)$ and hence induces an endomorphism $\bar{\alpha}$ of $W(b)$ and that

$$\det(I - t\alpha)^{\delta^{1+n}} = \det(I - t\bar{\alpha}).$$

This shows that $(1-t)\Pi P_A(qt)$ is a polynomial, the degree of which is shown to be d^n by showing $\bar{\alpha}$ is nonsingular. The main point in the proof of nonsingularity is that α maps $L(b/q)$ into $L(b)$ and if we set

$$\Phi(X^w) = X^{wq}$$

for each monomial, and set $\beta = 1/F \circ \Phi$ then β maps $L(b)$ into $L(b/q)$ and $\alpha \circ \beta = I$. From the existence of a one-sided inverse for α, the nonsingularity of $\bar{\alpha}$ may be deduced but the proof is not immediate. The degree of $P_A(t)$ as rational function of t is now easily obtained.

To show that $P_S(t)$ is a polynomial, it is necessary to construct a decomposition of $\det(I - t\bar{\alpha})$ as product of characteristic polynomials. The basic fact is that for each subset A the endomorphism α of $L(b)$ is stable on the subspace $L^A(b)$ consisting of all elements of $L(b)$ which are divisible by $\Pi_{i \in A} X_i$. Furthermore, if $L_A(b)$ denotes the image of $L(b)$ under the specialization, $X_i \to 0$ for each $i \in S - A$, and if α_A is the corresponding endomorphism of $L_A(b)$ and if α_A^A is the restriction of α_A to $L_A^A(b) = L_A(b) \cap L^A(b)$ then it is trivially true that

$$\det(I - t\alpha) = (1-t) \prod_A \det(I - t\alpha_A^A),$$

the product being over all nonempty subsets of S. The corresponding decomposition of $\det(I - t\bar{\alpha})$ is somewhat more difficult to verify, but the final result is

$$P_S(qt) = \det(I - t\bar{\alpha}^S),$$

where $\bar{\alpha}^S$ is the restriction of $\bar{\alpha}$ to $\mathfrak{W}^S$, the image of $L^S(b)$in $\mathfrak{W}(b)$.

§5. DUAL THEORY

For b' real, let

$$L_-(b') = \{ \sum_{dw_0 = w_1 + \cdots + W_{n+1}} A_w 1/X^w \mid A_w \in \Omega, \quad \operatorname{Inf}(\operatorname{ord} A_w + b'w_0) > -\infty \},$$

a subspace of $\Omega[[X_0^{-1}, X_1^{-1}, \ldots, X_{n+1}^{-1}]]$.

For $b' < b$ we define a pairing of $L_-(b')$ with $L(b)$ by setting

$$\langle \xi^*, \xi \rangle = \text{constant term of } \hat{\xi}^* \xi,$$

for each $\xi^* \in L(b')$, $\xi \in L(b')$, where $\hat{\xi}^*$ is obtained from ξ^* by replacing X_0 by $-X_0$.

In this way we obtain endomorphisms

$$D_i^* = -(E_i + \gamma_- \pi X_0 f_i)$$
$$\alpha^* = \gamma_-[1/(F(X))] \circ \Phi$$

dual to D_i and α, respectively. Here γ_- is defined by linearity and by the condition that for $w \in Z^{n+2}$,

$$\gamma_- X^w = X^w \text{ if all } w_i \leq 0, \quad 0 \text{ otherwise.}$$

We define

$$\mathfrak{L}^* = \{ \sum_{dw_0 = w_1 + \cdots + w_{n-1}} A_w 1/X^w \mid A_w \in \Omega \}$$
$$\mathfrak{L} = L(b) \cap \Omega[X_0, X_1, \ldots, X_{n+1}].$$

Let $\mathfrak{K} = \{ \xi^* \in \mathfrak{L}^* \mid D_i^* \xi^* = 0, \ i = 1, 2, \ldots, n+1 \}$. The spectral theory of α^* may be used to show that $\mathfrak{K}$ is in $L_-(b')$ for each $b' > 0$, that it is dual to $\mathfrak{W}(b)$ (and hence of finite dimension) and that

$$\det(I - t\bar{\alpha}) = \det(I - t(\alpha^* \mid \mathfrak{K})).$$

Let $\mathfrak{K}^S$ be the annihilator of $L^S(b)$ in $\mathfrak{K}$, then $\mathfrak{K}/\mathfrak{K}^S$ is dual to $\mathfrak{W}^S$ and

$$P_S(qt) = \det(I - t\alpha_S^*),$$

where α_S^* is the endomorphism of $\mathfrak{K}/\mathfrak{K}^S$ induced by the restriction of α^* to $\mathfrak{K}$.

The object of our theory is the construction of an isomorphism Θ of $\mathfrak{K}/\mathfrak{K}^S$ onto $\mathfrak{W}^S$ such that

$$q^{n+1}(\bar{\alpha}^S)^{-1} = \Theta \circ \alpha_S^* \circ \Theta^{-1}.$$

To achieve this we discard the condition that the coefficients of $f(X)$ are roots of the polynomial $t^q - t$. We construct the desired mapping in the case in which $f(X)$ is a diagonal form, $\Sigma a_i X_i^d$ and extend this first to the case in which $f(X)$ approximates a diagonal form and finally to the general case. The remainder of the lecture is devoted to the development of this program.

§6. ALGEBRAIC THEORY OF $\mathfrak{K}$

Let $a_1, \ldots, a_{n+1}$ be units in $\mathfrak{O}$, let $h(X)$ be a form of degree d in $\mathfrak{O}[X_1, \ldots, X_{n+1}]$, and let

$$f(X, \Gamma) = \sum_{i=1}^{n+1} a_i X_i^d + \Gamma h(X),$$

where Γ is a new variable. We further assume that $a_1, \ldots, a_{n+1}$ and the coefficients of h are sufficiently close to roots of $t^q - t$. For each $i \in S$ let $f_{i,\Gamma} = E_i f(X, \Gamma)$.

Let $$\mathfrak{L}_\Gamma = \Omega(\Gamma) \otimes \mathfrak{L}$$

and let $$D_{i,\Gamma} = E_i + \pi X_0 f_{i,\Gamma},$$

an endomorphism of $\mathfrak{L}_\Gamma$ for each $i \in S$.

Let $\mathbf{A} = \{u \in Z_+^{n+2} \mid du_0 = u_1 + \cdots + u_{n+1},\ 0 \leq u_i < d \text{ for each } i \in S\}$. Then $\{\pi^u \circ X^u\}_{u \in \mathbf{A}}$ represents a basis of $\mathfrak{L}_\Gamma / \Sigma_{i=1}^{n+1} D_{i,\Gamma}\mathfrak{L}_\Gamma$. Let $\mathfrak{L}_\Gamma^* = \mathfrak{L}^* \otimes \Omega(\Gamma)$, the dual space of $\mathfrak{L}_\Gamma$ and using the same pairing as before we obtain endomorphisms

$$D_{i,\Gamma}^* = -(E_i + \gamma_{-\pi} X_0 f_{i,\Gamma})$$

for each $i \in S$. It is shown that

$$\mathfrak{K}_\Gamma = \{\xi^* \in \mathfrak{L}_\Gamma^* \mid D_{i,\Gamma}^* \xi^* = 0 \text{ for each } i \in S\}$$

is dual to the factor space $\mathfrak{L}_\Gamma / \Sigma D_{i,\Gamma}\mathfrak{L}_\Gamma$, and that there exists a basis

$\{\xi^*_{u,\Gamma}\}_{u\in\mathbf{A}}$ dual to the indicated basis of the factor space. Explicitly, for each $u \in \mathbf{A}$,

$$\xi^*_{u,\Gamma} = \frac{1}{\mathfrak{g}(\Gamma)} \sum_{dw_0 = w_1 + \cdots + w_{n+1}} \frac{G_{w,u}(\Gamma)}{R(\Gamma)^{w_0}\pi^{w_0}} \frac{1}{X^w}$$

where $\mathfrak{g}(\Gamma)$ is a fixed element of $\Omega[\Gamma]$, $G_{w,u}(\Gamma) \in \mathfrak{O}[\Gamma]$ and $R(\Gamma)$ is the resultant of the polynomials $f_{1,\Gamma}, \ldots, f_{n+1,\Gamma}$. By a deeper analysis, there exists a constant e such that for $w_0 \neq 0$,

$$\operatorname{ord} G_{w,u}(\Gamma) \geq e - (N+1)n \log w_0 / \log p,$$

N being the dimension of $\mathfrak{W}^S$ and the ord of a polynomial being the minimal ordinal of the coefficients.

Let $\mathbf{A}' = \{u \in \mathbf{A} \mid 0 < u_i < d \text{ for each } i \in S\}$ then $\{\xi^*_{u,\Gamma}\}_{u\in\mathbf{A}'}$ represents a basis of $\mathfrak{K}_\Gamma/\mathfrak{K}^S_\Gamma$, $\mathfrak{K}^S_\Gamma$ being the annihilator in $\mathfrak{K}_\Gamma$ of the elements of $\mathfrak{L}_\Gamma$ which are divisible by $\Pi_{i=1}^{n+1} X_i$.

§7. TRANSCENDENTAL THEORY OF $\mathfrak{K}$

We now view Γ as a variable element of Ω and define $\mathfrak{K}_\Gamma$ for each $\Gamma \in \Omega$ to be the subspace of $\mathfrak{L}^*$ consisting of elements ξ^* such that

$$D^*_{i,\Gamma}\xi^* = 0 \qquad \text{for each } i \in S.$$

Of course $D^*_{i,\Gamma}$ is viewed as endomorphism of $\mathfrak{L}^*$.

7.1. NEAR ZERO

For each Γ close to zero in the p-adic sense there exists a natural mapping

$$\xi^* \to \gamma_- \xi^* \exp(-\pi X_0 \Gamma h)$$

of $\mathfrak{K}_0$ onto $\mathfrak{K}_\Gamma$. This mapping is in fact an isomorphism and induces an isomorphism, T_Γ of $\mathfrak{K}_0/\mathfrak{K}^S_0$ onto $\mathfrak{K}_\Gamma/\mathfrak{K}^S_\Gamma$. Relative to our chosen bases $\{\xi^*_{u,0}\}_{u\in\mathbf{A}'}$ of $\mathfrak{K}_0/\mathfrak{K}^S_0$ and $\{\xi^*_{u,\Gamma}\}_{u\in\mathbf{A}'}$ of $\mathfrak{K}_\Gamma/\mathfrak{K}^S_\Gamma$, the mapping T_Γ is represented by a matrix C_Γ whose coefficients are power series in Γ converging everywhere in $\mathfrak{P}$. This matrix satisfies an ordinary differential equation

$$\frac{\partial C_\Gamma}{\partial_\Gamma} = C_\Gamma B,$$

where B is an $N \otimes N$ matrix whose coefficients are rational functions of Γ with poles only among the zeros of $\mathfrak{g}(\Gamma)R(\Gamma)$. We note at this point that by changing the coefficients $a_1, \ldots, a_{n+1}$ in $f(X, \Gamma)$ slightly, we may be sure that no root of $\mathfrak{g}(\Gamma)$ is a root of unity.

7.2. GENERAL

We now restrict Γ to $W = \{\Gamma \in \mathfrak{D} \mid \operatorname{ord} R(\Gamma) = 0\}$. We construct

$$\alpha_\Gamma^* = \gamma_- \frac{1}{F(X, \Gamma)} \circ \Phi,$$

an isomorphism of $\mathfrak{R}_{\Gamma^q}$ onto $\mathfrak{R}_\Gamma$, $F(X, \Gamma)$ denoting the power series $\exp(\pi X_0 f(X, \Gamma) - \pi X_0^q f(X^q, \Gamma^q))$. It is seen that α_Γ^* induces an isomorphism, $\alpha_{\Gamma,S}^*$ of $\mathfrak{R}_{\Gamma^q}/\mathfrak{R}_{\Gamma^q}^S$ onto $\mathfrak{R}_\Gamma/\mathfrak{R}_\Gamma^S$. If $\mathfrak{g}(\Gamma)\mathfrak{g}(\Gamma^q) \neq 0$ then $\mathfrak{g}(\Gamma^q)\alpha_{\Gamma,S}^*$ is represented by a matrix whose coefficients are series of rational functions converging uniformly in W, and hence the matrix representing $\alpha_{\Gamma,S}^*$ is analytic on the set obtained by removing from W the zeros of $\mathfrak{g}(\Gamma^q)$. It is convenient to define $W' = \{\Gamma \in W \mid \mathfrak{g}(\Gamma)\mathfrak{g}(\Gamma^q) \neq 0\}$. Since $\alpha_{\Gamma,S}^*$ as a mapping has an inverse for each $\Gamma \in W$, the determinant of the matrix representing $\alpha_{\Gamma,S}^*$ on W' is never zero on that set. Thus (§10) both the matrix and its inverse are analytic functions on W'.

If we return to the case in which Γ is close to zero, we note that the diagram

$$\begin{array}{ccc}
\mathfrak{R}_{\Gamma^q}/\mathfrak{R}_{\Gamma^q}^S & \xrightarrow{T_{\Gamma^q}} & \mathfrak{R}_0/\mathfrak{R}_0^S \\
{\scriptstyle \alpha_{\Gamma,S}^*}\downarrow & & \downarrow{\scriptstyle \alpha_{0,S}^*} \\
\mathfrak{R}_\Gamma/\mathfrak{R}_\Gamma^S & \xrightarrow[T_\Gamma]{} & \mathfrak{R}_0/\mathfrak{R}_0^S
\end{array}$$

commutes and gives the matrix relation

$$\alpha_{\Gamma,S}^* = C_{\Gamma^q}^{-1}\alpha_{0,S}^* C_\Gamma$$

for $\Gamma \in \mathfrak{P}$. It follows from Krasner's uniqueness theorem (see §10) that $\alpha_{\Gamma,S}^*$ on W is determined by its specification on a neighborhood of zero, and the above relation shows that the latter is determined by C_Γ and $\alpha_{0,S}^*$.

§8. FUNCTIONAL EQUATION

We first consider the diagonal case ($\Gamma = 0$). By constructing the basis of $\mathfrak{K}_0$ we verify that

$$\xi^* \longrightarrow D_{1,0}D_{2,0} \cdot \cdot \cdot D_{n+1,0}\xi^*$$

is a mapping, Θ_0' of $\mathfrak{K}_0$ into $L^S(b)$. By passage to quotients we obtain, $\bar{\Theta}_0'$, an isomorphism of $\mathfrak{K}_0/\mathfrak{K}_0^S$ onto $\mathfrak{W}_0^S$. [Generally $\mathfrak{W}_\Gamma(b) = L(b)/\Sigma D_{i,\Gamma}\, L(b)$ for $\Gamma \in W$, and $\mathfrak{W}_\Gamma^S$ denotes the image in $\mathfrak{W}_\Gamma(b)$ of $L^S(b)$].

We verify that the diagram

$$\begin{array}{ccc} \mathfrak{K}_0/\mathfrak{K}_0^S & \xrightarrow{\bar{\Theta}_0'} & \mathfrak{W}_0^S \\ {\scriptstyle \alpha_{0,S}*}\downarrow & & \downarrow{\scriptstyle (\bar{\alpha}_0{}^S)^{-1}} \\ \mathfrak{K}_0/\mathfrak{K}_0^S & \xrightarrow[\bar{\Theta}_0']{} & \mathfrak{W}_0^S \end{array}$$

commutes except for the factor q^{n+1} which appears as indicated in §5.

For $\text{ord}\Gamma > b$ we obtain from the two preceding diagrams and duality, the diagram

$$\begin{array}{ccccccc} \mathfrak{K}_{\Gamma^q}/\mathfrak{K}_{\Gamma^q}^S & \xrightarrow{T_{\Gamma^q}{}^{-1}} & \mathfrak{K}_0/\mathfrak{K}_0^S & \longrightarrow & \mathfrak{W}_0^S & \xrightarrow{(T^t_{\Gamma^q})^{-1}} & \mathfrak{W}_{\Gamma^q}^S \\ {\scriptstyle \alpha_{\Gamma,S}*}\downarrow & & {\scriptstyle \alpha_{0,S}*}\downarrow & & \downarrow{\scriptstyle (\bar{\alpha}_0{}^S)^{-1}} & & \downarrow{\scriptstyle (\bar{\alpha}^S)^{-1}} \\ \mathfrak{K}_\Gamma/\mathfrak{K}_\Gamma^S & \xrightarrow[T_\Gamma{}^{-1}]{} & \mathfrak{K}_0/\mathfrak{K}_0^S & \longrightarrow & \mathfrak{W}_0^S & \xrightarrow[(T^t_\Gamma)^{-1}]{} & \mathfrak{W}_\Gamma^S. \end{array}$$

The mapping T^t_Γ is obtained from T_Γ by duality, and since $\text{ord}\Gamma > b$, the mapping may be deduced from the automorphism

$$\xi \longrightarrow \xi \cdot \exp(\pi X_0 \Gamma h)$$

of $L(b)$. From this diagram we define

$$\overline{\Theta'_\Gamma} = (T_\Gamma)^{-1} \circ \overline{\Theta'_0} \circ (T^{-t}_{\Gamma^q})^{-1}$$

for $\text{ord}\Gamma > b$, and deduce

$$q^{n+1}(\bar{\alpha}_\Gamma^S)^{-1} = \bar{\Theta}_\Gamma' \circ \alpha^*_{\Gamma,S} \circ (\bar{\Theta}'_{\Gamma^q})^{-1}$$

Consider the matrices representing each side of this relation. The matrix representing $(\bar{\alpha}_\Gamma^S)^{-1}$ is the transpose of the inverse of the matrix representing $\alpha^*_{\Gamma,S}$, and hence (§7) is analytic on W'. Suppose $\overline{\Theta'_\Gamma}$ is represented by a rational matrix. The differential equation satisfied by it and by its determinant have singular points only among the zeros of $\mathfrak{g}(\Gamma)R(\Gamma)$. With the aid of the theory of the Wronskian, we may conclude that the poles of this matrix and the zeros of its determinant lie among the zeros of $R(\Gamma)\mathfrak{g}(\Gamma)$. This would show that the matrices representing each side of the displayed relation are analytic on W' and coincide on a neighborhood of zero, hence coinciding on W'. In particular, if $z \in W$, $z^q = z$, then $z \in W$ and the matrices representing $q^{n+1}(\bar{\alpha}_z^S)^{-1}$ and representing $\alpha^*_{z,S}$ would be equivalent.

The functional equation of the zeta function of the hypersurface

$$f(X, z) \equiv 0 \bmod \mathfrak{P}$$

follows directly. This reduces the proof of the functional equation to the verification of the rationality of $\overline{\Theta'_\Gamma}$.

§9. THE RATIONALITY OF $\overline{\Theta'_\Gamma}$

We consider the space $\mathfrak{M}$ of all infinite sums $\Sigma A_w X^w$, where w runs over all elements of Z^{n+2} such that $dw_0 = w_1 + \cdots + w_{n+1}$. For each $i \in S$ let γ_i^+ be the endomorphism of this space defined by

$$\gamma_i^+ X^w = \begin{cases} X^w \text{ if } w_i > 0, \\ 0 \text{ otherwise.} \end{cases}$$

If $A = \{1, 2, \ldots, r\}$, a nonempty subset of S, let

$$\gamma_A^+ = \gamma_1^+ \circ \gamma_2^+ \circ \cdots \circ \gamma_r^+$$
$$D_A = D_{1,\Gamma} \circ D_{2,\Gamma} \circ \cdots \circ D_{r,\Gamma}$$

so that both γ_A^+ and D_A are endomorphisms of $\mathfrak{M}$. For each ordered partition $\mathfrak{p} = \{A_0, A_1, \ldots, A_m\}$ of S, let

$$D_\mathfrak{p} = (-1)^m D_{A_1} \circ \gamma_{A_1}^+ \circ D_{A_2} \circ \gamma_{A_2}^+ \circ \cdots D_{A_m} \circ \gamma_{A_m} \circ D_{A_0}$$

Finally let

$$\Theta_\Gamma = \Sigma D_\mathfrak{p},$$

and the sum is over all ordered partitions of S. Trivially Θ_Γ is an endomorphism of $\mathfrak{M}$, and by a purely combinatorial argument it is shown that $\mathfrak{K}_\Gamma$ is mapped into $\mathfrak{L}^S$, the set of all elements of $\mathfrak{L}$ which are divisible by $\Pi_{i=1}^{n+1} X_i$. An elementary consequence is

$$\langle \xi^*_{v,\Gamma}, \Theta_\Gamma \xi^*_{u,\Gamma} \rangle \in \Omega(\Gamma) \qquad \text{for each } u, v \in \mathbf{A}.$$

For Γ close to zero we have the mapping

$$\Theta'_\Gamma : \xi^* \longrightarrow (\exp(-\pi X_0 \Gamma h) \circ \Theta'_0 \circ \gamma_- \exp(\pi X_0 \Gamma h))\xi^*$$

of $\mathfrak{K}_\Gamma$ into $L^S(b)$. It is shown that for $\xi^* \in \mathfrak{K}_\Gamma$, with Γ close to zero,

$$\Theta_\Gamma \xi^* \equiv \Theta'_\Gamma \xi^* \bmod \sum_{i=1}^{n+1} D_{i,\Gamma} L^S(b).$$

The assertion that $\overline{\Theta'_\Gamma}$ is represented by a rational matrix follows without difficulty, since this mapping is obtained from Θ'_Γ by passage to quotients.

§10. THEORY OF KRASNER

We can summarize some of the pertinent results of Krasner. A subset W of Ω is said to be ultraopen about a point $z \in W$ if $\operatorname{ord}(x - z)$ assumes only a finite set of distinct values as x runs through the complement of W in Ω. The set W is said to be quasiconnected if it is ultraopen about each point in W. In particular, the complement in a disk of a finite set of disks is quasiconnected. If W is quasiconnected, a function $f(x)$ defined on W is said to be an *analytic element* of *support* W—providing there exists a sequence of rational functions with coefficients in Ω and without poles in W which converges uniformly towards $f(x)$ on W. The uniqueness theorem asserts that two analytic elements with support W coincide on W if they coincide on a subset with limit point in W.

Two analytic elements f, f^* are said to be equivalent if there exists a sequence $f = f_0, f_1, \ldots, f_S = f^*$ of analytic elements of which each pair of consecutive terms have nondisjoint supports and coincide on the intersection of their supports. If f and f^* have nondisjoint supports then they coincide on the intersection of their supports. Thus an equivalence class F determines a single valued function on the union of the supports of the elements of the class, called an *analytic function*. Two analytic functions coincide if they are equal on a subset of the intersection of their supports and the subset has a limit point.

If f and g are analytic elements of support W, then the same holds for $f + g$ and fg while f/g is an analytic function on the subset of W at which g does not vanish.

REFERENCES

For detailed proofs of the material in §5 to §9 of this chapter we refer the reader to the author's article "On the zeta function of a hypersurface II," *Annals Math.*, 1964. The material in §4 is covered by articles of Serre and myself in *Pub. Math.* (*IHES*), *Paris*, **12**(1962). Serre's exposition in *Semminaire Bourbaki*, *1959–1960*, No. 198 is useful in connection with §2 and §3. For §1 see our *IHES* article referred to above and §1 and §4(a) in it. The quoted work of Krasner is given in the *Comptes Rendues Notes:* **238**(1954), 2385–2387; **239**(1954), 468–470; **244**(1957), 1304–1306 and 1599–1602.

Picard Groups of Moduli Problems

David Mumford

The purpose of this lecture is to describe a single specific calculation which gives a modern formulation of an old fact. However, I want to devote a large part of this lecture to the explanation of the machinery which has been developed to give a new and, I think, enlightening setting to a whole group of old questions.

Severi, for one, raised the question: look at maximal families of (irreducible) space curves—is the parameter space of such families rational [10]? A more intrinsic question is whether the moduli variety for nonsingular curves of genus g is rational; in other words, look at the parameter space of the universal family of nonsingular curves of genus g and ask whether this is rational;† this question

† Actually, there is no such family. But if $g \geq 3$, then almost all such curves admit no automorphisms, and there is a universal family of the automorphism-free nonsingular curves.

may be very difficult. However, it can be approximated by any number of weaker questions: is this space unirational, or is it regular in the sense that its function field does not admit everywhere regular differential forms (cf. [5], Chapter 7, §2)? Or, still weaker, is the Picard variety of its function field trivial (cf. [6], Chapter 6, §1)? One of the principal results of our theory is that the last statement is true in characteristic 0. In the same line, can we determine various cohomology groups of this moduli variety?

Now all these questions, especially the last two, suffer from a certain vagueness because of our uncertainty about

1. Whether to look only at birational invariants of the function field,
2. Or, if we want to look at invariants of a definite model, which model to select (since there is no universal family of nonsingular curves),
3. If we settle for the usual moduli variety (i. e., the *coarse* one, cf. [7]), it has singularities (cf. [9]) and is not compact.

If we want an answer which has some pretense of being a basic fact, or of being more than idle, we certainly need to start with the *correct* variety, that is, the one which is most relevant to the set of all non-singular curves with whatever structure is contained therein. Now the real clue here, I contend, is that we must not ask for the cohomology or the Picard group simply of a variety; there is a much better object, which is much more intrinsically related to the moduli problem and which possesses equally (a) a function field, (b) a Picard group, and (c) both étale and coherent cohomology theories. The invariants of this object—call it X—are the basic pieces of information.

In the first section, I want to describe the whole class of objects of which our X is an example. These objects, "topologies," were discovered by Grothendieck, and are the basic concept on which his theory of étale cohomology is constructed. In fact, it was chiefly in order to better understand this important concept that I made the calculations described in this paper. In the second section, I want to describe the étale topology proper, and its relation to the Zariski and the classical topology. In the third section, I want to introduce the topologies relevant to the problem of moduli. All this is nothing but definitions, and I hope that they possess enough intrinsic symmetry and interest to make the reader bear with their mounting abstractness. In the fourth section, I try to alleviate this abstractness by giving the full gory details of the topology relevant to the computations described later. In the fifth section, I describe precisely in two different ways the Picard groups associated to the moduli problem. In the last two sections, for $g = 1$, we give two separate computations of this group.

§1. TOPOLOGIES

In the classical definition of a topology, we start with a basic set X, the space, and we are given a collection A of subsets of X, called the open subsets. Suppose we try to eliminate the set X from our description and develop the theory from A alone: then we will have to endow A with extra structure to compensate for the loss of X. First of all, we make A into a category $\boldsymbol{A}$ by defining:

$$\begin{aligned}\mathrm{Hom}(U, V) &= \text{set with one element } f_{U,V}, \text{ if } U \subset V \\ &= \text{empty set, if } U \not\subset V \\ &\quad (\text{all } U, V \in A).\end{aligned}$$

Notice that the operation of intersecting two open sets U, V can be defined in terms of this category:

1.1.

$U \cap V$ is the product of U and V in $\boldsymbol{A}$, that is, it fits into a diagram

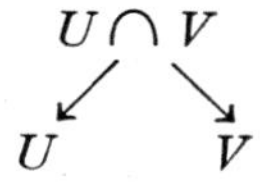

and has the universal mapping property: for all $W \in A$, and for all maps f, g as below, there is a unique h making the diagram commute:

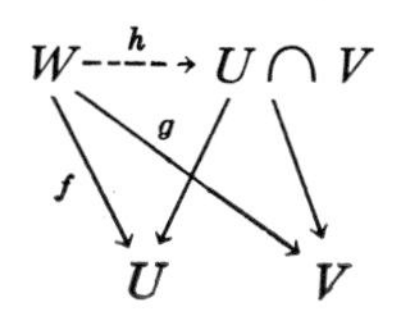

Similarly, arbitrary unions of open sets can be defined as *sums* in the category $\boldsymbol{A}$:

1.2.

If $U = \bigcup_{i \in I} U_i$, then with respect to the inclusions

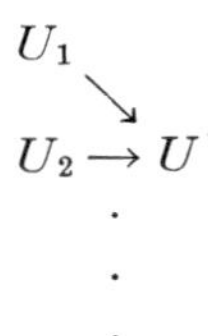

U is the categorical sum of the U_i's.

Moreover, the whole space X as an object of A—but not as a set—can be recovered as the final object of $\boldsymbol{A}$; X is the unique element Y of A such that for all other $U \in A$, there is one and only one map from U to Y.

Now suppose that we want to define the concept of a sheaf $\mathfrak{F}$ (of sets) on X purely in terms of $\boldsymbol{A}$. This goes as follows: first of all we must have a presheaf. This will be a collection of sets $\mathfrak{F}(U)$, one for each $U \in A$; and a collection of restriction maps, that is, if $U \subset V$, or if, equivalently, there is an element $f_{U,V} \in \text{Hom}(U, V)$, then we must have a map

$$\text{res}_{U,V} : \mathfrak{F}(V) \longrightarrow \mathfrak{F}(U).$$

This is nothing more than a contravariant functor $\mathfrak{F}$ from $\boldsymbol{A}$ to the category (Sets). In order to be a sheaf, it must have an additional property:

1.3.

If U_α is a *covering* of U, that is, each U_α is contained in U and

$$\bigcup_\alpha U_\alpha = U,$$

then an element x of $\mathfrak{F}(U)$ is determined by its restrictions to the subsets U_α; and every set of elements $x_\alpha \in \mathfrak{F}(U_\alpha)$, such that x_α and x_β always have the same restriction to $U_\alpha \cap U_\beta$, come from such an x.

To define sheaves, it is now clear that we may as well start with any category $\mathcal{C}$, instead of $\boldsymbol{A}$, and call its objects the open sets, provided that:

a. If U, V are open sets, $\operatorname{Hom}(U, V)$ contains at most one element.
b. Finite products and arbitrary sums of objects in $\mathcal{C}$ exist; $\mathcal{C}$ has a final object X.
   Also this turns out to be essential:

c. $$V \cap [\bigcup_{i \in I} U_i] = \bigcup_{i \in I} (V \cap U_i)$$

   where $\cap$, $\cup$ denote products and sums.

Then sheaves are simply contravariant functors $\mathfrak{F}$ from $\mathcal{C}$ to (Sets) such that, whenever $U = \bigcup_{i \in I} U_i$, the following diagram of sets is exact:

$$\mathfrak{F}(U) \rightarrow \prod_{i \in I} \mathfrak{F}(U_i) \rightrightarrows \prod_{i,j \in I} \mathfrak{F}(U_i \cap U_j).$$

Moreover, the "global sections" $\Gamma(\mathfrak{F})$ of a sheaf $\mathfrak{F}$ are nothing but the elements of the set $\mathfrak{F}(X)$. If we look at sheaves of abelian groups instead of sheaves of Sets, then we can define the higher cohomology groups as well as Γ $(= H^0)$. Namely, we verify in the standard way:

a. The category of abelian sheaves is an abelian category with lots of injective objects.
b. Γ is a left-exact functor from this category to the category (abelian groups).

Hence, as usual, if $\mathfrak{F}$ is an abelian sheaf, put $H^i(\mathfrak{F})$ $(i \geq 0)$ equal to the ith derived functor of Γ (cf. [4], §3.2; [1], Ch. 2, §2).

So far, the theory is essentially trivial: it is nothing more than an exercise in avoiding the explicit mention of points. Grothendieck's fantastic idea is to enlarge the set of possibilities by dropping the assumption that $\operatorname{Hom}(U, V)$ contains at most one element; for example, open sets may even have nontrivial automorphisms. Notice first of all that then it is no longer sufficient to say simply that open sets U_α cover the open set U: it will be necessary to specify particular maps

$$p_\alpha : U_\alpha \rightarrow U$$

with respect to which U is covered by the U_α's. Moreover, it is generally not enough to say that the U_α's cover U only when U is the categorical sum of the U_α's: usually there are other collections of maps $\{p_\alpha\}$ which we will want to call coverings. The concept which emerges from these ideas is the following:

Definition. A "topology" T is a category $\mathcal{C}$ whose objects are called open sets and a set of "coverings." Each covering is a set of morphisms in $\mathcal{C}$, where all the morphisms have the same image; that is, it is a set of the form:

$$\{U_\alpha \xrightarrow{p_\alpha} U\}.$$

The axioms are:

a. Fibred products† $U_1 \times_V U_2$ of objects in $\mathcal{C}$ exist.

b. $\{U' \xrightarrow{p} U\}$ is a covering if p is an isomorphism; if $\{U_\alpha \xrightarrow{p_\alpha} U\}$ is a covering and if, for all α,

$$\{U_{\alpha,\beta} \xrightarrow{q_{\alpha,\beta}} U_\alpha\}$$

is a covering, then the whole collection

$$\{U_{\alpha,\beta} \xrightarrow{p_\alpha \circ q_{\alpha,\beta}} U\}$$

is a covering.

c. To generalize property (c) under 1.3, if $\{U_\alpha \xrightarrow{p_\alpha} U\}$ is a covering, and $V \rightarrow U$ is any morphism, then

$$\{V \times_U U_\alpha \xrightarrow{q_\alpha} V\}$$

is a covering (q_α being the projection of the fibre product on its first factor).

† In any category, given morphisms $p : X \rightarrow Z$ and $q : Y \rightarrow Z$, a fibre product is a commutative diagram:

$$\begin{array}{ccccc} & & W & & \\ & {}^{u}\swarrow & & \searrow^{v} & \\ X & & & & Y \\ & {}_{p}\searrow & & \swarrow_{q} & \\ & & Z & & \end{array}$$

such that for all objects W' and morphisms $u' : W' \rightarrow X$, $v' : W' \rightarrow Y$ such that $p \circ u' = q \circ v'$, there is a unique morphism $t : W' \rightarrow W$ such that $u' = u \circ t$, $v' = v \circ t$. This object W is usually written

$$X \times_Z Y$$

and referred to alone as the fibre product of X and Y over Z.

In general, we want to assume that $\mathcal{C}$ possesses a final object X, but this is not necessary. We want to generalize the concept of a sheaf to an arbitrary topology:

Definition. A sheaf (of sets) on T is a contravariant functor $\mathfrak{F}$ from $\mathcal{C}$ to the category (Sets) such that, for all coverings $U_\alpha \xrightarrow{p_\alpha} U$ in T, the following diagram of sets is exact:

$$\mathfrak{F}(U) \to \prod_{\alpha} \mathfrak{F}(U_\alpha) \rightrightarrows \prod_{\alpha,\beta} \mathfrak{F}(U_\alpha \times_U U_\beta)$$

(the arrows being the usual maps given by the functor $\mathfrak{F}$, contravariant to p_α and to the projections of $U_\alpha \times_U U_\beta$ to U_α and to U_β).

Exactly as before, each sheaf $\mathfrak{F}$ of abelian groups has a group of global sections:

$$\Gamma(\mathfrak{F}) = \mathfrak{F}(X)$$

(X the final object) and hence, by the method of derived functors, higher cohomology groups $H^i(T, \mathfrak{F})$.

A topology in the classical sense gives a topology in an obvious way. To give the theory some content, consider the following example:

Let a group π act freely and discontinuously on a topological space X; that is, for all $x \in X$, there is an open neighborhood U of x such that $U \cap U^\sigma = \emptyset$ for all $\sigma \in \pi$, $\sigma \neq e$. For every set S and action of π on S, we can construct the topological space $\mathcal{S} = (X \times S)/\pi$ (endowing S with the discrete topology). With two π sets S and T and a π-linear map $f : S \to T$, we obtain a local homeomorphism

$$\begin{array}{ccc} (X \times S)/\pi & \xrightarrow{\tilde{f}} & (X \times T)/\pi \\ \| & & \| \\ \mathcal{S} & & \mathfrak{I} \end{array}$$

that makes $\mathcal{S}$ into a covering space of $\mathfrak{I}$. Let the category $\mathcal{C}$ consist in the set of such spaces $\mathcal{S}$ and such maps $\tilde{f}$; let the coverings consist of maps $\tilde{f}_\alpha : \mathcal{S}_\alpha \to \mathfrak{I}$ such that, equivalently, $\mathfrak{I} = \bigcup_\alpha \tilde{f}_\alpha(\mathcal{S}_\alpha)$ or $T = \bigcup_\alpha f_\alpha(S_\alpha)$. The final object in this topology is the topological space X/π, since every other open set has a unique projection

$$\mathcal{S} = (X \times S)/\pi \to X/\pi$$

in the category. In other words, what has happened is that the open sets are no longer subsets of X/π; they are covering spaces of X/π.

If X is simply connected and connected, then X is just the universal covering space of X/π, and the topology consists in fact in *all* covering spaces $\mathfrak{S}$ of X/π, and all continuous maps $\mathfrak{S} \to \mathfrak{T}$ making the following diagram commute:

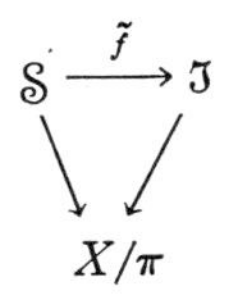

On the other hand, this topology is actually independent of X: we may as well "call" the π-sets S themselves the open sets, and call the π-linear maps $f : S \to T$ the morphisms. Then the space X corresponds to the π-set π, (say with left multiplication as the action of π on itself), and the final object X/π corresponds to the π-set $\{0\}$, with trivial action of π. We shall call this topology T_π.

In this form, it is easy to give an explicit description of a sheaf $\mathfrak{F}$ on the topology. Let π, considered only as a set with the *group* π acting on the left, be denoted $\langle\pi\rangle$. Then the right action of π on $\langle\pi\rangle$ makes π into a group of automorphisms of the π-set $\langle\pi\rangle$. But the group of automorphisms of $\langle\pi\rangle$ obviously acts on the set $\mathfrak{F}(\langle\pi\rangle)$ for every sheaf $\mathfrak{F}$. Let $M = \mathfrak{F}(\langle\pi\rangle)$. Then M itself becomes a π-set. I claim that $\mathfrak{F}$ is canonically determined by the π-set M.

a. Let S be a π-set on which π acts transitively. Then there is a π-linear surjection

$$\langle\pi\rangle \xrightarrow{p} S$$

making $\langle\pi\rangle$ into a covering of S. By applying the sheaf axiom to this covering, we check that $\mathfrak{F}(S)$ is isomorphic to the subset M^h of M of elements, left fixed by $h \subset \pi$, where h is the stabilizer of $p(e)$.

b. If S is any π-set, then S is the disjoint union of π-subsets S_α on which π acts transitively. If i_α is the inclusion of S_α in S, apply the sheaf axiom to the covering

$$\{S_\alpha \xrightarrow{i_\alpha} S\}.$$

We check that, via $\mathfrak{F}(i_\alpha)$,

$$\mathfrak{F}(S) \cong \prod_\alpha \mathfrak{F}(S_\alpha).$$

Conversely, given the π-set M, the isomorphisms in (a) and (b) define a sheaf $\mathfrak{F}$: hence to give a sheaf (of sets) $\mathfrak{F}$ in this topology and to give a π-set M are one and the same thing. In particular, a sheaf of abelian groups $\mathfrak{F}$ is the same thing as a π-module M. As the π-set $\{0\}$ is the final object in T_π, we find by means of (a) that the global sections $\Gamma(\mathfrak{F})$ of the sheaf $\mathfrak{F}$ are just the invariant elements M^π of M. Now it is well known that the category of π-modules is an abelian category, and that

$$M \longrightarrow M^\pi$$

is a left-exact functor on this category. Its derived functors are known as the cohomology groups of π with coefficients in M:

$$H^i(\pi, M)$$

(cf. [8], §10.6). Therefore, we find:

$$H^i(T_\pi, \mathfrak{F}) \cong H^i(\pi, M).$$

One final set of concepts: if T_1 and T_2 are two topologies with final object, a *continuous map* F from T_1 to T_2 consists in a functor from the category of open sets of T_2 to the category of open sets of T_1 such that:

a. It takes the final object to the final object.
b. It takes fibre products in T_2 to fibre products in T_1.
c. It takes coverings in T_2 to coverings in T_1.

For the sake of tradition, if U is an open set in T_2, we let $F^{-1}(U)$ denote the open set in T_1 associated to U by this functor; in other words, requirement (b) means:

$$F^{-1}(U \underset{U}{\times} U_2) \cong (F^{-1}(U_1) \underset{F^{-1}(U)}{\times} F^{-1}(U_2)).$$

If F is a continuous map, then F induces a map F_* from sheaves on T_1 to sheaves on T_2: let $\mathfrak{F}$ be a sheaf on T_1. Define

$$F_*(\mathfrak{F})(U) = \mathfrak{F}(F^{-1}(U))$$

for all open sets U in T_2. This is clearly a sheaf. By standard techniques (cf. [4] and [1], Ch. 2, §4), we find that there is a canonical homomorphism:

$$H^i(T_2, F_*(\mathfrak{F})) \longrightarrow H^i(T_1, \mathfrak{F}).$$

Moreover, let U be an open set in a topology T. Then "U with its induced topology" is a topology T_U defined as follows:

a. Its open sets are morphisms $V \to U$ in T.
b. Its morphisms are commutative diagrams:

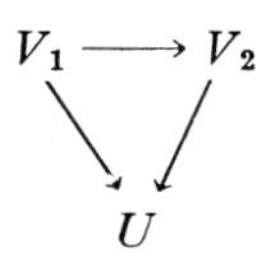

c. A set of morphisms

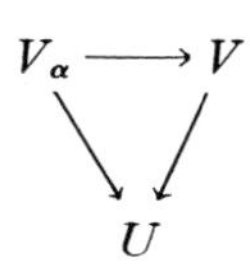

is a covering, if the set of morphisms $\{V_\alpha \to V\}$ is a covering in T.

Then there is a canonical continuous "inclusion" map:

$$i : T_U \to T,$$

that is, to the open set V in T, associate the open set $i^{-1}(V)$ which is the projection:

$$p_2 : V \times U \to U.$$

§2. ÉTALE AND CLASSICAL TOPOLOGIES

From now on, we will be talking about schemes. For the sake of simplicity, we will work over an algebraically closed field k, and all schemes will be assumed separated and of finite type over k, *without further mention.*

Definition. Let $f : X \to Y$ be a morphism. Then if, for all closed points $y \in Y$, $f^{-1}(y)$ is a finite set and for all $x \in f^{-1}(y)$, the induced homomorphism

$$f^* : \mathfrak{o}_y \to \mathfrak{o}_x$$

gives rise to an isomorphism of the completions of these rings

$$\hat{f}^* : \hat{\mathfrak{o}}_y \xrightarrow{\sim} \hat{\mathfrak{o}}_x,$$

then f is *étale.*

As an exercise, the reader might prove that this is equivalent to assuming:

a. f is flat, that is, for all $x \in f^{-1}(y)$, $\boldsymbol{o}_x$ is a flat $\boldsymbol{o}_y$-module,
b. The scheme-theoretic fibre $f^{-1}(y)$ is a reduced finite set, that is, $f^{-1}(y)$ is a finite set, and for all $x \in f^{-1}(y)$, $\boldsymbol{m}_x = f^*(\boldsymbol{m}_y) \cdot \boldsymbol{o}_x$.

Clearly, "étale" is the scheme-theoretic analog of "local homeomorphism" for topological spaces. Now let X be a scheme.

Definition. The étale topology $X_{\text{ét}}$ of X consists of

a. The category whose objects are étale morphisms $p : U \to X$, and whose morphisms are arbitrary X-morphisms; in other words, given $U \xrightarrow{p} X$, $V \xrightarrow{q} X$, then $\text{Hom}(p, q)$ is the set of commutative diagrams

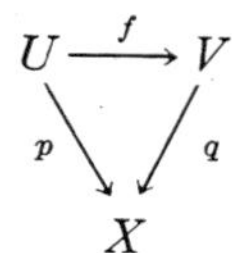

(For simplicity, we shall refer to the objects of this category as schemes U, the étale morphism p to X being understood).

b. The coverings consist in arbitrary sets of morphisms $\{U_\alpha \xrightarrow{p_\alpha} U\}$ provided that

$$U = \bigcup_\alpha p_\alpha(U_\alpha).$$

Let X_{Zar} be the Zariski topology on X: its category consists in the open *subsets* of X and the inclusion maps between them; and a set of inclusion maps $p_\alpha : U_\alpha \subset U$ is said to be a covering if

$$U = \bigcup_\alpha U_\alpha.$$

These two topologies are related by a continuous map

$$\sigma : X_{\text{ét}} \to X_{\text{Zar}}.$$

Namely, if $U \subset X$ is an open subset, the inclusion morphism i of U in X is obviously étale, so that i is an open set in $X_{\text{ét}}$. The reader should check to see that the map from U to i extends to a functor from the category of X_{Zar} to the category of $X_{\text{ét}}$, which takes coverings to coverings and fibre products to fibre products.

If $k = \mathbf{C}$, the field of complex numbers, we can compare $X_{\text{ét}}$ with the classical topology too. The set of closed points of X forms an analytic set $X_{\mathbf{C}}$, and has an underlying topology inherited from the usual topology on $\mathbf{C}$: call this X_{cx}. Unfortunately, there is no continuous map in either direction between $X_{ét}$ and X_{cx}. However, there is a third topology related to both: let open sets consist in analytic sets U and holomorphic maps

$$f : U \to X_{\mathbf{C}},$$

which are local homeomorphisms—as usual, coverings are just sets of maps

$$\begin{array}{ccc} U_\alpha & \xrightarrow{f_\alpha} & U \\ & \searrow \quad \swarrow & \\ & X_{\mathbf{C}} & \end{array}$$

such that $U = \bigcup_\alpha f_\alpha(U_\alpha)$. Call this topology X_{cx}^*. Then there are continuous maps

$$\begin{array}{ccc} & X_{cx}^* & \\ {}^{a}\swarrow & & \searrow{}^{b} \\ X_{cx} & & X_{ét}, \end{array}$$

since

a. An open set in X_{cx} is an "open" subset $U \subset X_{\mathbf{C}}$; and this defines the inclusion map

$$i : U \to X_{\mathbf{C}},$$

which is a holomorphic local homeomorphism.

b. An open set in $X_{ét}$ is an étale morphism $f : U \to X$ of a scheme U to the scheme X; and this defines the holomorphic local homeomorphism

$$f_{\mathbf{C}} : U_{\mathbf{C}} \to X_{\mathbf{C}}$$

of the corresponding analytic sets.

On the other hand, although $\boldsymbol{a}$ is not an isomorphism of topologies, it is very nearly one in the following sense:

Definition. Let $f : T_1 \to T_2$ be a continuous map of topologies. f is an *equivalence* of T_1 and T_2 if

a. The functor f^{-1} from the category of open sets of T_2 to that of T_1 is fully faithful,

b. Every open set U in T_1 admits a covering in T_1 of the form $\{f^{-1}(V_\alpha) \xrightarrow{g_\alpha} U\}$, with suitable open sets V_α in T_2,

c. A collection of maps $\{V_\alpha \xrightarrow{g_\alpha} V\}$ in T_2 is a covering, if the collection of maps $\{f^{-1}(V_\alpha) \xrightarrow{f^{-1}(g_\alpha)} f^{-1}(V)\}$ in T_1 is a covering.

We leave it to the reader to check several simple points: $\boldsymbol{a}$ is an equivalence of topologies; if $f : T_1 \to T_2$ is an equivalence of topologies, f_* defines an equivalence between the category of sheaves on T_1 and the category of sheaves on T_2; hence if $\mathfrak{F}$ is a sheaf of abelian groups on T_1, the canonical homomorphism:

$$H^i(T_1, \mathfrak{F}) \xleftarrow{\sim} H^i(T_2, f_*\mathfrak{F}),$$

is an isomorphism. In fact, there is no significant difference between equivalent topologies. For this reason, we often speak of "the continuous map" from X_{cx} to $X_{\text{ét}}$, although strictly speaking this does not exist. Finally, there is a very nice result of M. Artin: let $\mathbf{Z}/n$ denote the sheaf on X^*_{cx}

$$\mathbf{Z}/n(U) = \bigoplus_{\substack{\text{connected components of} \\ U \text{ in complex topology}}} \mathbf{Z}/n;$$

(this is the same as the sheaf associated to the presheaf which simply assigns the group $\mathbf{Z}/n$ to every open set U.) We shall denote $b_*(\mathbf{Z}/n)$ simply by $\mathbf{Z}/n$; since the connected components of a scheme U in its complex and in its Zariski topologies are the same, we have:

$$b_*(\mathbf{Z}/n)(U) = \bigoplus_{\substack{\text{connected components} \\ \text{of } U \text{ in Zariski topology}}} \mathbf{Z}/n.$$

If X is nonsingular, M. Artin has proven that the canonical homomorphism

$$H^i(X_{\text{ét}}, \mathbf{Z}/n) \to H^i(X^*_{\text{cx}}, \mathbf{Z}/n) \xleftarrow{\sim} H^i(X_{\text{cx}}, \mathbf{Z}/n)$$

is an isomorphism. This result assures us that, at least for nonsingular varieties, the étale topology, defined purely in terms of schemes, captures much of the topological information contained in the a priori finer complex topology.

To complete this comparison of the topologies associated to a scheme X, we must mention three other topologies, defined over any k, which are interesting. The idea behind these topologies is to enlarge the category as much as you want, but to keep the coverings relatively limited. In all of them, an open set is an *arbitrary* morphism

$$f : U \to X,$$

and a map between two open sets f_1 and f_2 is a commutative diagram:

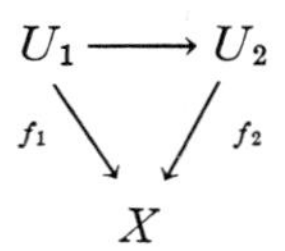

The restriction on the coverings involves new classes of morphisms, defined as follows:

Definition. A morphism $f : X \to Y$ is *flat* if for all $x \in X$, the local ring $\boldsymbol{o}_x$ is a flat module over $\boldsymbol{o}_{f(x)}$. Moreover, f is *smooth* if it is flat and if the scheme-theoretic fibres of f are nonsingular varieties (not necessarily connected).

To understand smoothness better, the reader might check that it is equivalent to requiring, for all $x \in X$, that the completion $\hat{\boldsymbol{o}}_x$ is isomorphic, as $\hat{\boldsymbol{o}}_{f(x)}$-algebra, to

$$\hat{\boldsymbol{o}}_{f(x)}[[X_1, \ldots, X_n]]$$

for some n.

For the purposes of §3, it is very important to know that smooth morphisms are also characterized by the following property (cf. [3], exposé 3, Theorem 3.1).

2.1.

Let A be a finite-dimensional commutative local k-algebra, and let $I \subset A$ be an ideal. Let a commutative diagram of solid arrows be given:

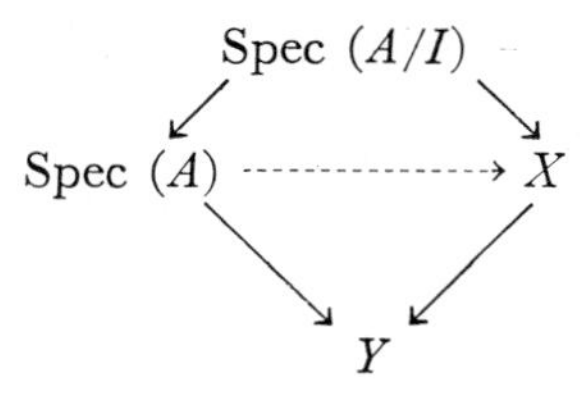

Then there exists a morphism denoted by the dotted arrow filling in the commutative diagram.

This should be understood as a kind of "homotopy lifting property," so that smooth morphisms are somewhat analogous to fibre spaces.

We can now define three topologies,

$$X^*_{\text{ét}},\ X^*_{\text{smooth}},\ \text{and}\ X^*_{\text{flat}},$$

by defining a covering as a collection of morphisms $\{U_\alpha \xrightarrow[f_\alpha]{} U\}$ such that $U = \cup_\alpha f_\alpha(U_\alpha)$ and f_α is étale; f_α is smooth; f_α is flat, respectively. You can check to see that all our topologies are related by continuous maps as follows:

$$X^*_{\text{flat}} \to X^*_{\text{smooth}} \to X^*_{\text{ét}} \to X_{\text{ét}} \to X_{\text{Zar}}.$$

The important fact about these maps is that, in particular, they set up isomorphisms between the cohomology of X^*_{smooth}, $X^*_{\text{ét}}$ and $X_{\text{ét}}$. Therefore, as far as cohomology is concerned, any one of these three topologies is just as good as the others.

§3. MODULI TOPOLOGIES

For this entire section, fix a nonnegative integer g. We first recall the basis of the moduli problem for curves of genus g:

Definition. A "curve" (over k, of genus g) is a connected, reduced, one-dimensional scheme X, such that

$$\dim H^1(X, \mathfrak{o}_X) = g.$$

Definition. A "family of curves" over S (or, parametrized by S) is a flat, projective morphism of schemes

$$\pi : \mathfrak{X} \to S,$$

whose fibres over all closed points are curves.

Definition. A "morphism" F of one family $\pi_1 : \mathfrak{X}_1 \to S_1$ to another $\pi_2 : \mathfrak{X}_2 \to S_2$ is a diagram of morphisms of schemes:

$$\begin{array}{ccc} \mathfrak{X}_1 & \longrightarrow & \mathfrak{X}_2 \\ {\scriptstyle \pi_1}\downarrow & & \downarrow{\scriptstyle \pi_2} \\ S_1 & \longrightarrow & S_2 \end{array}$$

making $\mathfrak{X}_1$ into the fibre product of S_1 and $\mathfrak{X}_2$ over S_2. F is smooth/flat/étale if the morphism from S_1 to S_2 is smooth/flat/étale.

Definition. Given a family of curves $\pi : \mathfrak{X} \to S$ and a morphism $g : T \to S$, the "induced family of curves" over T is the projection:

$$p_2 : \mathfrak{X} \times_S T \to T.$$

The most natural problem is to seek a universal family of curves, that is, one such that every other one is induced from it by a unique morphism of the parameter spaces. As indicated in the introduction, the usual compromises made in order that this existence problem has a solution are exactly what we want to avoid now. Instead, we want to define a topology; in the ideal case, if a universal family of curves had existed, this would be one of the standard topologies on the universal parameter space. Inasmuch as such a family does not exist (unless stringent conditions on the curves in our families are adopted), this topology is a new object.

Definition (Provisional Form). The moduli topologies $\mathfrak{M}^*_{\text{ét}}$, $\mathfrak{M}^*_{\text{smooth}}$, and $\mathfrak{M}^*_{\text{flat}}$ are as follows:

a. Their open sets are families of curves.
b. Morphisms between open sets are morphisms between families.
c. A collection of such morphisms

$$\begin{array}{ccc} \mathfrak{X}_\alpha & \longrightarrow & \mathfrak{X} \\ {\scriptstyle \pi_\alpha}\downarrow & & \downarrow{\scriptstyle \pi} \\ S_\alpha & \xrightarrow[g_\alpha]{} & S \end{array}$$

is called a covering, if $S = \bigcup_\alpha g_\alpha(S_\alpha)$ and if each g_α is étale, smooth, or flat, respectively.

The first thing to check is that this is a topology and, in particular, that fibre products exist in our category. However, unlike the examples considered in §2, there is not necessarily a final object in our category. Such a final object would be a universal family of curves. A second point is that, if $\pi : \mathfrak{X} \to S$ is any family of curves, the topology induced on the open set π is equivalent to the topology $S^*_{\text{ét}}$, S^*_{smooth}, or S^*_{flat} on S.

A less trivial fact is that absolute products exist in our category. Let $\pi_i : \mathfrak{X}_i \to S_i$ $(i = 1, 2)$ be two families of curves: I shall sketch the construction of the product family. First, over the scheme

$S_1 \times S_2$, we have two induced families of curves,

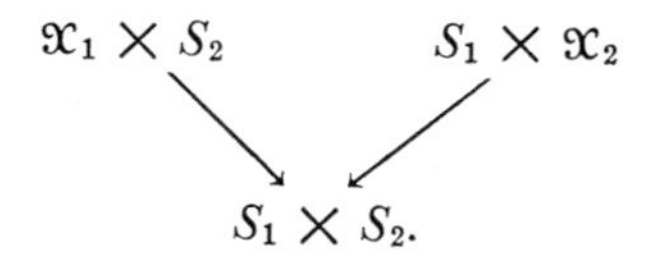

Now suppose $\mathfrak{Y} \to T$ is a third family of curves, and that the following morphisms are morphisms of families:

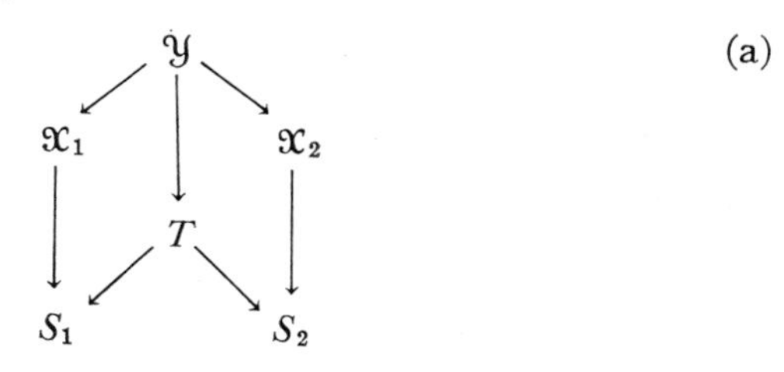

To have such morphisms is obviously equivalent to having (1) a morphism $T \to S_1 \times S_2$, and (2) isomorphisms *over* T of the three families of curves:

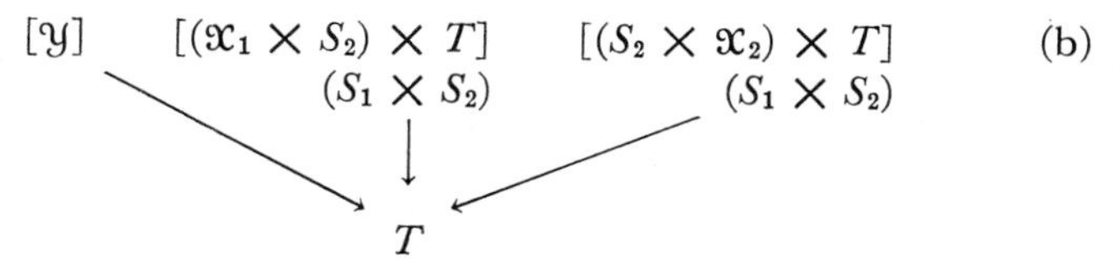

But now we must digress for a minute; consider, á la Grothendieck, the following class of universal mapping properties which can be used to define auxiliary schemes. Let S be a scheme, and let

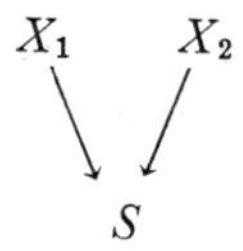

be two morphisms. Look at all pairs (T, Φ) consisting of schemes T over S (i. e., with given morphism to S) and isomorphisms over T:

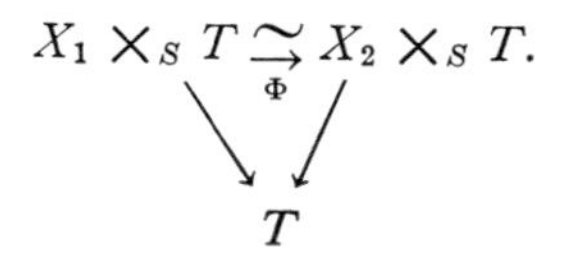

If there is one such pair (T, Φ) such that for every other such pair (T', Φ'), there is a unique morphism (over S)

$$f : T' \to T$$

making the following diagram commute:

$$\begin{array}{ccc} X_1 \times_S T' & \xrightarrow{\Phi'} & X_2 \times_S T' \\ \downarrow{\scriptstyle 1_{X_1} \times f} & & \downarrow{\scriptstyle 1_{X_2} \times f} \\ X_1 \times_S T & \xrightarrow{\Phi} & X_2 \times_S T \end{array}$$

then (T, Φ) is uniquely determined up to canonical isomorphism by this property. And T is denoted

$$\mathrm{Isom}_S(X_1, X_2).$$

Now returning to our families of curves, suppose that the scheme

$$I = \mathrm{Isom}_{S_1 \times S_2}(\mathfrak{X}_1 \times S_2, S_1 \times \mathfrak{X}_2)$$

exists. Then, in situation (a), we get not only a canonical morphism from T to $S_1 \times S_2$ but even a canonical morphism from T to I. Now over I, the two families of curves induced from $\mathfrak{X}_1/S_1$ and $\mathfrak{X}_2/S_2$ are canonically identified: call this family $\mathfrak{X}/I$. Then the situation (a) is obviously equivalent with a morphism from the family Y/T to the family $\mathfrak{X}/I$. In other words, $\mathfrak{X}/I$ is the only possible product of the families $\mathfrak{X}_1/S_1$ and $\mathfrak{X}_2/S_2$. Fortunately, I does exist in our case. This is a consequence of a general result of Grothendieck's (cf. [2], exposé 221), and we will pass over this point completely.

Definition. The product of the families $\pi_i : \mathfrak{X}_i \to S_i$ $(i = 1, 2)$ will be denoted:

$$\pi : (\mathfrak{X}_1, \mathfrak{X}_2) \to \mathrm{Isom}(\pi_1, \pi_2).$$

Since products do exist in the common category of the topologies $\mathfrak{M}^*$, there is no reason not to add a final object M to this category in a perfectly formal way. In order to enlarge the topology, though, we have to define the coverings of the final object M. The point is, however, that if $\pi : \mathfrak{X} \to S$ is part of a covering of M, and if $\pi' : \mathfrak{X}' \to S'$ is any other family of curves whatsoever, then the morphism from the product family

$$(\mathfrak{X}, \mathfrak{X}') \to \mathrm{Isom}(\pi, \pi')$$

to the family π' must be part of a covering of π'. In particular, the projection from $\mathrm{Isom}(\pi, \pi')$ to S' must be étale, smooth, or flat according to the case involved. This leads to:

Definition. A family of curves $\pi : \mathfrak{X} \to S$ is *étale, smooth,* or *flat over M* if, for all other families $\pi' : \mathfrak{X}' \to S'$, the projection from $\mathrm{Isom}(\pi, \pi')$ to S' is étale, smooth, or flat.

If we use criterion 2.1 for smoothness given at the end of §2 (p. 46), the condition that π is smooth over M can be reformulated. In fact, after unwinding all the definitions by various universal mapping properties, this condition comes out as follows.

3.1.

Let A be a finite-dimensional commutative local k-algebra, and let $I \subset A$ be an ideal. Suppose we are given a diagram of solid arrows:

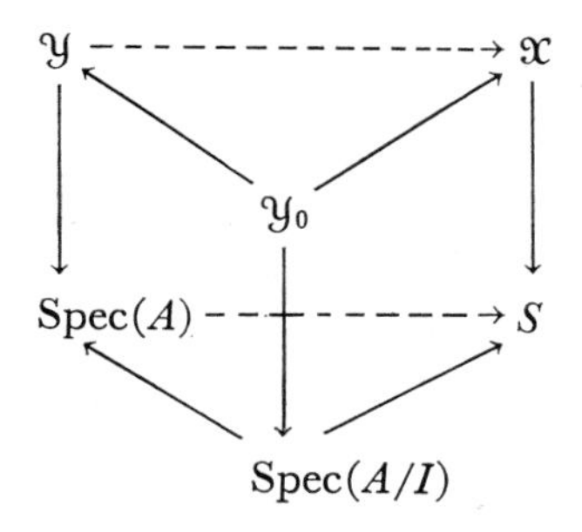

where $\mathfrak{Y}/\mathrm{Spec}(A)$ and $\mathfrak{Y}_0/\mathrm{Spec}(A/I)$ are families of curves, and where the two solid squares are morphisms of families of curves. Then there should be a morphism of families denoted by the dotted arrows filling in the commutative diagram.

Such families have been considered already: compare, especially, the thesis of M. Schlessinger. The important thing is that plenty of such families exist. In particular, if C is any curve over k, we certainly want C to be part of such a family. This can be proven by the method of "linear rigidifications" (cf. [7], §5.2 and §7.2). A fortiori, plenty of families π flat over M exist too.

With families étale over M, it is another matter. In fact, unless we stick to curves C without global vector fields (i. e., everywhere finite derivations), such families do not exist. Let us analyze what it means for $\pi : \mathfrak{X} \to S$ to be étale over M. Let C be any curve over k, and let

$$p : C \to \text{Spec}(k)$$

be the trivial family given by C. Then if π is étale over M, $\text{Isom}(\pi, p)$ must be étale over $\text{Spec}(k)$; that is, $\text{Isom}(\pi, p)$ must consist in a finite set of reduced points. But the points of $\text{Isom}(\pi, p)$ represent isomorphisms of C with the fibres $\pi^{-1}(s)$ of the family π. Therefore, if π is étale over M, the following is satisfied.

3.2.

For all curves C over k, C occurs only a finite number of times in the family $\pi : \mathfrak{X} \to S$, that is C is only isomorphic to a finite number of curves $\pi^{-1}(s)$. Moreover, if C occurs at all in π, the group of automorphisms of C is finite.

Now conversely, the smoothness of π and (3.2) (i.e., 3.1 and 3.2), guarantee the étaleness of π. To see this, let $\pi' : \mathfrak{X}' \to S'$ be any other family of curves. Assume (3.1) and (3.2). Then we know that $\text{Isom}(\pi, \pi')$ is smooth over S'; for it also to be étale over S' means simply that $\text{Isom}(\pi, \pi')$ has only a finite number of closed points over every closed point $s' \in S'$. But let C be the curve $\pi'^{-1}(s')$. There is an isomorphism between the set of closed points of $\text{Isom}(\pi, \pi')$ over s' and the set of isomorphisms of C with the curves $\pi^{-1}(s)$ (s a closed point of S). Therefore, the finiteness of this set follows from 3.2.

Definition. A family $\pi : \mathfrak{X} \to S$ of curves satisfying (3.1) and (3.2) will be called a "modular" family of curves.

Modular families have the following very nice property. Let $\pi_i : \mathfrak{X}_i \to S_i$ be two modular families of curves, and suppose the curve C occurs in π_1 over the point $s_1 \in S_1$ and in π_2 over the point $s_2 \in S_2$, that is,

$$\pi_1^{-1}(s_1) \cong C \cong \pi_2^{-1}(s_2).$$

I claim that S_1 and S_2 are formally isomorphic at the points s_1, s_2; in other words, the complete local rings $\hat{\mathfrak{o}}_{s_1}$ and $\hat{\mathfrak{o}}_{s_2}$ are isomorphic. To see this, fix an isomorphism τ of $\pi_1^{-1}(s_1)$ and $\pi_2^{-1}(s_2)$. Then τ determines a point

$$t \in \text{Isom}(\pi_1, \pi_2)$$

lying over s_1 and s_2. But since both π_1 and π_2 are modular, $\text{Isom}(\pi_1, \pi_2)$

is étale over both S_1 and S_2. Therefore, via the projections, we get isomorphisms:

$$\hat{o}_{s_1} \cong \hat{o}_t \cong \hat{o}_{s_2}.$$

More precisely, two modular families containing the same curve are related by an étale correspondence at the point where this curve occurs. As a consequence, for example, either all or none of such families are nonsingular, and they all have the same dimension.

Another very important property of modular families is that any morphism between two such families is necessarily étale. Assume that

$$\begin{array}{ccc} \mathcal{Y} & \longrightarrow & \mathcal{X} \\ {\scriptstyle \varpi}\downarrow & & \downarrow{\scriptstyle \pi} \\ T & \longrightarrow & S \end{array}$$

is a morphism of modular families. This morphism defines an isomorphism of $\mathcal{Y}/T$ and the family induced by $\mathcal{X}/S$ over T: so it defines a morphism of T to $\mathrm{Isom}(\varpi, \pi)$ by the universal mapping property defining Isom. We get the diagram

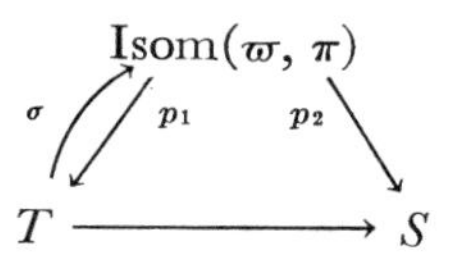

where $p_1 \circ \sigma = 1_T$, and $p_2 \circ \sigma = g$. Since p_1 is étale, a section, such as σ, of p_1 defines an isomorphism of T with an open component

$$I_0 \subset \mathrm{Isom}(\varpi, \pi).$$

Since p_2 is étale, the restriction of p_2 to I_0 is étale; hence g is étale.

We now return to our topologies.

Definition (*Final Form*). The moduli topologies $\mathfrak{M}^*_{\text{smooth}}$, and $\mathfrak{M}^*_{\text{flat}}$ are as follows:

a. Their open sets are families of curves, and a final object M.
b. Their morphisms are morphisms of families of curves, and projections onto the final object M,
c. A collection of such morphisms with image a family $\pi : \mathcal{X} \to S$ is called a covering exactly as before; a collection of projections of families $\pi_\alpha : \mathcal{X}_\alpha \to S_\alpha$ onto the final object M is called a covering

of M if: (1) each family π_α is smooth, or flat over M, and (2) every curve C occurs in one of the families π_α.

It is clear that a topology $\mathfrak{M}^*_{\text{ét}}$ could be defined in the same way, but then the final object M would have no coverings at all. This is because some curves have an infinite group of automorphisms, and hence do not occur in any modular families. One result is that sheaves on this topology would not be sufficiently restricted; the topology is too loosely tied together and would not be useful.

However, suppose that we happen to be interested only in nonsingular curves. This is perhaps short sighted, but never mind. By considering only families of nonsingular curves, we can modify $\mathfrak{M}^*_{\text{smooth}}$, for example, and get a smaller topology. Now if the genus g is at least 2, it is well known that such nonsingular curves have only a finite group of automorphisms. It is to be expected that they belong to modular families, and indeed this is the case. Therefore, we can define an étale moduli topology by looking only at nonsingular curves and modular families. We make the definition in analogy to the scheme topology $X_{\text{ét}}$ rather than $X^*_{\text{ét}}$:

Definition. The moduli topology $\mathfrak{M}_{\text{ét}}$ is as follows:

a. Open sets are modular families of nonsingular curves, and a final object M.
b. Morphisms are morphisms of families of curves, and projections onto the final object M.
c. A collection of morphisms:

$$\begin{array}{ccc} \mathfrak{X}_\alpha & \longrightarrow & \mathfrak{X} \\ \downarrow & & \downarrow \\ S_\alpha & \xrightarrow[g_\alpha]{} & S \end{array}$$

is a covering if $S = \bigcup_\alpha g_\alpha(S_\alpha)$; a collection of projections of families $\pi_\alpha : \mathfrak{X}_\alpha \to S_\alpha$ onto the final object M is a covering if every curve C occurs in one of the families π_α.

In the rest of this paper, this is the topology we will be interested in; therefore, we will refer to it simply as $\mathfrak{M}$, *rather than* $\mathfrak{M}_{\text{ét}}$.

It is, I think, a very important topology. At a future occasion, I hope to give some deeper results about this topology and compute some of its cohomology groups. For the present, I just want to mention a few nice facts about it:

a. The induced topology on an open set $\pi : \mathfrak{X} \longrightarrow S$ is equivalent to the étale topology $S_{\text{ét}}$ on S.
b. If $\pi : \mathfrak{X} \longrightarrow S$ is an open set, S is a nonsingular $3g - 3$-dimensional variety.
c. The so-called "higher level moduli schemes" form (for $n \geq 3$, n prime to the characteristic of k) modular families

$$\pi_n : \mathfrak{X}_n \longrightarrow S_n$$

each of which is, by itself, a covering over M. Moreover, $\text{Isom}(\pi_n, \pi_n)$ is a finite Galois covering of S_n.

§4. THE ELLIPTIC TOPOLOGY

The last topology that I want to define is the one which we shall study closely in §§6 and 7. It is essentially the topology $\mathfrak{M}_{\text{ét}}$ in the case $g = 1$, except that certain modifications are necessary to extend the definition given in §3 when $g \geq 2$. With this topology everything can be made very explicit, and hopefully the abstractness of all our definitions will be enlivened by this case. This topology is the classical proving ground for all notions of moduli, and, as such, it is found in various forms in hundreds of places.

The difficulty in using the definitions of §3 when $g = 1$ is that a nonsingular curve of genus 1 admits a structure of a group scheme, and therefore it has an infinite group of automorphisms. But by a minor modification, we can make everything go through. The key is to consider not curves, but *pointed* curves, that is, curves with a distinguished base point.

Definition. A nonsingular pointed curve of genus 1 is an "elliptic curve."

Definition. A "family of pointed curves" is a family of curves $\pi : \mathfrak{X} \longrightarrow S$ with a given section $\varepsilon : S \longrightarrow \mathfrak{X}$ (i. e., $\pi \circ \varepsilon = 1_S$). If $g = 1$, and the curves are nonsingular, this is called a "family of elliptic curves".

We can define a modular family of elliptic curves just as before.

Since modular families of elliptic curves do exist, it makes sense to state the next definition.

Definition. The topology $\mathfrak{M}$ is as follows:

a. Its open sets are modular families of elliptic curves, and a final object M,
b. Its morphisms are (étale) morphisms of families of elliptic curves, and projections of every open set to M.
c. Coverings of a family $\pi : \mathfrak{X} \to S$ are collections of morphisms of families:

$$\begin{array}{ccc} \mathfrak{X}_\alpha & \longrightarrow & \mathfrak{X} \\ {\scriptstyle \pi\alpha}\downarrow & & \downarrow{\scriptstyle \pi} \\ S_\alpha & \xrightarrow{f\alpha} & S \end{array}$$

such that $S = \bigcup_\alpha f_\alpha(S_\alpha)$; coverings of M are collections of projections of families π_α to M, provided that every elliptic curve occurs in one of the families π_α.

We want to describe this topology explicitly. First, we shall outline the basic facts about elliptic curves, and then indicate step by step, without complete proofs, how this leads to our final description. We shall assume from now on that the characteristic of k is not 2 or 3, so as to simplify the situation.

The basic fact is that elliptic curves are exactly the curves obtained as double coverings of the line ramified in four distinct points. Therefore, they are the curves C described by equations

$$y^2 = (x - \alpha_1)(x - \alpha_2)(x - \alpha_3)(x - \alpha_4).$$

Since the group of automorphisms acts transitively on the curve C, we can assume that the distinguished point e on C is the point $x = \alpha_4$, $y = 0$. By a projective transformation in the coordinate x, we can put α_4 at ∞, and the equation becomes:

$$y^2 = (x - \alpha_1')(x - \alpha_2')(x - \alpha_3'),$$

where e is now the unique point of this curve over $x = \infty$.

In the language of schemes, the conclusion is that every elliptic curve is isomorphic as *pointed* curve to the subscheme of $\mathbf{P}_2$ defined by homogeneous ideal

$$\mathfrak{A} = (X_2^2X_0 - (X_1 - \alpha_1'X_0)(X_1 - \alpha_2'X_0)(X_1 - \alpha_3'X_0))$$

together with the distinguished point

$$X_0 = 0; X_1 = 0; X_2 \neq 0.$$

It can be shown that this representation is essentially unique; in fact, the triple $(\alpha_1', \alpha_2', \alpha_3')$ is uniquely determined by the curve up to permutations and to affine substitutions of the form

$$\beta_i' = A\alpha_i' + B.$$

It follows easily from this that elliptic curves are *classified* by the number:

$$j = -64 \left[\frac{(\lambda - 2) \cdot (2\lambda - 1) \cdot (\lambda + 1)}{\lambda \cdot (\lambda - 1)} \right]^2 \tag{1}$$

where $$\lambda = \frac{\alpha_3' - \alpha_1'}{\alpha_2' - \alpha_1'}.$$

Why is this? First, λ determines the triple $(\alpha_1', \alpha_2', \alpha_3')$ up to affine transformations. And, if we permute the α_i''s, λ is transformed into one of six numbers:

$$\lambda, 1 - \lambda, \frac{1}{\lambda}, \frac{\lambda - 1}{\gamma}, \frac{1}{1 - \lambda}, \frac{\lambda}{\lambda - 1}.$$

Also, the values $\lambda = 0$ and $\lambda = 1$ are excluded, since the three numbers α_1', α_2', and α_3' are distinct. It can be checked that j is unchanged by any of these substitutions in λ, and, conversely, that only λ's related by these substitutions give the same j. The factor -64 arose historically, and turns out to be crucial if we specialize to characteristic 2. In characteristics other than 2, it is obviously harmless!

How about automorphisms of elliptic curves as *pointed* curves? Every elliptic curve C obviously possesses the automorphism

$$\begin{aligned} x &\longrightarrow x \\ y &\longrightarrow -y \end{aligned}$$

corresponding to its being a double covering of the x-line. We will call this the *inversion* ρ of C. A very important fact is that if $\pi : \mathfrak{X} \longrightarrow S$, $\varepsilon : S \longrightarrow \mathfrak{X}$ is any family of elliptic curves, then the inversions of all the fibres piece together to an automorphism $P : \mathfrak{X} \longrightarrow \mathfrak{X}$, of the family π; we will also call this the inversion of π. A related fact is that ρ commutes with any other automorphism α of C. Since $k(x)$ is the field of functions on C fixed by the inversion, such an α will take $k(x)$ into itself; that is, it will be given by a projective transformation in x. Also since α leaves e fixed, it leaves $x = \infty$ fixed; and it must permute the other three branch points $\alpha_1', \alpha_2', \alpha_3'$. It is now an elementary result that such an α occurs only in two cases:

a. $j = 0$; $\lambda = 2, \frac{1}{2}$, or -1; $\alpha_1', \alpha_2', \alpha_3'$ of the form $\beta, \beta + \gamma, \beta + 2\gamma$.
b. $j = 12^3$; $\lambda = -\omega$ or $-\omega^2$ (ω a cube root of 1); $\alpha_1', \alpha_2', \alpha_3'$ of the form $\beta + \gamma, \beta + \omega\gamma, \beta + \omega^2\gamma$.

Now normalizing the first case by choosing $\alpha_1' = -1$, $\alpha_2' = 0$, $\alpha_3' = 1$, we find that C possesses the automorphism σ of order 4:

$$x^\sigma = -x$$
$$y^\sigma = i \cdot y$$

such that σ^2 is the inversion. Normalizing the second case by choosing $\alpha_1' = 1$, $\alpha_2' = \omega$, $\alpha_3' = \omega^2$, we find that C possesses the automorphism τ of order 6:

$$x^\tau = \omega \cdot x$$
$$y^\tau = -y$$

such that τ^3 is the inversion. These are the only automorphisms.

Now, what about modular families. Since only one parameter j is involved, it is natural to expect that modular families are always parametrized by nonsingular curves S. This is true. The most natural thing would be to look for a modular family parametrized by j itself. The following is an example of such a family:

$$y^2 = x^3 + A \cdot (x + 1)$$

where

$$A = \frac{27}{4} \cdot \frac{12^3 - j}{j}.$$

We check that if $j \neq 0, 12^3$, then A is finite and the roots of $x^3 + A(x + 1)$ are all distinct—so we have an elliptic curve. And we can compute its j-invariant in an elementary way, and it is the j we had at the start.

In the language of schemes, let

$$\mathbf{A}_j = \operatorname{Spec} k[j]$$
$$S = \mathbf{A}_j - (0, 12^3),$$

and let $\mathfrak{X}$ be the closed subscheme of $\mathbf{P}_2 \times S$ defined by the vanishing of the section

$$X_2^2 \cdot X_0 - X_1^3 - \frac{27}{4} \cdot \frac{12^3 - j}{j} \cdot (X_1 X_0^2 + X_0^3)$$

of the sheaf $\boldsymbol{o}(3)$. Let ϵ be the morphism

$$S \xrightarrow{\sim} (0, 0, 1) \times S \subset \mathfrak{X}.$$

Then a rigorous analysis of the infinitesimal deformations of an elliptic curve shows that this is a modular family.

Can we extend this family π to cover the points $j = 0$ and 12^3? For the value $j = 0$, A is infinite; and for $j = 12^3$, our equation degenerates. But even a priori it is clear that there has to be trouble. If π is a modular family, then $\mathrm{Isom}(\pi, \pi)$ must be étale over S. Now for each closed point $t \in S$, the closed points of $\mathrm{Isom}(\pi, \pi)$ over t stand for: (a) closed points $t' \in S$ such that $\pi^{-1}(t)$ and $\pi^{-1}(t')$ are isomorphic, plus (b) isomorphisms of $\pi^{-1}(t)$ and $\pi^{-1}(t')$. If S is an open set in the j-line, $\pi^{-1}(t)$ and $\pi^{-1}(t')$ can never be isomorphic unless $t = t'$. Therefore, the number of points in $\mathrm{Isom}(\pi, \pi)$ over t equals the order of the group of automorphisms of $\pi^{-1}(t)$. For $j \neq 0, 12^3$, this is 2, so $\mathrm{Isom}(\pi, \pi)$ is a double covering of S; and $\mathrm{Isom}(\pi, \pi)$ could not have four or six points over $j = 0$ or $j = 12^3$. The real problem here is that j is not the "right" parameter at $j = 0$ and 12^3. At $j = 0$, $\sqrt{j}$ or something analytically equivalent is needed; at $j = 12^3$, $\sqrt[3]{j - 12^3}$ is needed. This works out as follows. Let $\pi : \mathfrak{X} \to S$ be *any* modular family. In particular, S is a nonsingular curve. Suppose we define a function on the closed points of S by assigning to the point $s \in S$ the j-invariant of the curve $\pi^{-1}(s)$. It can be proven that this function is a morphism:

$$S \xrightarrow{j} \mathbf{A}_j.$$

We can then prove the following.

4.1.

Each component of S dominates $\mathbf{A}_j$ and the ramification index of j at a closed point $s \in S$ is 1, 2, or 3 according to whether $j(s) \neq 0$ and 12^3, $j(s) = 0$, or $j(s) = 12^3$.

We now want to return to the problem of giving an explicit description of the topology $\mathfrak{M}$. The morphism j is one invariant which we can attach to the family $\pi : \mathfrak{X} \to S$. Unfortunately, a given j may correspond to more than one family π. A second invariant is needed. The key is to use more strongly the particular modular family over $\mathbf{A}_j - (0, 12^3)$ which we have constructed. With this as a reference point, so to speak, we will get the second invariant. Let $\pi_0 : \mathfrak{X}_0 \to S_0$ denote this one family. We use the diagram:

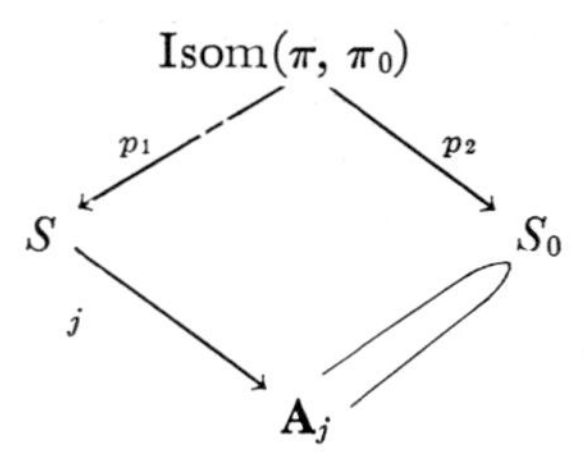

The first thing to notice is that this is commutative: let t be a closed point of $\mathrm{Isom}(\pi, \pi_0)$. If $s = p_1(t)$ and $s_0 = p_2(t)$, then t represents an isomorphism of $\pi^{-1}(s)$ and $\pi_0^{-1}(s_0)$. Therefore, $\pi^{-1}(s)$ and $\pi_0^{-1}(s_0)$ have the same j-invariant, that is, $p_1(t)$ and $p_2(t)$ have the same image in $\mathbf{A}_j$.

Now what is $\mathrm{Isom}(\pi, \pi_0)$? Over a closed point $s \in S$, its points represent isomorphisms of $\pi^{-1}(s)$ with curves $\pi_0^{-1}(s_0)$, $s_0 \in S_0$. In other words, $\mathrm{Isom}(\pi, \pi_0)$ has no points over s if $j(s) = 0$ or 12^3; two points otherwise. $\mathrm{Isom}(\pi, \pi_0)$ is a double étale covering of the open set:

$$j^{-1}(S_0) \subset S.$$

This covering extends uniquely to a covering I of all of S (not necessarily étale!)†. The covering I/S is the second invariant. I claim that j and I/S determine the modular family π uniquely.

Indication of Proof. The first step is to check that there is at most

† By a double covering T/S, I mean a second nonsingular curve T, and a finite, flat, surjective morphism $f : T \to S$ of degree 2, étale over an open dense subset $S' \subset S$. Now either Isom is the disjoint union of two copies of $j^{-1}(S_0)$; and then I is the disjoint union of two copies of S; or Isom is the normalization of $j^{-1}(S_0)$ in a quadratic extension of its function field, and then I is the normalization of S in this field.

one family $\mathfrak{X}/S$ extending the restriction of this family to the open subset $j^{-1}(S_0)$. After this, we may assume $j(S) \subset S_0$. Let $\mathcal{Y}$ be the given family of elliptic curves over $I = \text{Isom}(\pi, \pi_0)$. Then we have a diagram of morphisms of families:

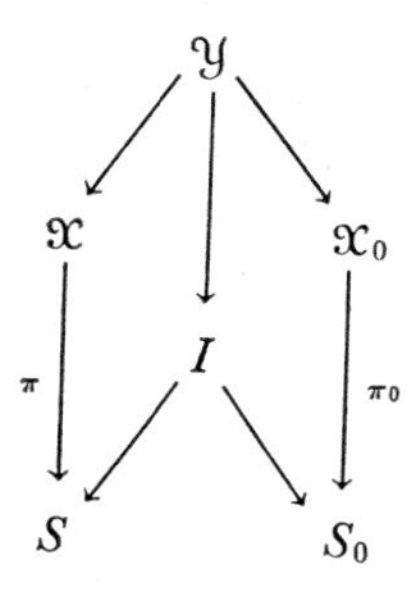

The family $\mathcal{Y}/I$ is determined by j and I/S, because it is just the family induced over I by the base extension

$$I \rightarrow S \xrightarrow{j} S_0$$

from the standard family $\mathfrak{X}_0$. On the other hand, $\mathcal{Y}$ is also induced from $\mathfrak{X}$ via the double étale covering I/S. Therefore, $\mathcal{Y}$ is a double étale covering of $\mathfrak{X}$. We could recover $\mathfrak{X}$ from $\mathcal{Y}$ if we knew the involution ι of $\mathcal{Y}$ interchanging the two sheets of this covering. But let P_0 be the inversion of the family π_0: this is an involution of $\mathfrak{X}_0$ over S_0. Let $\bar{\iota}$ be the involution of I corresponding to the covering I/S: this is an automorphism of I over S_0 too. Since the diagram sets up an identification

$$\mathcal{Y} = I \times_{S_0} \mathfrak{X}_0,$$

$\bar{\iota}$ and P_0 induce an involution $\bar{\iota} \times P_0$ of $\mathcal{Y}$. We check that $\iota = \bar{\iota} \times P_0$.

Q.E.D.

The next question is whether there are any restrictions on j and I/S for these to come from a modular family. Besides the restriction (4.1) on j mentioned above, it turns out that the following is the only further restriction.

4.2.
I is ramified over all points s of S where $j(s) = 0$ or 12^3.

Turning all this around, we can make it into a second definition of the topology $\mathfrak{M}$:

Definition. The topology $\mathfrak{M}$ is as follows:

a. Its open sets are morphisms j of nonsingular curves S to $\mathbf{A}_j$ satisfying restriction (4.1), plus double coverings I/S satisfying restriction (4.2); and a final object M.

b. Its morphisms are commutative diagrams:

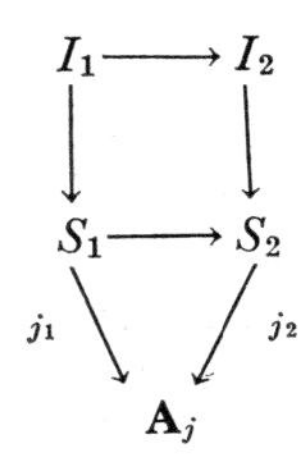

making I_1 into the fibre product $S_1 \times_{S_2} I_2$; and projections of every open set onto M,

c. Coverings of $(j, I/S)$ are collections of morphisms

$$\begin{array}{ccc} I_\alpha & \longrightarrow & I \\ \downarrow & & \downarrow \\ S_\alpha & \xrightarrow{f_\alpha} & S \end{array}$$

such that $S = \bigcup_\alpha f_\alpha(S_\alpha)$; coverings of M are collections of projections of open sets $(j_\alpha, I_\alpha/S_\alpha)$ onto M such that $\mathbf{A}_j = \bigcup_\alpha j_\alpha(S_\alpha)$.

Note that, because of restriction (4.1), given a morphism of open sets:

$$\begin{array}{ccc} I_1 & \longrightarrow & I_2 \\ \downarrow & & \downarrow \\ S_1 & \xrightarrow{f} & S_2 \end{array}$$

the morphism f is necessarily étale.

Let us work out (absolute) products in these terms to see how it all fits together. Say $(j_1, I_1/S_1)$ and $(j_2, I_2/S_2)$ are two open sets. Suppose we want to map a third open set $(j, I/S)$ to both:

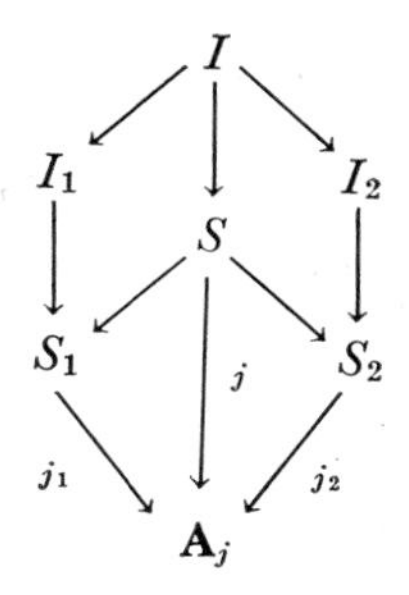

Then first we get a morphism f_1 from S to $S_1 \times_{\mathbf{A}} S_2$. But S is non-singular, and f maps each component of S to an open subset of $S_1 \times_{\mathbf{A}} S_2$; therefore, f_1 factors through the normalization of $S_1 \times_{\mathbf{A}} S_2$. Denote this normalization by T, and let $f_2 : S \to T$ be the morphism that factors f_1. Let I_1' and I_2' be the double coverings of T induced by I_1/S_1 and I_2/S_2. Then pulling these double coverings all the way back to S, we get isomorphisms of both with I/S, hence an isomorphism between them. Exactly as in §3, we get a factorization of f_2 via $S \xrightarrow{f_3} \mathrm{Isom}_T(I_1', I_2')$. But what is this Isom? At points where I_1' and I_2' are unramified, it is just the "quotient" double covering; that is, if I_1' is defined by extracting $\sqrt{f_1}$, and I_2' by $\sqrt{f_2}$, then Isom is the double covering given by $\sqrt{f_1/f_2}$. Since I_1' and I_2' are ramified over exactly the same points of T, this "quotient" covering extends to an étale double covering I_3' over all of T. It turns out that I_3' is a closed subscheme of $\mathrm{Isom}_T(I_1', I_2')$ and f_3 factors via

$$S \xrightarrow{f_4} I_3'.$$

This I_3' is the S of the product open set. Over I_3', I_1 and I_2 can be canonically identified to the I of the product open set.

§5. THE PICARD GROUPS

Now we come to the Picard groups, which are one of the interesting invariants of our topologies. There are two quite different ways to define these groups. One is a direct method going back to the moduli problem itself; the other is a cohomological method using our topologies. We will first explain the direct method:

Fix, as before, the genus g.

Definition. An "invertible sheaf" L (on the moduli problem itself) consists in two sets of data:

a. For all families of nonsingular curves (of genus g) $\pi : \mathfrak{X} \to S$, an invertible sheaf $L(\pi)$ on S.
b. For all morphisms F between such families:

$$\begin{array}{ccc} \mathfrak{X}_1 & \longrightarrow & \mathfrak{X}_2 \\ {\scriptstyle \pi_1}\downarrow & & \downarrow{\scriptstyle \pi_2} \\ S_1 & \xrightarrow{f} & S_2 \end{array}$$

an isomorphism $L(F)$ of $L(\pi_1)$ and $f^*(L(\pi_2))$.†

The second set of data should satisfy a compatibility condition with respect to composition of morphisms:

Let

$$\begin{array}{ccccc} \mathfrak{X}_1 & \longrightarrow & \mathfrak{X}_2 & \longrightarrow & \mathfrak{X}_3 \\ {\scriptstyle \pi_1}\downarrow & & {\scriptstyle \pi_2}\downarrow & & {\scriptstyle \pi_3}\downarrow \\ S_1 & \underset{f}{\longrightarrow} & S_2 & \underset{g}{\longrightarrow} & S_3 \end{array}$$

be a composition of the morphism F from π_1 to π_2, and G from π_2 to π_3. Then the diagram:

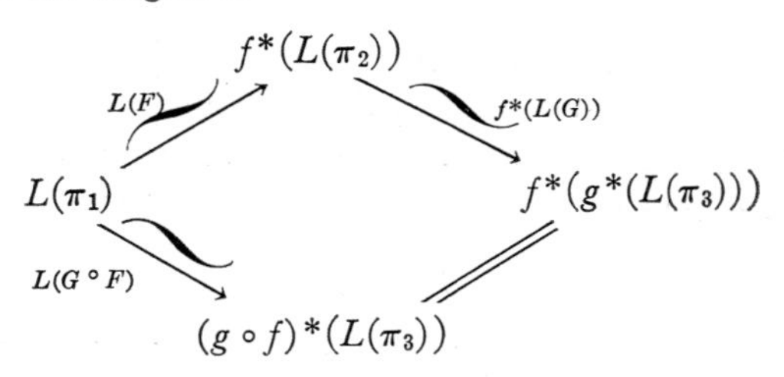

should commute.

This definition has an obvious translation into the language of fibred categories, which is left to the reader who has a taste for that approach. Loosely speaking, an invertible sheaf is simply a pro-

† Note that the morphism F is the whole diagram, while f is simply the morphism from S_1 to S_2. In the sequel, we will denote morphisms of families by capital letters and the component morphism of base spaces by the same small letters.

cedure for attaching canonically a one-dimensional vector space to every nonsingular curve of genus g: Start with L as above. If C/k is such a curve, let

$$\pi : C \longrightarrow \mathrm{Spec}(k)$$

be the projection. Then $L(\pi)$ is a one-dimensional vector space (over k) attached to C. Conversely, if this procedure is "canonical" enough, then given a family $\pi : \mathfrak{X} \longrightarrow S$, the one-dimensional vector spaces attached to the curves $\pi^{-1}(s)(s \in S_k)$ should form a line bundle over S; and its sections then form an invertible sheaf $L(\pi)$.

Example. Given any $\pi : \mathfrak{X} \longrightarrow S$ as above, let

$$E(\pi) = R^1\pi_*(\boldsymbol{o}_X).$$

This is known to be a locally free sheaf on S of rank g. Let

$$L(\pi) = \Lambda^g\{R^1\pi_*(\boldsymbol{o}_X)\}.$$

This is an invertible sheaf on S. Moreover, for all morphisms of families:

$$\begin{array}{ccc} \mathfrak{X}_1 & \longrightarrow & \mathfrak{X}_2 \\ {\scriptstyle \pi_1}\downarrow & & \downarrow{\scriptstyle \pi_2} \\ S_1 & \xrightarrow{f} & S_2 \end{array}$$

there is a canonical identification of $E(\pi_1)$ and $f^*(E(\pi_2))$, hence of $L(\pi_1)$ and $f^*(L(\pi_2))$. This is, therefore, an invertible sheaf on the moduli problem. It corresponds to attaching to each curve C the one-dimensional vector space

$$\Lambda^g\{H^1(C, \boldsymbol{o}_C)\}.$$

It is clear what is meant by an isomorphism of two invertible sheaves.

Definition. The set of isomorphism classes of such invertible sheaves is called $\mathrm{Pic}(\mathfrak{M})$.

As usual, $\mathrm{Pic}(\mathfrak{M})$ is an abelian group. Given L and M, two invertible sheaves, define $L \otimes M$ by

$$(L \otimes M)(\pi) = L(\pi) \otimes M(\pi)$$
$$(L \otimes M)(F) = L(F) \otimes M(F).$$

This induces the product on the set of isomorphism classes $\mathrm{Pic}(\mathfrak{M})$.

Now we give the second definition of Pic($\mathfrak{M}$). Recall that, by definition, a scheme X is a particular type of topological space, together with a given sheaf of rings $\boldsymbol{o}_X$. Now that we have generalized the concept of a topological space, it is clear that an important type of object to look at will be a topology T, together with a given sheaf of rings $\boldsymbol{o}_T$. This combination is known as a "site." For example, if X is a scheme it is not only the Zariski topology which comes with the sheaf of rings $\boldsymbol{o}_X$. Recall the five topologies on X and the continuous maps:

$$X^*_{\text{flat}} \to X^*_{\text{smooth}} \to X^*_{\text{ét}} \to X_{\text{ét}} \to X_{\text{Zar}}.$$

Let $\pi : U \to X$ be a morphism, that is, an open set in X^*_{flat}. Then define† a sheaf $\boldsymbol{o}$ on X_{flat} by

$$\boldsymbol{o}(U \to X) = \Gamma(U, \boldsymbol{o}_U).$$

By taking direct images, this also defines a sheaf $\boldsymbol{o}$ on X^*_{smooth}, $X^*_{\text{ét}}$, $X_{\text{ét}}$ and X_{Zar}; on X_{Zar} this is just the original sheaf $\boldsymbol{o}_X$. Thus each of these topologies is a site.

What is more important now is that the topologies $\mathfrak{M}$ are also sites. Let $\pi : \mathfrak{X} \to S$ be an open set in $\mathfrak{M}$, that is, a modular family of nonsingular curves. Let

$$\boldsymbol{o}(X \xrightarrow{\pi} S) = \Gamma(S, \boldsymbol{o}_S).$$

This defines a sheaf of rings $\boldsymbol{o}$ on $\mathfrak{M}$, except for the ring $\boldsymbol{o}(M)$: this is simply determined by the sheaf axiom. Fix a covering of $\mathfrak{M}$ by open sets $\{\mathfrak{X}_\alpha \xrightarrow{\pi_\alpha} S_\alpha\}$. Let the product of π_α and π_β be the open set

$$\mathfrak{X}_{\alpha,\beta} \xrightarrow{\pi_{\alpha,\beta}} S_{\alpha,\beta}.$$

Then $\boldsymbol{o}(M)$ is the kernel of the usual homomorphism

$$\prod_\alpha \boldsymbol{o}(\mathfrak{X}_\alpha \to S_\alpha) \to \prod_{\alpha,\beta} \boldsymbol{o}(\mathfrak{X}_{\alpha,\beta} \to S_{\alpha,\beta}).$$

In fact, if $g \geq 3$, it is known that $\boldsymbol{o}(M)$ is just k. In any case, this defines $\boldsymbol{o}$, and it brings $\mathfrak{M}$ into a familiar context: we can now develop a theory of coherent sheaves, and their cohomology on $\mathfrak{M}$,

† This is not obviously a sheaf; it is so as a consequence of the theory of descent (cf. [3], exposé 8).

as well as a general theory of (étale) cohomology. Moreover, in addition to $\boldsymbol{o}$ we get the two auxiliary sheaves:

a. $\boldsymbol{o}^*$, defined by $\boldsymbol{o}^*(\mathfrak{X} \xrightarrow{\pi} S) =$ group of units in $\boldsymbol{o}(\mathfrak{X} \xrightarrow{\pi} S)$.
b. $\boldsymbol{K}$, defined as the sheaf associated to the presheaf $\tilde{\boldsymbol{K}}(\mathfrak{X} \xrightarrow{\pi} S) =$ total quotient ring of $\boldsymbol{o}(\mathfrak{X} \xrightarrow{\pi} S)$.

The ring of global sections of $\boldsymbol{K}$ is, so to speak, the function field of the moduli problem. Now the second definition of Pic($\mathfrak{M}$) is simply the cohomology group:

$$H^1(\mathfrak{M}, \boldsymbol{o}^*).$$

Sketch of Proof of Isomorphism. The first thing to do is to set up a map between these groups. The map goes like this: let L be an invertible sheaf on the moduli problem. Then we will associate to L an element:

$$\lambda \in H^1(\mathfrak{M}, \boldsymbol{o}^*).$$

First choose any collection of families $\pi_\alpha : \mathfrak{X}_\alpha \to S_\alpha$ which is a covering of the final object M. Then $L(\pi_\alpha)$ is an invertible sheaf on S_α. By replacing S_α with a suitable set of (Zariski) open subsets and replacing π_α by the set of induced families over these subsets, we can assume that for each α there is an isomorphism:

$$L(\pi_\alpha) \underset{\phi_\alpha}{\overset{\sim}{\to}} \boldsymbol{o}_{S_\alpha}$$

For each α, choose such an isomorphism. For all α, β, let

$$\pi_{\alpha,\beta} : (\mathfrak{X}_\alpha, \mathfrak{X}_\beta) \to \mathrm{Isom}(\pi_\alpha, \pi_\beta) = I_{\alpha,\beta}$$

be the product of the families π_α and π_β. Let p_1 and p_2 denote the projections of $\mathrm{Isom}(\pi_\alpha, \pi_\beta)$ onto S_α and S_β. By definition of an invertible sheaf, we are given isomorphisms of $p_1^*(L(\pi_\alpha))$ and $p_2^*(L(\pi_\beta))$ with $L(\pi_{\alpha,\beta})$. Now look at the composite isomorphism:

$$\begin{aligned}
\boldsymbol{o}_{I_{\alpha,\beta}} &= p_1^*(\boldsymbol{o}_{S_\alpha}) \\
&\overset{\sim}{\to} p_1^*(L(\pi_\alpha)) && \text{via } \phi_\alpha \\
&\cong L(\pi_{\alpha,\beta}) \\
&\cong p_2^*(L(\pi_\beta)) \\
&\overset{\sim}{\leftarrow} p_2^*(\boldsymbol{o}_{S_\beta}) && \text{via } \phi_\beta \\
&= \boldsymbol{o}_{I_{\alpha,\beta}}.
\end{aligned}$$

This isomorphism is set up by multiplication by a unit:

$$\sigma_{\alpha,\beta} \in \Gamma(I_{\alpha,\beta}, \boldsymbol{o}^*_{I_{\alpha,\beta}}) = \boldsymbol{o}^*(\pi_{\alpha,\beta}).$$

I claim that, for the covering $\{\pi_\alpha\}$ of $\mathfrak{M}$, $\{\sigma_{\alpha,\beta}\}$ forms a 1-Czech cocycle in the sheaf $\boldsymbol{o}^*$. This is checked using the compatibility property for the invertible sheaf L (cf., last part of the definition of an invertible sheaf). Then this cocycle induces an element λ_1 in the first Czech cohomology group for this covering, hence an element λ_2 of $H^1(\mathfrak{M}, \boldsymbol{o}^*)$.

Now suppose the isomorphisms ϕ_α are varied? The only possible change is to replace ϕ_α by $\phi'_\alpha = \sigma_\alpha \cdot \phi_\alpha$, where σ_α means multiplication by the unit:

$$\sigma_\alpha \in \Gamma(S_\alpha, \boldsymbol{o}^*_{S_\alpha}) = \boldsymbol{o}^*(\pi_\alpha)$$

But then $\sigma_{\alpha,\beta}$ is replaced by the homologous cocycle:

$$\sigma'_{\alpha,\beta} = p_1^*(\sigma_\alpha) \cdot p_2^*(\sigma_\beta^{-1}) \cdot \sigma_{\alpha,\beta}.$$

Therefore even λ_1 is unaltered. Now suppose the covering $\{\pi_\alpha\}$ is changed. Any two coverings are dominated by a finer covering, so we can assume that the new covering is finer. It is immediate that the new λ_1 is just the element of the new Czech cohomology group induced by the old λ_1 under restriction. Therefore, λ_2 is unaltered.

This defines a map from $\mathrm{Pic}_1(\mathfrak{M})$ (the first group) to $\mathrm{Pic}_2(\mathfrak{M})$ (the second group). To show that this is a surjective, we first use the fact that (for any sheaf F),

$$H^1(\mathfrak{M}, F) = \varinjlim_{\text{coverings } \mathfrak{A}} H^1(\mathfrak{A}, F)$$

where $H^1(\mathfrak{A}, -)$ denotes the first Czech cohomology group for the covering $\mathfrak{A}$. Now suppose $\lambda_2 \in H^1(\mathfrak{M}, \boldsymbol{o}^*)$ is given. Then λ_2 is induced by a $\lambda_1 \in H^1(\mathfrak{A}, \boldsymbol{o}^*)$ for some covering $\mathfrak{A}$. And λ_1 is defined by some cocycle $\{\sigma_{\alpha,\beta}\}$ in $\boldsymbol{o}^*$, (if $\mathfrak{A}$ is the covering $\pi_\alpha : \mathfrak{X}_\alpha \to S_\alpha$). Now suppose $\pi : \mathfrak{X} \to S$ is any modular family of nonsingular curves. Then

$$\{I_\alpha = \mathrm{Isom}(\pi, \pi_\alpha) \to S\}$$

is an étale covering of S. Moreover, via the natural projection

$$I_\alpha \times_S I_\beta \to \mathrm{Isom}(\pi_\alpha, \pi_\beta),$$

the cocycle $\{\sigma_{\alpha,\beta}\}$ induces a cocycle $\{\tau_{\alpha,\beta}\}$ for the covering $\{I_\alpha \to S\}$ of S and the sheaf $\mathbf{o}_S^*$. We then require a theorem of Grothendieck:

Theorem 90 (Hilbert-Grothendieck). Let $\{U_\alpha \xrightarrow{q_\alpha} X\}$ be a flat covering of X; for all α, let L_α be an invertible sheaf on U_α; and for all α, β, let $\phi_{\alpha,\beta}$ be an isomorphism on $U_\alpha \times_X U_\beta$ of the sheaves $p_1^*(L_\alpha)$ and $p_2^*(L_\beta)$. Assume an obvious compatibility of isomorphisms on $U_\alpha \times_X U_\beta \times_X U_\gamma$ (for all α, β, γ). Then there is an invertible sheaf L on X, and for all α, isomorphisms ψ_α on U_α of L_α and $q_\alpha^*(L)$ such that, on $U_\alpha \times_X U_\beta$, the diagram:

$$\begin{array}{ccc} p_1^*(L_\alpha) & \xrightarrow[\phi_{\alpha,\beta}]{\sim} & p_2^*(L_\beta) \\ {\scriptstyle p_1^*(\psi_\alpha)} \wr\downarrow & & \downarrow\wr {\scriptstyle p_2^*(\psi_\alpha)} \\ p_1^*(q_\alpha^*(L)) & = & p_2^*(q_\beta^*(L)) \end{array}$$

commutes. Moreover, L and ψ_α are uniquely determined, up to canonical isomorphisms. (cf. [3], exposé 8, Theorem 1.1).

There is a shorthand which is used in connection with this theorem: given the L_α, the isomorphisms $\{\phi_{\alpha,\beta}\}$ are called "descent data" for $\{L_\alpha\}$. The L obtained is said to be gotten by "descending" the sheaves L_α to X (that is, reversing the process, the L_α are gotten by lifting L to U_α).

Apply this theorem with $U_\alpha = I_\alpha$, $X = S$, $L_\alpha = \mathbf{o}_{I_\alpha}$, and $\phi_{\alpha,\beta}$ given by $\sigma_{\alpha,\beta}$. The L constructed is to be our $L(\pi)$. We leave it to the reader to construct the isomorphisms $L(F)$ required for an invertible sheaf; and to check that this L does induce λ_2 when the process is reversed.

Finally, why is the map injective? If λ_2 were 0, then for a suitable covering λ_1 would be 0, and for suitable choices of the ϕ_α's, the cocycle $\sigma_{\alpha,\beta}$ itself would come out 1. The question is then, if $\sigma_{\alpha,\beta} = 1$ for all α, β show that $L = \mathbf{o}$ (the trivial invertible sheaf). What we need to do is to construct, for every family $\pi : \mathfrak{X} \to S$, an isomorphism

$$\psi(\pi) : L(\pi) \xrightarrow{\sim} \mathbf{o}_S,$$

such that, for every morphism F of families:

$$\begin{array}{ccc} \mathfrak{X}_1 & \longrightarrow & \mathfrak{X}_2 \\ {\scriptstyle \pi_1}\downarrow & & \downarrow{\scriptstyle \pi_2} \\ S_1 & \xrightarrow{f} & S_2 \end{array}$$

the diagram:

$$\begin{array}{ccc} L(\pi_1) & \xrightarrow[\sim]{L(F)} & f^*(L(\pi_2)) \\ \wr\downarrow{\scriptstyle \psi(\pi_1)} & & \wr\downarrow{\scriptstyle f^*(\psi(\pi_2))} \\ \mathbf{o}_{S_1} & = & f^*(\mathbf{o}_{S_2}) \end{array}$$

commutes. Exactly as before, we use the induced étale covering

$$\{I_\alpha = \mathrm{Isom}(\pi, \pi_\alpha) \xrightarrow{q_\alpha} S\}.$$

The family of curves $\mathcal{Y}_\alpha$ over I_α induced via q_α from $\mathfrak{X}/S$ is canonically isomorphic to the family induced from $\mathfrak{X}_\alpha/S_\alpha$. But we are given an isomorphism of $L(\pi_\alpha)$ and $\mathbf{o}_{S_\alpha}$. This induces an isomorphism of $L(\mathcal{Y}_\alpha/I_\alpha)$ and $\mathbf{o}_{I_\alpha}$; hence an isomorphism

$$q_\alpha^*(L(\pi)) \underset{\psi_\alpha}{\overset{\sim}{\rightarrow}} \mathbf{o}_{I_\alpha}.$$

The fact that $\sigma_{\alpha,\beta} = 1$ can be easily seen to imply that the diagram of sheaves on $I_\alpha \times_S I_\beta$:

$$\begin{array}{ccc} p_1^*(q_\alpha^*(L(\pi))) & \xrightarrow[\sim]{p_1^*(\psi_\alpha)} & p_1^*(\mathbf{o}_{I_\alpha}) \\ \| & & \| \\ p_2^*(q_\beta^*(L(\pi))) & \xrightarrow[p_2^*(\psi_\beta)]{\sim} & p_2^*(\mathbf{o}_{I_\beta}) \end{array}$$

commutes. In order words, both L and $\mathbf{o}_S$ satisfy the conclusions of Theorem 90 for the setup $U_\alpha = I_\alpha$, $X = S$, $L_\alpha = \mathbf{o}_{I_\alpha}$, and $\phi_{\alpha,\beta} = 1$. Therefore, the uniqueness half of that theorem states that there is a canonical isomorphism of L and $\mathbf{o}_S$. This is to be $\psi(\pi)$. We omit the rest of the details.

§6. COMPUTATIONS: DIRECT METHOD

We return to the case $g = 1$, and its topology $\mathfrak{M}$. In this section, for $\mathrm{char}(k) \neq 2, 3$, we shall give a direct computation of $\mathrm{Pic}(\mathfrak{M})$. In the next section, for $k = \mathbf{C}$, we shall give a transcendental computation of this same group.

Let L be an invertible sheaf on the moduli problem. First of all, let us try to extract some numerical invariants directly from L. Start with a family of curves $\pi : \mathfrak{X} \to S$. Any such family has one nontrivial automorphism: the inversion ρ of order 2. By definition of an invertible sheaf, the morphism of families:

$$\begin{array}{ccc} \mathfrak{X} & \xrightarrow{\rho} & \mathfrak{X} \\ {\scriptstyle\pi}\downarrow & & \downarrow{\scriptstyle\pi} \\ S & \xrightarrow[1_S]{} & S \end{array}$$

induces an automorphism $L(\rho)$ of $L(\pi)$. Since ρ has order 2, so does $L(\rho)$. But $L(\rho)$, as any automorphism of an invertible sheaf, is given by multiplication by an element $\alpha \in \Gamma(S, \mathbf{o}_S^*)$. Therefore, $\alpha^2 = 1$; hence on each connected component S_i of S, α equals $+1$ or -1. In particular, suppose $S = \mathrm{Spec}(k)$, and $\mathfrak{X} = C$ is an elliptic curve. Then we have defined a number:

$$\alpha(C) = \pm 1.$$

Moreover, if $\pi : \mathfrak{X} \to S$ is any family, then the fact that the inversion ρ for π induces the inversion on each fibre $\pi^{-1}(s)$ of the family implies that the function $\alpha \in \Gamma(S, \mathbf{o}_S^*)$ has value $\alpha(\pi^{-1}(s))$ at the point $s \in S$. This shows that α is a "continuous" function of C; that is, if we have a family $\pi : \mathfrak{X} \to S$ with connected base S, then α is constant on the set of curves $\pi^{-1}(s)$ occuring as fibres in the family π. Actually this shows that α is constant on all curves; either $\alpha(C) = +1$ for all C, or $\alpha(C) = -1$. Namely, it is easy to exhibit a family π with connected base S, such that every C occurs in π. For example, take the family of all nonsingular cubic curves; or take the modular family of cubic curves

$$y^2 = x(x - 1)(x - \lambda),$$

where $\lambda \neq 0, 1, \infty$. Therefore, in fact, we have defined one number $\alpha(L)$ equal to ± 1. And, quite clearly, this gives a homomorphism

$$\operatorname{Pic}(\mathfrak{M}) \xrightarrow{\alpha} \mathbf{Z}/2.$$

In fact, this same method goes further. After all, there are two elliptic curves with bigger groups of automorphisms. Let C_A be the curve with a group of automorphisms of order 4 (i. e., $j = 0$); let C_B be the curve with a group of order 6 (i. e., $j = 12^3$). Pick generators σ and τ of $\operatorname{Aut}(C_A)$ and $\operatorname{Aut}(C_B)$. Note that σ^2 is the inversion of C_A and τ^3 is the inversion of C_B. Let

$$\pi_A : C_A \longrightarrow \operatorname{Spec}(k)$$
$$\pi_B : C_B \longrightarrow \operatorname{Spec}(k)$$

be the trivial families. Then L gives us one-dimensional vector spaces $L(\pi_A)$ and $L(\pi_B)$, *and* L gives us an action of $\operatorname{Aut}(C_A)$ on $L(\pi_A)$ and of $\operatorname{Aut}(C_B)$ on $L(\pi_B)$. In particular, σ acts on $L(\pi_A)$ by multiplication by a fourth root of 1: call it $L(\sigma)$; and τ acts on $L(\pi_B)$ by multiplication of a sixth root of 1: call it $L(\tau)$. Clearly,

$$L(\sigma)^2 = \alpha(L)$$
$$L(\tau)^3 = \alpha(L).$$

If we also fix a primitive twelfth root of 1, ζ, then we can determine uniquely an integer β mod 12 by the equations:

$$\zeta^{6\beta} = \alpha(L);\ \zeta^{3\beta} = L(\sigma);\ \zeta^{2\beta} = L(\tau).$$

Then this associates an invariant $\beta(L) \in \mathbf{Z}/12$ to each invertible sheaf L. It is easy to see that this is a homomorphism:

$$\operatorname{Pic}(\mathfrak{M}) \xrightarrow{\beta} \mathbf{Z}/12.$$

Actually, β is not quite as nice as α, in that to define β we had to make three arbitrary choices, namely, σ, τ, and ζ. Our next step is to simultaneously make β more canonical and to prove that β is surjective. Recall the invertible sheaf Λ on $\mathfrak{M}$ given as an example in §3:

$$\Lambda(\mathfrak{X} \xrightarrow{\pi} S) = R^1\pi_*(\boldsymbol{o}_{\mathfrak{X}})$$

(with the obvious compatibility morphisms for each morphism of families). The interesting fact is that $\beta(\Lambda)$ is a generator of $\mathbf{Z}/12$. To verify this, all we have to check is that $\Lambda(\sigma)$ [resp. $\Lambda(\tau)$] is a *primitive* fourth root (resp. a sixth root) of 1. But this means simply that $\mathrm{Aut}(C_A)$ [resp. $\mathrm{Aut}(C_B)$] acts faithfully on $\Lambda(\pi_\alpha)$ [resp. $\Lambda(\pi_B)$]. Now by definition:

$$\Lambda(\pi_A) = H^1(C_A, \mathbf{o}_{C_A})$$
$$\Lambda(\pi_B) = H^1(C_B, \mathbf{o}_{C_B}).$$

We could say, at this point, that it is a classical fact that these actions are faithful. But this is not hard to check:

Proof of Faithfulness.

a. By Serre duality, for any curve C, $H^1(C, \mathbf{o}_C)$ is canonically dual to the vector space of regular differentials on C.

b. If C is the elliptic curve:

$$y^2 = x^3 + Ax + B,$$

then the differential dx/y is regular, and is a basis of the space of such differentials.

c. C_A is the curve

$$y^2 = x^3 - x = x(x+1)(x-1)$$

and σ may be taken to be

$$x \longmapsto -x$$
$$y \longmapsto iy.$$

Then $dx/y \longmapsto i(dx/y)$, so the action of $\mathrm{Aut}(C_A)$ is faithful.

d. C_B is the curve

$$y^2 = x^3 - 1 = (x-1)(x-\omega)(x-\omega^2)$$

and τ may be taken to be

$$x \longmapsto \omega \cdot x$$
$$y \longmapsto -y.$$

Then $dx/y \longmapsto -\omega(dx/y)$, so the action of $\mathrm{Aut}(C_B)$ is faithful.

Q.E.D.

Therefore β is indeed surjective. But also β can be normalized by the requirement:

$$\beta(\Lambda) \equiv 1 \pmod{12}.$$

Then β becomes completely canonical.

The last step is that β is injective, completing the proof of:

Main Theorem. If char(k) $\neq 2, 3$, and if g $= 1$, then there is a canonical isomorphism

$$\mathrm{Pic}(\mathfrak{M}) \cong \mathbf{Z}/12.$$

Sketch of Rest of Proof. Let L be an invertible sheaf on the moduli problem such that $\beta(L) \equiv 0 \pmod{12}$. Then all automorphisms of all elliptic curves C induce trivial automorphisms of the corresponding vector spaces $L(C/\mathrm{Spec}(k))$. We must set up consistent isomorphisms of all the invertible sheaves $L(\pi)$ with the sheaves $\boldsymbol{o}_S$. But say $\pi : \mathfrak{X} \rightarrow S$ is a modular family of curves containing every elliptic curve as a fibre. Then according to the results of §5, it is sufficient to set up an isomorphism ϕ of this one $L(\pi)$ and $\boldsymbol{o}_S$ provided that the compatibility property written out in §5 is satisfied.

Look at the diagram:

$$\begin{array}{c} \mathrm{Isom}(\pi, \pi) \\ \downarrow f \\ \{\text{Normalization of } S \times_{\mathbf{A}} S\} \\ \downarrow g \\ S \times_{\mathbf{A}_j} S \\ p_1 \searrow \quad \swarrow p_2 \\ S \end{array}$$

(cf. §4, last part). Recall that f is an étale double covering. Let $q_i = p_i \circ g \circ f$. By definition of an invertible sheaf, we are given an isomorphism ψ of $q_1^*(L)$ and $q_2^*(L)$. We can use the fact that $\beta(L) \equiv 0$ to show that there is actually an isomorphism ψ_0 of $p_1^*(L)$ and $p_2^*(L)$ which induces ψ via $f^* \circ g^*$. Set theoretically, we see this is as follows: let t and t' be two closed points of $\mathrm{Isom}(\pi, \pi)$ over the same point $\bar{t}$ of $S \times_{\mathbf{A}} S$. Let $\bar{L}_1$ and $\bar{L}_2$ be the one-dimensional vector spaces obtained by restricting the invertible sheaves $p_1^*(L)$ and $p_2^*(L)$ to the one-point subscheme $\{\bar{t}\}$. If $s_i = p_i(\bar{t})$, then $\bar{L}_i = L(\pi^{-1}(s_i))$. Moreover, t and t' define two isomorphisms τ and τ' of $\pi^{-1}(s_1)$ and $\pi^{-1}(s_2)$. By hypothesis, $L(\tau' \circ \tau^{-1})$ is the identity! Therefore, $L(\tau) = L(\tau')$. But $L(\tau)$ and $L(\tau')$ are just the isomorphisms of $\bar{L}_1$ and $\bar{L}_2$ given by looking at the action of ψ at the points t and t'. Therefore, ψ induces a *unique* isomorphism ψ_0 of $\bar{L}_1$ and $\bar{L}_2$ at $\bar{t}$. One must still check that this isomorphism ψ_0 is given by functions in the local rings of $S \times_{\mathbf{A}} S$ (this scheme is not normal, so this is not obvious). We omit this technical point.

Now the compatibility property of ψ shows immediately that ψ_0 is descent data for the invertible sheaf $L(\pi)$ on S with respect to the morphism $j : S \to \mathbf{A}_j$. Also j is clearly a flat covering of $\mathbf{A}_j$. Therefore, we can apply Theorem 90 of §5! In other words, we find an invertible sheaf L_0 on $\mathbf{A}_j$, and an isomorphism ϕ of $L(\pi)$ with $j^*(L_0)$ such that the following commutes:

$$\begin{array}{ccc} p_1^*(L(\pi)) & \xrightarrow[\psi]{\sim} & p_2^*(L(\pi)) \\ {\scriptstyle p_1^*(\phi)}\downarrow\wr & & \downarrow\wr{\scriptstyle p_2^*(\phi)} \\ p_1^*(j^*(L_0)) & = & p_2^*(j^*(L_0)) \end{array} \tag{2}$$

But now every invertible sheaf on the affine line is trivial, that is, $L_0 \cong \boldsymbol{o}_{\mathbf{A}}$. Use this isomorphism to set up an isomorphism of L with $\boldsymbol{o}_S$. Finally, the compatibility property follows immediately from (2).

Q.E.D.

§7. COMPUTATIONS: TRANSCENDENTAL METHOD

Now assume $k = \mathbf{C}$. We shall give a completely different approach to Pic($\mathfrak{M}$) which has the virtue of generalizing to higher genus in various ways. This approach is based on:

Definition. An "analytic family of elliptic curves" is a morphism $\pi : \mathfrak{X} \to S$ of analytic spaces, which is proper and flat, plus a section $\varepsilon : S \to \mathfrak{X}$ of π, such that the fibres of π are elliptic curves.

We can now define a modular analytic family in two ways: either by the same properties used to define an (algebraic) modular family;† or else by defining the j-morphism from the base S to the complex j-plane and requiring that

a. S is a nonsingular one-dimensional complex space.
b. j is open.
c. j has ramification index 1, 2, 3 at $x \in S$ according to $j(x) \neq 0, 12^3$, $j(x) = 0$, or $j(x) = 12^3$.

† The lifting property goes over verbatim. But instead of asking that each elliptic curve only occur a finite number of times in a modular family $\pi : \mathfrak{X} \to S$, we should ask that it occur only over the points of a discrete subset $\Delta \subset S$.

A morphism of families is defined exactly as before, using analytic maps rather than algebraic ones.

Definition. The topology $\mathfrak{M}_{cx}$ is as follows:

a. Its open sets are analytic modular families of elliptic curves $\pi : \mathfrak{X} \to S$, and a final object M,
b. Its morphisms and coverings are exactly as in $\mathfrak{M}$.

We check to see that products exist in this topology and that they have exactly the same interpretation as before. Moreover, we get a continuous map of topologies:

$$\mathfrak{M}_{cx} \xrightarrow{\alpha} \mathfrak{M},$$

just as, in §2, we found a continuous map from the complex topology to the étale topology on a scheme. For all integers n, define a sheaf $\mathbf{Z}/n$ on $\mathfrak{M}_{cx}$ by

$$\mathbf{Z}/n[\mathfrak{X} \xrightarrow{\pi} S] = \bigoplus_{\substack{\text{topological components} \\ S\alpha \text{ of } S}} \mathbf{Z}/n$$

The direct image $\alpha_* (\mathbf{Z}/n)$ of this sheaf is simply the "same" sheaf:

$$\mathbf{Z}/n[\mathfrak{X} \xrightarrow{\pi} S] = \bigoplus_{\substack{\text{topological components} \\ \text{(in Zariski topology) of } S}} \mathbf{Z}/n.$$

An immediate extension of Artin's result tells us that the canonical homomorphism

$$H^i(\mathfrak{M}, \mathbf{Z}/n) \to H^i(\mathfrak{M}_{cx}, \mathbf{Z}/n)$$

is an isomorphism.†

This gives us a transcendental approach to the cohomology groups $H^i(\mathfrak{M}, \mathbf{Z}/n)$. These are related to the Picard group by virtue of the standard exact sequences of sheaves:

$$0 \to \mathbf{Z}/n \to \boldsymbol{o}^* \xrightarrow{n} \boldsymbol{o}^* \to 0,$$

where n indicates the homomorphism $f \mapsto f^n$ (cf. [1], p. 102). The

† The stronger form in which Artin gave his result is that if $g : X_{cx} \to X_{\acute{e}t}$ is the canonical map, then:

$$R^i g_* (\mathbf{Z}/n) = (0), \qquad i > 0.$$

This gives $R^i\alpha_* (\mathbf{Z}/n) = (0)$, $(i > 0)$ as a corollary because $\mathfrak{M}$ (respectively, $\mathfrak{M}_{cx}$) induces on an open set $\mathfrak{X} \xrightarrow{\pi} S$ the topology $S_{\acute{e}t}$ (respectively, S_{cx}).

cohomology sequence tells us:

$$0 \to H^0(\mathfrak{M}, \mathbf{Z}/n) \to H^0(\mathfrak{M}, \boldsymbol{o}^*) \xrightarrow{n} H^0(\mathfrak{M}, \boldsymbol{o}^*) \to H^1(\mathfrak{M}, \mathbf{Z}/n) \to \operatorname{Pic}(\mathfrak{M}) \to \operatorname{Pic}(\mathfrak{M}) \to H^2(\mathfrak{M}, \mathbf{Z}/n).$$

Via these sequences, we can work out the structure of $\operatorname{Pic}(\mathfrak{M})$, given that of $H^i(\mathfrak{M}, \mathbf{Z}/n)$. This is because we can prove by general arguments that

a. $H^0(\mathfrak{M}, \boldsymbol{o}^*)$ has the subgroup $\mathbf{C}^*$ of constant functions, with factor group isomorphic to $\mathbf{Z}^a$.
b. $\operatorname{Pic}(\mathfrak{M})$ has a subgroup $\operatorname{Pic}^\tau(\mathfrak{M})$ of the type $\mathbf{R}^b/\mathbf{Z}^c$, where the lattice $\mathbf{Z}^c$ spans $\mathbf{R}^b$ (it need not be discrete), with finitely generated factor group.

Corollary. If there is a prime p such that $H^1(\mathfrak{M}, \mathbf{Z}/p) = (0)$, then $H^0(\mathfrak{M}, \boldsymbol{o}^*) = \mathbf{C}^*$, and $\operatorname{Pic}(\mathfrak{M})$ is finitely generated.

Corollary. If there is a prime p such that $H^1(\mathfrak{M}, \mathbf{Z}/p) = H^2(\mathfrak{M}, \mathbf{Z}/p) = (0)$, then $\operatorname{Pic}(\mathfrak{M})$ is a finite group, and

$$\operatorname{Pic}(\mathfrak{M}) = \varinjlim H^1(\mathfrak{M}, \mathbf{Z}/n),$$

where the limit is taken with respect to the ordering:

$$n_1 \geq n_2 \quad \text{if} \quad n_2 \mid n_1,$$

and the maps

$$\mathbf{Z}/n_2 \xrightarrow{n_1/n_2} \mathbf{Z}/n_1.$$

(The proofs are obvious.)

We now go on to consider the topology $\mathfrak{M}_{\mathrm{cx}}$. The point is that there is one open set in $\mathfrak{M}_{\mathrm{cx}}$ which is very well known:

Let $\mathfrak{H} = \{z \in \mathbf{C} \mid \operatorname{Im}(z) > 0\}$.

Let $\mathbf{Z} \oplus \mathbf{Z}$ act on the analytic space $\mathbf{C} \times \mathfrak{H}$ so that the generators act by:

$$(x, z) \mapsto (x + 1, z)$$
$$(x, z) \mapsto (x + z, z).$$

Let $\mathfrak{X} = (\mathbf{C} \times \mathfrak{H}/\mathbf{Z} \oplus \mathbf{Z})$.

Let $\pi : \mathfrak{X} \to \mathfrak{H}$ be induced by $p_2 : \mathbf{C} \times \mathfrak{H} \to \mathfrak{H}$.

Let $\epsilon : \mathfrak{H} \to \mathfrak{X}$ be induced by the section $\mathfrak{H} \xrightarrow{\sim} (0) \times \mathfrak{H} \subset \mathbf{C} \times \mathfrak{H}$.

Then π (and ϵ) define a modular analytic family of elliptic curves. Moreover, every elliptic curve occurs in π, so it is a covering of M.

Let $\Gamma = SL(2; \mathbf{Z})$

$$= \text{group of integral } 2 \times 2 \text{ matrices} \begin{pmatrix} a & b \\ c & d \end{pmatrix}$$

such that $ad - bc = 1$.

Let Γ act on $\mathfrak{H}$ via

$$\begin{pmatrix} a & b \\ c & d \end{pmatrix} \times (z) \mapsto \left(\frac{az + b}{cz + d}\right)$$

Call this morphism $\tau_0 : \Gamma \times \mathfrak{H} \to \mathfrak{H}$.

Let Γ act on $\mathbf{C} \times \mathfrak{H}$ via

$$\begin{pmatrix} a & b \\ c & d \end{pmatrix} \times (x, z) \mapsto \left(\frac{x}{cz + d}, \frac{az + b}{cz + d}\right)$$

Then we check that the action of Γ normalizes the action of $\mathbf{Z} \oplus \mathbf{Z}$, hence it induces an action of Γ on $\mathfrak{X}$. Denote by $\tau : \Gamma \times \mathfrak{X} \to \mathfrak{X}$ the morphism giving this action. Clearly, π and ϵ commute with this action of Γ, so that we have made Γ into a group of automorphisms of the family $\mathfrak{X}/\mathfrak{H}$. This action of Γ has the following interpretation: via the diagram

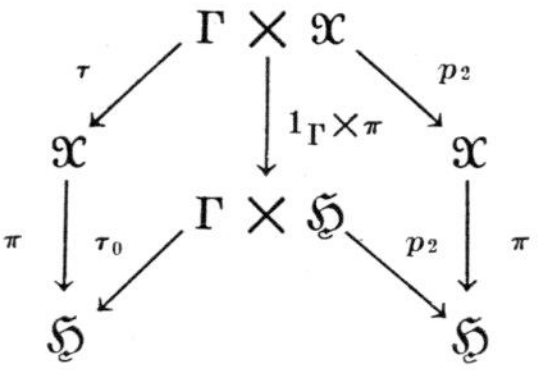

$$\begin{array}{ccccc} & & \Gamma \times \mathfrak{X} & & \\ & \swarrow^{\tau} & \downarrow^{1_\Gamma \times \pi} & \searrow^{p_2} & \\ \mathfrak{X} & & & & \mathfrak{X} \\ \downarrow^{\pi} & & \Gamma \times \mathfrak{H} & & \downarrow^{\pi} \\ & \swarrow^{\tau_0} & & \searrow^{p_2} & \\ \mathfrak{H} & & & & \mathfrak{H} \end{array} \tag{3}$$

the family of elliptic curves $\Gamma \times \mathfrak{X}/\Gamma \times \mathfrak{H}$ is made into the product of $\mathfrak{X}/\mathfrak{H}$ with itself; in particular,

$$\Gamma \times \mathfrak{H} = \text{Isom}(\pi, \pi).$$

The effect of this is to make a connection between the topology $\mathfrak{M}_{cx}$ and the topology T_Γ of the discrete group Γ (cf. §1). We recall:

Definition. The topology T_Γ is as follows:

a. Its open sets are Γ-sets S, that is, sets plus action of Γ.
b. Its morphisms are Γ-linear maps between Γ-sets.
c. Its coverings are collections $S_\alpha \xrightarrow{p\alpha} S$ of morphisms such that

$$S = \bigcup_\alpha p_\alpha(S_\alpha).$$

For our purpose, we need a slight modification of this topology.
Definition. Let Γ_n be the subgroup of Γ of matrices such that

$$\begin{pmatrix} a & b \\ c & d \end{pmatrix} \equiv \begin{pmatrix} 1 & 0 \\ 0 & 1 \end{pmatrix} \pmod{n}$$

Definition. Let T'_Γ be the following topology:

a. Its open sets are Γ-sets S such that, for all $x \in S$, the subgroup of Γ of elements leaving x fixed is contained in Γ_3; and a final object M.
b. Its morphisms are Γ-linear maps of Γ-sets, and projections of Γ-sets to M.
c. Its covering are collections $S_\alpha \xrightarrow{p\alpha} S$ of morphisms such that

$$S = \bigcup_\alpha p_\alpha(S_\alpha);$$

and any collections of morphisms to M.

There is a continuous map:

$$T_\Gamma \xrightarrow{\beta} T'_\Gamma$$

such that β^{-1} of a Γ-set S is S; and $\beta^{-1}(M)$ is the Γ-set $\{e\}$ with one element. It is easy to check that β_* sets up an equivalence between the category of abelian sheaves on T_Γ and the category of abelian sheaves on T'_Γ. Therefore, cohomologically T_Γ and T'_Γ are identical. In fact, as we saw in §1, these categories of sheaves are equivalent to the category of Γ-modules (where the group of global sections of a sheaf is equal to the subgroup of Γ-invariants of the corresponding module). Therefore, the cohomology of T_Γ and T'_Γ is also the same as the cohomology of the group Γ.

Finally, there is a continuous map

$$\mathfrak{M}_{cx} \xrightarrow{\gamma} T'_\Gamma$$

which is as follows:

Definition. Let S be a Γ-set in T'_Γ; give S the discrete topology. Then $\gamma^{-1}(S)$ is the family:

$$\begin{array}{c} \mathfrak{X} \times S/\Gamma \\ \downarrow \\ \mathfrak{H} \times S/\Gamma \end{array}$$

where Γ acts on $\mathfrak{X} \times S$ and $\mathfrak{H} \times S$ by a product of τ and τ_0 with the given action on S.

This makes sense only provided that Γ acts freely on $\mathfrak{H} \times S$ (hence on $\mathfrak{X} \times S$). But if an element $a \in \Gamma$ leaves fixed some element of S, then by definition of T'_Γ, $a \in \Gamma_3$; then it is easy to check that a acts on $\mathfrak{H}$ without fixed points. Therefore, the action is free. Of course, $\gamma^{-1}(M)$ is to be M. The key point to check is that fibre products in T'_Γ go into fibre products in $\mathfrak{M}_{cx}$. We omit the proof, except to say that this fact follows readily from the fact that diagram (3) makes $\Gamma \times \mathfrak{X}/\Gamma \times \mathfrak{H}$ into the product of $\mathfrak{X}/\mathfrak{H}$ with itself.

Recapitulating, we have unwound the structure of M by the following continuous maps:

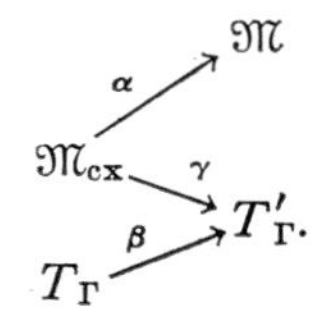

The final step is to prove that, via γ, we get an isomorphism:

$$H^i(T'_\Gamma, \mathbf{Z}/n) \xrightarrow{\sim} H^i(\mathfrak{M}_{cx}, \mathbf{Z}/n)$$

This follows from the Leray spectral sequence, once we know that:

$$R^i\gamma_*(\mathbf{Z}/n) = (0), \qquad i > 0;$$

and this is equivalent to knowing that $\mathbf{Z}/n$ has no higher cohomology in the induced topology on the open set $\mathfrak{X}/\mathfrak{H}$ in $\mathfrak{M}_{cx}$. But this is just the classical topology on $\mathfrak{H}$; and since $\mathfrak{H}$ is homeomorphic to a cell, $\mathbf{Z}/n$ has no higher cohomology in this topology.

Corollary. There are canonical isomorphisms:

$$H^i(\mathfrak{M}, \mathbf{Z}/n) = H^i(\Gamma, \mathbf{Z}/n) \qquad \text{for all } i.$$

Now it is well known that

a. $H^i(\Gamma, M) = (0)$, $i \geq 2$, for any Γ-module M which is p-torsion, $p \neq 2, 3$,
b. $H^1(\Gamma, M) = \text{Hom}(\mathbf{Z}/12, M)$ for any abelian group M with trivial Γ action.

Putting all the results of this section together, we have proven again that $\text{Pic}(\mathfrak{M}) \cong \mathbf{Z}/12$.

REFERENCES

1. Artin, M., *Grothendieck Topologies*, Mimeographed notes, Harvard University, Cambridge, Mass., 1962.
2. Grothendieck, A., Fondements de la géométrie algébrique, *Collected Bourbaki Talks*, mimeographed by the Secrétariat Mathématique, Paris, 1962.
3. Grothendieck, A., *Séminaire de géométrie algébrique*, Institut des hautes études scientifique, Paris, 1960–61.
4. Grothendieck, A., Sur quelques points d'algèbre homologique, *Tôhoku Math. Jour.*, **9**(1957), 119.
5. Lang, S., *Introduction to algebraic geometry*, Interscience, N.Y., 1958.
6. Lang, S., *Abelian varieties*, Interscience, N.Y., 1959.
7. Mumford, D., *Geometric invariant theory*, Springer-Verlag, Berlin-Göttingen-Heidelberg, 1965.
8. Northcott, D., *An introduction to homological algebra*, Cambridge University Press, Cambridge, 1960.
9. Rauch, H., The singularities of the moduli space, *Bull. Amer. Math. Soc.*, **68**(1962), 390.
10. Severi, F., La géométrie algébrique italienne (esp. p. 37), in *Colloque de géométrie algébrique*, Georges Thone, Liége, and Masson, Paris, 1949.

Zeta and L Functions

Jean-Pierre Serre

The purpose of this lecture is to give the general properties of zeta functions and Artin's L functions in the setting of *schemes*. I will restrict myself mainly to the formal side of the theory; for the connection with l-adic cohomology and Lefschetz's formula, see Tate's lecture.

§1. ZETA FUNCTIONS

1.1. DIMENSION OF SCHEMES

All schemes considered below are supposed to be *of finite type over* **Z**. Such a scheme X has a well-defined *dimension* denoted by $\dim X$. It is the maximum length n of a chain

$$Z_0 \subset Z_1 \subset \cdots \subset Z_n, \qquad Z_i \neq Z_{i+1}$$

of closed irreducible subspaces of X. If X itself is irreducible, with generic point x, and if $k(x)$ is the corresponding residue field, one has:

$$\dim X = \text{Kronecker dimension of } k(x). \tag{1}$$

(The Kronecker dimension of a field E is the transcendence degree of E over the prime field, augmented by 1 if $\text{char} E = 0$.)

1.2. CLOSED POINTS

Let X be a scheme and let $x \in X$. The following properties are equivalent:

a. $\{x\}$ is closed in X.

b. The residue field $k(x)$ is finite.

The set of closed points of X will be denoted by $\bar{X}$; we view it as a discrete topological space, equipped with the sheaf of fields $k(x)$; we call $\bar{X}$ the *atomization* of X. If $x \in \bar{X}$, the *norm* $N(x)$ of x is the number of elements of $k(x)$.

1.3. ZETA FUNCTIONS

The zeta function of a scheme X is defined by the eulerian product

$$\zeta(X, s) = \prod_{x \in \bar{X}} \frac{1}{1 - 1/N(x)^s}. \tag{2}$$

It is easily seen that there are only a finite number of $x \in \bar{X}$ with a given norm. This is enough to show that the above product is a *formal Dirichlet series* $\Sigma a_n/n^s$, with integral coefficients. In fact, that series converges, as the following theorem shows:

Theorem 1. The product $\zeta(X, s)$ converges absolutely for

$$R(s) > \dim X.$$

(As usual, $R(s)$ denotes the *real part* of s.)

Lemma. (a) Let X be a finite union of schemes X_i. If Theorem 1 is valid for each of the X_i's, it is valid for X. (b) If $X \to Y$ is a finite morphism, and if Theorem 1 is valid for Y, it is valid for X.

Using this lemma (which is elementary) and induction on dimension, one reduces Theorem 1 to the case

$$X = \text{Spec } A[T_1, \ldots, T_n],$$

where the ring A is either $\mathbf{Z}$ or $\mathbf{F}_p$. In the first case, $\dim X = n + 1$, and the product (2) gives (after collecting some terms together):

$$\zeta(X, s) = \prod_p \frac{1}{1 - p^{n-s}} = \zeta(s - n).$$

In the second case, $\dim X = n$, and $\zeta(X, s) = 1/(1 - p^{n-s})$. In both cases, we have absolute convergence for $R(s) > \dim X$.

1.4. ANALYTIC CONTINUATION OF ZETA FUNCTIONS

One *conjectures* that $\zeta(X, s)$ can be continued as a meromorphic function in the entire s-plane; this, at least, has been proved for many schemes. However, in the general case, one knows only the following much weaker:

Theorem 2. $\zeta(X, s)$ can be continued analytically (as a meromorphic function) in the half-plane $R(s) > \dim X - \frac{1}{2}$.

The singularities of $\zeta(X, s)$ in the strip

$$\dim X - \tfrac{1}{2} < R(s) \leqq \dim X$$

are as follows:

Theorem 3. Assume X to be irreducible, and let E be the residue field of its generic point.

a. If $\operatorname{char} E = 0$, the only pole of $\zeta(X, s)$ in $R(s) > \dim X - \frac{1}{2}$ is $s = \dim X$, and it is a simple pole.

b. If $\operatorname{char} E = p \neq 0$, let q be the highest power of p such that E contains the field $\mathbf{F}_q$. The only poles of $\zeta(X, s)$ in $R(s) > \dim X - \frac{1}{2}$ are the points

$$s = \dim X + \frac{2\pi i n}{\log(q)}, \qquad n \in \mathbf{Z},$$

and they are simple poles.

Corollary 1. For any nonempty scheme X, the point $s = \dim X$ is a pole of $\zeta(X, s)$. Its order is equal to the number of irreducible components of X of dimension equal to $\dim X$.

Corollary 2. The domain of convergence of the Dirichlet series $\zeta(X, s)$ is the half-plane $R(s) > \dim X$.

Theorem 2 and Theorem 3 are deeper than Theorem 1. Their proof uses the "Riemann hypothesis for curves" of Weil [7] combined with the technique of "fibering by curves" (i.e., maps $X \to Y$ whose fibers are of dimension 1). One may also deduce them from the estimates of Lang-Weil [5] and Nisnevič [6].

1.5. SOME PROPERTIES AND EXAMPLES

$\zeta(X, s)$ depends only on the *atomization* $\bar{X}$ of X. In particular, it does not change by radicial morphism, and we have

$$\zeta(X_{\text{red}}, s) = \zeta(X, s). \tag{3}$$

If X is a disjoint union (which may be infinite) of subschemes X_i, we have

$$\zeta(X, s) = \prod \zeta(X_i, s),$$

with absolute convergence for $R(s) > \dim X$. It is even enough that $\bar{X}$ be the disjoint union of the $\bar{X}_i$'s. For instance, if $f : X \to Y$ is a morphism, we may take for X_i's the fibers $X_y = f^{-1}(y)$, $y \in \bar{Y}$, and we get:

$$\zeta(X, s) = \prod_{y \in \bar{Y}} \zeta(X_y, s). \tag{4}$$

(This, with $Y = \operatorname{Spec}(\mathbf{Z})$, was the original definition of Hasse-Weil.) Note that the X_y's are schemes over the finite fields $k(y)$; that is, they are "algebraic varieties."

If $X = \operatorname{Spec}(A)$, where A is the ring of integers of a number field K $\zeta(X, s)$ coincides with the classical zeta function ζ_K attached to K. For $A = \mathbf{Z}$, we get Riemann's zeta.

If $\mathbf{A}^n(X)$ is the affine n-space over a scheme X, we have

$$\zeta(\mathbf{A}^n(X), s) = \zeta(X, s - n).$$

Similarly,

$$\zeta(\mathbf{P}^n(X), s) = \prod_{m=0}^{m=n} \zeta(X, s - m).$$

1.6. SCHEMES OVER A FINITE FIELD

Let X be a scheme over $\mathbf{F}_q$. If $x \in \bar{X}$, the residue field $k(x)$ is a finite extension of $\mathbf{F}_q$; let $\deg(x)$ be its degree. We have

$$N(x) = q^{\deg(x)},$$

and

$$\zeta(X, s) = Z(X, q^{-s}) \tag{5}$$

where $Z(X, t)$ is the power series defined by the product:

$$Z(X, t) = \prod_{x \in \bar{X}} \frac{1}{1 - t^{\deg(x)}}. \tag{6}$$

The product (6) converges for $|t| < q^{-\dim X}$.

Theorem 4 (Dwork). $Z(X, t)$ is a rational function of t.

(See[3] for the proof.)

In particular, $\zeta(X, s)$ is meromorphic in the whole plane and periodic of period $2\pi i/\log(q)$.

There is another expression of $Z(X, t)$ which is useful:

Let $k = \mathbf{F}_q$, and denote by k_n the extension of k with degree n. Let $X_n = X(k_n)$ be the set of points of X with value in k_n/k. Such a point P can be viewed as a *pair* (x, f), with $x \in \bar{X}$, and where f is a k-isomorphism of $k(x)$ into k_n. We have

$$\bigcup X_n = X(\bar{k}),$$

where $\bar{k}$ is the algebraic closure of k.

It is easily seen that the X_n's are *finite*. If we put:

$$\nu_n = \mathrm{Card}(X_n),$$

we have

$$\log Z(X, t) = \sum_{n=1}^{\infty} \frac{\nu_n t^n}{n}. \tag{7}$$

1.7. FROBENIUS

We keep the notations of 1.6. Let $F : X \to X$ be the "Frobenius morphism" of X into itself (i.e., F is the identity on the topological space X, and it acts on the sheaf O_X by $\varphi \mapsto \varphi^q$). If we make F operate on $X(\bar{k})$, the *fixed points* of the nth iterate F^n of F are *the elements of* X_n. In particular, the number ν_n is *the number* $\Lambda(F^n)$ *of fixed points of* F^n. This remark, first made by Weil, is the starting point of his interpretation of ν_n as a *trace*, in Lefschetz's style.

§2. *L* FUNCTIONS

2.1 FINITE GROUPS ACTING ON A SCHEME

Let X be a scheme, let G be a finite group, and suppose that G acts on X on the right; we also assume that the quotient $X/G = Y$

exists (i.e., X is a union of affine open sets which are stable by G). The atomization $\bar{Y}$ of Y may be identified with $\bar{X}/G$. More precisely, let $x \in \bar{X}$, let y be its image in $\bar{Y}$, and let $D(x)$ be the corresponding decomposition subgroup; we have $g \in D(x)$ if and only if g leaves x fixed. There is a natural epimorphism

$$D(x) \longrightarrow \text{Gal } k(x)/k(y).$$

Its kernel $I(x)$ is called the *inertia subgroup* corresponding to x; when $I(x) = \{1\}$, the morphism $X \longrightarrow Y$ is *étale* at x.

Since $D(x)/I(x)$ can be identified with $\text{Gal}(k(x)/k(y))$, it is a cyclic group, with a canonical generator F_x, called the *Frobenius element* of x.

2.2. ARTIN'S DEFINITION OF L FUNCTIONS

Let χ be a character of G (i.e. a linear combination, with coefficients in $\mathbf{Z}$, of irreducible complex characters). For each $y \in \bar{Y}$, and for each integer n, let $\chi(y^n)$ be the mean value of χ on the nth power F_x^n of the Frobenius element $F_x \in D(x)/I(x)$, where $x \in \bar{X}$ is any lifting of y. Artin's definition of the L function $L(X, \chi; s)$ is the following (cf. [1]):

$$\log L(X, \chi; s) = \sum_{y \in \bar{Y}} \sum_{n=1}^{\infty} \frac{\chi(y^n) N(y)^{-ns}}{n}. \tag{8}$$

When χ is the character of a linear representation $g \mapsto M(g)$, we have

$$L(X, \chi; s) = \prod_{y \in \bar{Y}} \frac{1}{\det(1 - M(F_x)/N(y)^s)}, \tag{9}$$

where $M(F_x)$ is again defined as the mean value of $M(g)$, for $g \mapsto F_x$.

Both expressions (8) and (9) converge absolutely when

$$R(s) > \dim X.$$

2.3. FORMAL PROPERTIES OF THE L FUNCTIONS

a. $L(X, \chi)$ depends on X only through its atomization $\bar{X}$.

b. $L(X, \chi + \chi') = L(X, \chi). L(X, \chi')$.

c. If $\bar{X}$ is the disjoint union of the $\bar{X}_i$'s, with X_i stable by G for each i, we have

$$L(X, \chi; s) = \prod L(X_i, \chi; s)$$

with absolute convergence for $R(s) > \dim X$.

d. Let $\pi : G \rightarrow G'$ be a homomorphism, and let $\pi_* X = X \times^G G'$ be the scheme deduced from X by "extension of the structural group." Let χ' be a character of G', and let $\pi^*\chi' = \chi' \circ \pi$ be the corresponding character of G. We have

$$L(X, \pi^*\chi') = L(\pi_* X, \chi'). \tag{10}$$

e. Let $\pi : G' \rightarrow G$ be a homomorphism, and let π^*X denote the scheme X on which G' operates through π. Let χ' be a character of G', and let $\pi_*\chi'$ be its direct image, which is a character of G (when G' is a subgroup of G, $\pi_*\chi'$ is the "induced character" of χ'). We have

$$L(X, \pi_*\chi') = L(\pi^*X, \chi'). \tag{11}$$

f. Let $X = \operatorname{Spec}(\mathbf{F}_{q^n})$, $Y = \operatorname{Spec}(\mathbf{F}_q)$, $G = \operatorname{Gal}(\mathbf{F}_{q^n}/\mathbf{F}_q)$, and χ an irreducible character of G. We have

$$L(X, \chi; s) = \frac{1}{1 - \chi(F)q^{-s}}, \tag{12}$$

where F is the Frobenius element of G.

It is not hard to see that *properties* (a) *to* (f) *uniquely characterize the L functions.*

g. If $\chi = 1$ (unit character), $L(X, 1) = \zeta(X/G)$.

h. If $\chi = r$ (character of the regular representation), we have

$$L(X, r) = \zeta(X).$$

By combining (h) and (b), one gets the following formula (which is one of the main reasons for introducing L functions):

$$\zeta(X) = \prod_{\chi \in \operatorname{Irr}(G)} L(X, \chi)^{\deg(\chi)}, \tag{13}$$

where $\operatorname{Irr}(G)$ denotes the set of *irreducible characters* of G, and $\deg(\chi) = \chi(1)$.

There is an analogous result for $\zeta(X/H)$, when H is a subgroup of G; one replaces the regular representation by the permutation representation of G/H.

2.4. SCHEMES OVER A FINITE FIELD

Let X be an $\mathbf{F}_q$-scheme and assume that the operations of G are $\mathbf{F}_q$-automorphisms of X. The scheme $Y = X/G$ is then also an $\mathbf{F}_q$-scheme.

On the set $X(\bar{k})$, we have two kinds of operators: the Frobenius endomorphism F (cf. 1.7) and the automorphisms defined by the elements of G; if $g \in G$, we have $F \circ g = g \circ F$.

If we put as usual $t = q^{-s}$, we can transform $L(X, \chi; s)$ into a function $\boldsymbol{L}(X, \chi; t)$ of t. An elementary calculation gives:

$$\log \boldsymbol{L}(X, \chi; t) = \sum_{n=1}^{\infty} \nu_n(\chi) t^n/n, \tag{14}$$

with

$$\nu_n(\chi) = \frac{1}{(G)} \sum_{g \in G} \chi(g^{-1}) \Lambda(gF^n), \tag{15}$$

where $(G) = \mathrm{Card}(G)$, and $\Lambda(gF^n)$ is the number of fixed points of gF^n (acting on $X(\bar{k})$).

(These formulae could have been used to *define* the L functions; they make the verification of properties (a) to (f) very easy.)

Remark. It is not yet known that $\boldsymbol{L}(X, \chi; t)$ is a *rational function* of t. However, this is true in the following special cases:

a. When X is projective and smooth over $\mathbf{F}_q$: this follows from l-adic cohomology (Artin-Grothendieck).
b. When Artin-Schreier or Kummer theory applies; that is, when G is cyclic of order p^N, or of order m prime to p, with m dividing $q - 1$. This can be proved by Dwork's method; the case $G = \mathbf{Z}/p\mathbf{Z}$ has been studied in some detail by Bombieri.

(Added in proof: The rationality of the L functions has now been proved by Grothendieck. See his Bourbaki's lecture, n° 279.)

2.5. ARTIN-SCHREIER EXTENSIONS

It would be easy—but too long—to give various examples of L functions, in particular for an abelian group G. I will limit myself to one such example:

Let Y be an $\mathbf{F}_q$-scheme, and let a be a section of the sheaf $\boldsymbol{O}_Y$. In the affine line $Y[T]$, let X be the closed subscheme defined by the equation

$$T^p - T = a.$$

If we put $G = \mathbf{Z}/p\mathbf{Z}$, the group G acts on X by $T \mapsto T + 1$, and

$X/G = Y$; we get in this way an *étale covering*. Let w be a primitive pth root of unity in $\mathbf{C}$, and let χ be the character of G defined by $\chi(n) = w^n$. The L function $L(X, \chi; t)$ is given by formula (14); its coefficients $\nu_n(\chi)$ can be written here in the following form:

$$\nu_n(\chi) = \sum_{y \in Y_n} w^{\mathrm{Tr}_n a(y)}, \tag{16}$$

where $Y_n = Y(k_n)$, and Tr_n is the trace map from $k_n = \mathbf{F}_{q^n}$ to $\mathbf{F}_p$. The above expression is a typical "exponential sum." If, for instance, we take for Y the multiplicative group $\mathbf{G}_m$, and put $a = \lambda y + \mu y^{-1}$, we get the so-called "Kloosterman sums." This connection between L functions and exponential sums was first noticed by Davenport-Hasse [2] and then used by Weil [8] to give estimates in the one-dimensional case.

2.6. ANALYTIC CONTINUATION OF L FUNCTIONS

Theorems 2 and 3 have analogues for L functions. First:

Theorem 5. $L(X, \chi; s)$ can be continued analytically (as a meromorphic function) in the half-plane $R(s) > \dim X - \frac{1}{2}$.

The singularities of $L(X, \chi; s)$ in the critical strip

$$\dim X - \tfrac{1}{2} < R(s) \leq \dim X$$

can be determined, or rather reduced to the classical case $\dim X = 1$. We use the following variant of the "fibering by curves" method:

Lemma. Let $f : X \to X'$ be a morphism which commutes with the action of the group G. Assume that all geometric fibers of f are irreducible curves. Then

$$L(X, \chi; s) = H(s) \cdot L(X', \chi; s - 1), \tag{17}$$

where $H(s)$ is holomorphic and $\neq 0$ for $R(s) > \dim X - \frac{1}{2}$.

This lemma gives a reduction process to dimension 1 (and even to dimension 0 if X is a scheme over a finite field). The result obtained in this way is a bit involved, and I will just state a special case:

Theorem 6. Assume that X is irreducible, and that G operates faithfully on the residue field E of the generic point of X. Let χ be a character of G, and let $\langle\chi, 1\rangle$ be the multiplicity of the identity character 1 in χ. The order of $L(X, \chi)$ at $s = \dim X$ is equal to $-\langle\chi, 1\rangle$.

Corollary. If χ is a non-trivial irreducible character, $L(X, \chi)$ is holomorphic and $\neq 0$ at the point $s = \dim X$.

2.7. ARTIN-ČEBOTAREV'S DENSITY THEOREM

Let Y be an irreducible scheme of dimension $n \geqq 1$. By using the fact that $\zeta(Y, s)$ has a simple pole at $s = n$, we get easily:

$$\sum_{y\in\bar{Y}} \frac{1}{N(y)^s} \sim \log \frac{1}{s-n} \qquad \text{for } s \to n. \tag{18}$$

A subset M of $\bar{Y}$ has a *Dirichlet density* m if we have

$$\left(\sum_{y\in M} \frac{1}{N(y)^s}\right)\Big/ \log \frac{1}{s-n} \to m \qquad \text{for } s \to n. \tag{19}$$

For $Y = \mathrm{Spec}(\mathbf{Z})$, this is the usual definition of the Dirichlet density of a set of prime numbers.

Now let X verify the assumptions of Theorem 6, and let $Y = X/G$. Assume that $\dim X \geqq 1$ and that G operates freely (i.e., $I(x) = \{1\}$ for all $x \in \bar{X}$). If $y \in \bar{Y}$, the Frobenius element F_x of a corresponding point $x \in \bar{X}$ is a well defined element of G, and its conjugation class F_y depends only on y.

Theorem 7. Let $R \subset G$ be a subset of G stable by conjugation. The set $\bar{Y}_R$ of elements $y \in \bar{Y}$ such that $F_y \subset R$ has Dirichlet density equal to $\mathrm{Card}(R)/\mathrm{Card}(G)$.

This follows by standard arguments from the corollary to Theorem 6.

Corollary. $\bar{Y}_R$ is infinite if $R \neq \emptyset$.

Remark. A slightly more precise result has been obtained by Lang [4] for "geometric" coverings and also for coverings obtained by extension of the ground field.

REFERENCES

1. Artin, E., Zur Theorie der L-Reihen mit allgemeinen Gruppencharakteren, *Abh. Hamb.*, **8**(1930), 292–306.
2. Davenport, H., and H. Hasse, Die Nullstellen der Kongruenzzetafunktionen im gewissen zyklischen Fällen. *Crelle Jour.*, **172**(1935), 151–182.
3. Dwork, B., On the rationality of the zeta function of an algebraic variety, *Amer. Jour. Math.*, **82**(1960), 631–648.
4. Lang, S., Sur les séries L d'une variété algébrique, *Bull. Soc. Math. France*, **84**(1956), 385–407.
5. Lang, S., and A. Weil, Number of points of varieties in finite fields, *Amer. Jour. Math.*, **76**(1954), 819–827.
6. Nisnevič, L., Number of points of algebraic varieties over finite fields (in Russian), *Dokl. Akad. Nauk*, **99**(1954), 17–20.
7. Weil, A., *Sur les courbes algébriques et les variétés qui s'en déduisent*, *Act. Sci. Ind.*, n°. 1041, Paris, Hermann, 1948.
8. Weil, A., On some exponential sums, *Proc. Nat. Acad. Sci. USA*, **34**(1948), 204–207.
9. Weil, A., Number of solutions of equations in finite fields, *Bull. Amer. Math. Soc.*, **55**(1949), 497–508.

Algebraic Cycles and Poles of Zeta Functions

John T. Tate

The following article is a slight modification of one which has appeared in the informal mimeographed proceedings of the A.M.S. Summer Institute on Algebraic Geometry held in Woods Hole, July, 1964. It unites material presented there (§1 and §2) with that presented at Purdue (roughly, §3 and §4). For the basic properties of zeta functions we refer to Serre's Woods Hole talk which is reproduced in this same volume for the convenience of the reader. Mumford's article contains an introductory discussion of étale cohomology.

The l-adic étale cohomology of algebraic varieties is much richer than the classical cohomology, in that Galois groups operate on

RESEARCH ON THIS PAPER SUPPORTED BY AN A. P. SLOAN FELLOWSHIP AND ALSO BY NATIONAL SCIENCE FOUNDATION GRANT G23833.

it. This opens up a new field of inquiry, even in the classical case. Although theorems seem scarce, the soil is fertile for conjectures; I ask your indulgence while I discuss some of these, together with some meager evidence, both computational and philosophical, for them. The main idea is, roughly speaking, that a cohomology class which is fixed under the Galois group should be algebraic when the ground field is finitely generated over the prime field. I have come to this idea by way of its relation to questions of orders of poles of zeta functions. Most of the signposts along the way became visible to me during conversations and/or correspondence with M. Artin, D. Mumford, and J.-P. Serre. I thank them heartily for their guidance.

§1. THE l-ADIC COHOMOLOGY

Throughout our discussion we shall consider the situation pictured below in which k is a field, $\bar{k}$ an algebraically closed extension

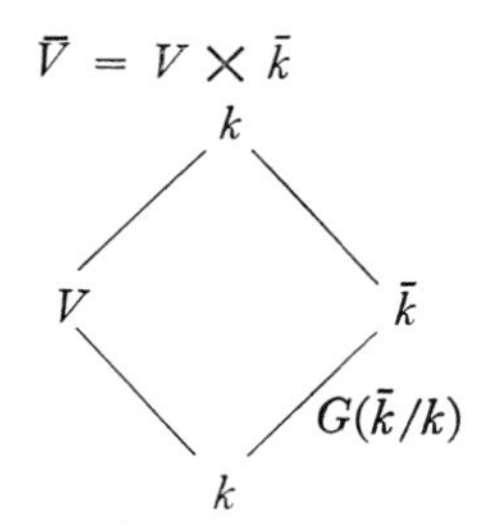

field, $G(\bar{k}/k)$ the group of automorphisms of $\bar{k}$ over k, and V an irreducible scheme projective and smooth over k, such that the scheme $\bar{V} = V \times_k \bar{k}$ obtained from V by base extension to $\bar{k}$ is irreducible. For each prime number l different from the characteristic of k, we put

$$H_l^i(\bar{V}) = \mathbf{Q}_l \underset{\mathbf{Z}_l}{\otimes} \left(\varprojlim_n H^i(\bar{V}_{\text{ét}}, \mathbf{Z}/l^n\mathbf{Z})\right) \tag{1}$$

where $\bar{V}_{\text{ét}}$ denotes the étale topology of $\bar{V}$. In the classical case, $\bar{k} = \mathbf{C}$, the comparison theorem of M. Artin allows us to replace "étale" by "classical" in this formula. The inverse limit is then isomorphic to $H^i(\bar{V}_{\text{classical}}, \mathbf{Z}_l)$, and consequently we have

$$H_l^i(\bar{V}) \simeq H^i(\bar{V}_{\text{classical}}, \mathbf{Q}_l) \simeq \mathbf{Q}_l \otimes_{\mathbf{Q}} H^i(\bar{V}_{\text{classical}}, \mathbf{Z}).$$

In the abstract case there is no good cohomology with rational coefficients, and it is the groups $H_l^i(\bar{V})$ that play the role we are accustomed to attribute to "cohomology with coefficients in $\mathbf{Q}_l$." I understand that the étale cohomologists have established finite dimensionality, Poincaré duality, Künneth formulas, and a Lefschetz fixed-point theorem for the groups H_l^i. The proper base change theorem shows that the groups H_l^i do not change if we replace $\bar{k}$ by a larger algebraically closed field. As Mike Artin says, the situation is just like the good old days.

In one respect the situation is even better, because the Galois group $G(\bar{k}/k)$ operates on the groups $H_l^i(\bar{V})$. Namely, it operates on the product $\bar{V} = V \times_k \bar{k}$ through the second factor and hence on the site $\bar{V}_{\text{ét}}$; the point is that the étale topology depends only on $\bar{V}$ and not on the arrow $\bar{V} \to \operatorname{Spec} \bar{k}$ which is used to define the classical topology when $\bar{k} = \mathbf{C}$.

There results a homomorphism

$$G(\bar{k}/k) \to \operatorname{Aut}_{\mathbf{Q}_l}(H_l^i(\bar{V})) \simeq \mathbf{GL}(b_i, \mathbf{Q}_l) \tag{2}$$

(where $b_i = \dim_{\mathbf{Q}_l} H_l^i = i$th Betti number). By using the base change theorem we see that the homomorphism (2) induces a topological isomorphism $G(k'/k) \xrightarrow{\sim} G_l^i$ between the group of a certain Galois extension k' over k and a certain closed subgroup G_l^i of $\mathbf{GL}(b_i, \mathbf{Q}_l)$. Thus the situation is exactly as described by Serre [4] in case $V = A$ is an abelian variety and $i = 1$, when $H_l^1(\bar{A})$ can be identified with the dual of Serre's $V_l(A)$. The group G_l^i is an l-adic Lie group, whose Lie algebra $\mathfrak{G}^i$ is unchanged if we replace k by an extension of finite type. These Lie algebras of Serre's raise a host of new problems, even, or perhaps especially, in the classical case.

For example, let X be a complex projective nonsingular variety. Then we can find a field $k \subset \mathbf{C}$ finitely generated over $\mathbf{Q}$, and a scheme V over k such that $\bar{V} = V \times_k \mathbf{C} \simeq X$. The Lie algebras

$$\mathfrak{G}_l^i \subset \operatorname{End}_{\mathbf{Q}_l}(H^i(X, \mathbf{Q}) \otimes_Q \mathbf{Q}_l)$$

which are obtained in the manner just discussed are *independent of the choice of k and V, and depend only on* $X/\mathbf{C}$. Almost nothing is known about them (cf. Serre [5]). Is their dimension and type independent of l? Are they reductive? Serre [6] has shown that the answers are affirmative in case X is a complex torus of dimension 1 whose j invariant is either real, or not an algebraic integer. The conjecture about algebraic cycles which I am going to discuss in a moment has the following consequence in the present situation: Let $\omega \in H^2(X, \mathbf{Q})$ be the cohomology class of a hyperplane section. For $x \in \mathfrak{G}_l^{2i}$, let $x\omega^i = \lambda_i(x)\omega^i$, with $\lambda_i(x) \in \mathbf{Q}_l$. Let $\theta \in H^{2i}(X, \mathbf{Q})$. Then (conjecturally) some multiple of θ is the class of an algebraic cycle of codimension i if and only if $x\theta = \lambda_i(x)\theta$ for all $x \in \mathfrak{G}_l^{2i}$.

§2. COHOMOLOGY CLASSES OF ALGEBRAIC CYCLES

The operation of $G(\bar{k}/k)$ on cohomology makes it imperative to keep track of "twisting" by roots of unity. If $G(\bar{k}/k)$ operates on a vector space H over $\mathbf{Q}_l$, we define the twistings of H to be the $G(\bar{k}/k)$-spaces $H(m) = H \otimes_{\mathbf{Q}_l} W^{\otimes m}$, for $m \in \mathbf{Z}$, where

$$W = \mathbf{Q}_l \underset{\mathbf{Z}_l}{\otimes} (\underset{\leftarrow}{\lim}\{\mu_{l^n}\}) \tag{3}$$

is a one-dimensional l-adic vector space on which $G(\bar{k}/k)$ operates according to its action on the group μ_{l^n} of l^nth roots of unity for all n. (For $m < 0$, we put $W^{\otimes m} = \mathrm{Hom}(W^{\otimes |m|}, \mathbf{Q}_l)$, so that $H(m)(n) \simeq H(m + n)$ for all $m, n \in \mathbf{Z}$). The canonical isomorphisms

$$H^i(\bar{V}_{\text{ét}}, \mathbf{Z}/l^n\mathbf{Z}) \otimes \mu_{l^n}^{\otimes m} \xrightarrow{\sim} H^i(\bar{V}_{\text{ét}}, \mu_{l^n}^{\otimes m})$$

(which are obtained by viewing $\mu_{l^n}^{\otimes m}$ as $\mathrm{Hom}(\mathbf{Z}/l^n\mathbf{Z}, \mu_{l^n}^{\otimes m})$ show that if we replace $\mathbf{Z}/l^n\mathbf{Z}$ by $\mu_{l^n}^{\otimes m}$ in the definition (1) of $H_l^i(\bar{V})$, then we replace $H_l^i(\bar{V})$ by its m-fold twisting $H_l^i(\bar{V})(m)$.

Let $d = \dim V$. As Verdier discussed in his talk at Woods Hole, the "orientation sheaf (modl^n)" on $\bar{V}$ is $\mu_{l^n}^{\otimes d}$, and there is a canonical isomorphism

$$\rho_V : H_l^{2d}(\bar{V})(d) \xrightarrow{\sim} \mathbf{Q}_l. \tag{4}$$

(For practical purposes, "canonical homomorphism" means $G(\bar{k}/k)$ homomorphism.) The l-adic Poincaré duality theorem states then that the cup product pairing:

$$H_l^i(\bar{V})(m) \otimes H_l^{2d-i}(\bar{V})(d - m) \to H^{2d}(\bar{V})(d) \simeq \mathbf{Q}_l$$

gives a perfect duality of finite dimensional vector spaces.

Thus, if X is an irreducible subscheme of $\bar{V}$ of codimension i, we can attach to X a cohomology class $c(x) \in H^{2i}(\bar{V})(i)$ which is characterized by the fact that

$$\rho_V(\eta \cup c(X)) = \rho_X(\eta \mid X)$$

for all $\eta \in H^{2(d-i)}(\bar{V})(d-i)$. When we extend c by additivity we obtain a homomorphism

$$\mathfrak{Z}^i(\bar{V}) \xrightarrow{c} H_l^{2i}(\bar{V})(i), \tag{5}$$

where $\mathfrak{Z}^i(\bar{V})$ denotes the free abelian group generated by the irreducible subschemes of codimension i on $\bar{V}$. These homomorphisms will carry intersection product into cup product:

$$c(X \cdot Y) = c(X) \cup c(Y),$$

whenever $X \cdot Y$ is defined.

Let $\mathfrak{Z}_h^i(\bar{V})$ denote the kernel of the homomorphism c in dimension i, (that is, the group of algebraic cycles of codimension i on $\bar{V}$ which are "l-adically homologically equivalent to zero") and put

$$\mathfrak{A}^i(\bar{V}) = \frac{\mathfrak{Z}^i(\bar{V})}{\mathfrak{Z}_h^i(\bar{V})}.$$

We have the following conjectural statements.

(a) $\mathfrak{Z}_h^i(\bar{V})$ is independent of l, or perhaps even:

(a′) $\mathfrak{Z}_h^i(\bar{V})$ consists exactly of the cycles numerically equivalent to zero.

(b) $\mathfrak{A}^i(\bar{V})$ is finitely generated, and the map

$$\mathfrak{A}^i(\bar{V}) \otimes_{\mathbf{Z}} \mathbf{Q}_l \xrightarrow{c \otimes 1} H^{2i}(\bar{V})(i)$$

is injective.

Statements (a) and (b) are true in characteristic zero, because we can then imbed k in $\mathbf{C}$ and factor the map c through the finitely generated $\mathbf{Z}$-module $H^{2i}(\bar{V}_{\text{classical}}, \mathbf{Z})$, for which

$$H_l^i(\bar{V}) \simeq H^i(\bar{V}_{\text{classical}}, \mathbf{Z}) \otimes \mathbf{Q}_l.$$

In the abstract case, nothing is known for codimensions $i > 1$, but for $i = 1$, all three statements (a), (a′) and (b) are true. Let

$$\mathfrak{Z}_n^1 \supset \mathfrak{Z}_a^1 \supset \mathfrak{Z}_l^1$$

denote the groups of divisors on $\bar{V}$ which are, respectively, numerically, algebraically, or linearly equivalent to zero. The map $c : \mathfrak{Z}^1(\bar{V}) \to H_l^2(\bar{V})(1)$ is obtained by passage to the limit from the composed maps

$$\mathfrak{Z}^1 \to \mathfrak{Z}^1/\mathfrak{Z}_l^1 \simeq H^1(\bar{V}_{\text{ét}}, \mathbf{G}_m) \xrightarrow{\delta_n} H^2(\bar{V}_{\text{ét}}, \mu_{l^n}),$$

where δ_n is the connecting homomorphism in the cohomology sequence derived from the exact sequence

$$0 \to \mu_{l^n} \to \mathbf{G}_m \xrightarrow{l^n} \mathbf{G}_m \to 0. \tag{6}$$

For each n, the kernel of δ_n is $l^n H^1(\bar{V}_{\text{ét}}, \mathbf{G}_m)$, and (a′) and (b) follow because $\mathfrak{Z}_a^1/\mathfrak{Z}_l^1$ is divisible, and $\mathfrak{Z}_n^1/\mathfrak{Z}_a^1$ is the torsion subgroup of the finitely generated group $\mathfrak{Z}^1/\mathfrak{Z}_a^1$.

From now on, we shall assume (a) and (b) hold in whatever situation is discussed. Each irreducible subscheme X of $\bar{V}$ is "defined" over a finite extension of k. Thus X is fixed by an open subgroup U of $G(\bar{k}/k)$, and the same is true of its class $c(x)$. There is a conjectural converse of this statement, namely:

Conjecture 1. If k is finitely generated over the prime field, the space $c(\mathfrak{A}^i(\bar{V}))\mathbf{Q}_l$ consists of those elements of $H_l^{2i}(\bar{V})(i)$ whose stabilizer is open in $G(\bar{k}/k)$, that is, which are annihilated by the corresponding Lie algebra.

Let $\mathfrak{A}^i(V)$ denote the subgroup of $\mathfrak{A}^i(\bar{V})$ generated by the algebraic cycles which are defined over k. If an element of $\mathfrak{A}^i(\bar{V})$ is fixed by $G(\bar{k}/k)$, then some nonzero multiple of it is in $\mathfrak{A}^i(V)$. Thus Conjecture 1 implies

$$c(\mathfrak{A}^i(V))\mathbf{Q}_l = [H_l^{2i}(\bar{V})(i)]^{G(\bar{k}/k)}, \tag{7}$$

for finitely generated k. On the other hand, if (7) holds for all (sufficiently large) finite extensions of k then Conjecture 1 is true.

Now let A and B be abelian varieties over k. If we combine the fundamental isomorphism

$$\mathrm{Hom}_k(A, B) \simeq \mathrm{Ker}(\mathfrak{A}^1(A \times \hat{B}) \to \mathfrak{A}^1(A) \times \mathfrak{A}^1(\hat{B}))$$

with the Künneth formula

$$H_l^1(A) \otimes H_l^1(\hat{B}) \simeq \mathrm{Ker}(H_l^2(A \times \hat{B}) \to H_l^2(A) \times H_l^2(\hat{B})),$$

we conclude from (7) applied to $V = A \times \hat{B}$ with $i = 1$ that

$$\mathrm{Hom}_k(A, B) \otimes \mathbf{Q}_l \xrightarrow{\sim} [H_l^1(A) \otimes H_l^1(\hat{B})(1)]^{G(\bar{k}/k)}$$

is an isomorphism. Reinterpreting the right-hand side in terms of points of finite order (via the Kummer sequence (6)) we find that this last is equivalent to

$$\mathrm{Hom}_k(A, B) \otimes \mathbf{Z}_l \xrightarrow{\sim} \mathrm{Hom}_{G(\bar{k}/k)}(A(l^\infty), B(l^\infty)), \tag{8}$$

where $A(l^\infty)$ denotes the $G(\bar{k}/k)$-module of points on A of order l^ν, all ν, with coefficients in k. In down to earth terms: if a group homomorphism $\varphi : A(l^\infty) \to B(l^\infty)$ commutes with the operation of the Galois group for a finitely generated k, then for every N there should exist a homomorphism of abelian varieties $\psi_N : A \to B$ such that ψ_N coincides with φ on the points of order l^N.

Mumford has verified (8) in case k is finite and A and B are of dimension 1, by lifting the Frobenius endomorphism to characteristic 0, à la Deuring, [1]. Results of Serre [6] show that (8) holds in the event that k is a number field with at least one real prime, and $A = B$ is of dimension 1. Of course, if (8) holds for A and B of dimension 1, then (7) holds with $V = A \times B$.

I can see no direct logical connection between Conjecture 1 and Hodge's conjecture [2] that a rational cohomology class of type (p, p) is algebraic, that is, a rational combination of classes of algebraic cycles. (In case of divisors, this is a well-known theorem of Lefschetz and is even true over $\mathbf{Z}$.) However, the two conjectures have an air of compatibility. For example, Grothendieck remarks that each of the two conjectures implies that the Künneth components $c_{a,b}$ of an algebraic class c on a product $V' \otimes V''$ are algebraic, a statement which seems unknown even in case of the diagonal on the product of a surface with itself in the classical case. By the "Künneth decomposition"

$$c = \sum_{a+b=2i} c_{a,b}$$

of a cohomology class $c \in H_l^{2i}(\bar{V}' \otimes \bar{V}'')(i)$, we mean its expression as a sum of classes $c_{a,b} \in H_l^{2i}(\bar{V}' \otimes \bar{V}'')(i)$ such that $c_{a,b}$ is in the image of $[H_l^a(\bar{V}') \otimes H_l^b(\bar{V}'')](i)$. Conjecture 1 implies that if

$$c \in c(\mathfrak{A}^i)\mathbf{Q}_l$$

then $c_{a,b} \in c(\mathfrak{A}^i)\mathbf{Q}_l$ for all a, b. Grothendieck conjectures that the same is true with $\mathbf{Q}$ instead of $\mathbf{Q}_l$, as would follow from Hodge's conjecture in the classical case.

§3. CONNECTIONS WITH ZETA FUNCTIONS (FINITE k)

Let $\varphi : \bar{V} \to \bar{V}$ be a $\bar{k}$-morphism, and let $\varphi_{i,l}$ denote the linear transformation of $H_l^i(\bar{V})$ induced by φ. Then the algebraic number $\Lambda(\varphi)$ of fixed points of φ is given by the Lefschetz formula

$$\Lambda(\varphi) = \sum_{i=0}^{2d} (-1)^i \operatorname{Trace}(\varphi_{i,l}). \tag{9}$$

It is generally conjectured that

(**c**) The characteristic polynomial $P_{i,l}(t) = \det(1 - \varphi_{i,l}t)$ has rational integral coefficients and is independent of l.

(**d**) Suppose that there exists an ample $\omega \in \mathfrak{A}^1(\bar{V})$ such that $\varphi^*\omega = q\omega$ for some integer $q > 0$. Then the endomorphisms $\varphi_{i,l}$ are semisimple, and if we write

$$\det(1 - \varphi_{i,l}t) = P_i(t) = \prod_{j=1}^{b_i} (1 - \alpha_{ij}t) \tag{10}$$

with complex α_{ij}, we have $|\alpha_{i,j}| = q^{i/2}$ for all j.

In characteristic 0, (c) is an immediate consequence of the existence of integral cohomology, and (d) can be proved by Kählerian methods (cf. Serre [4]). In characteristic p, both conjectures have been proved for curves and abelian varieties by Weil [10]. When φ is the Frobenius morphism, conjecture (d) is the famous conjecture of Weil [11] which started this whole business.

From now on we shall assume (c) and (d) hold in whatever situation is discussed. Let $k = \mathbf{F}_q$ be the finite field with q elements. For any scheme X over $\mathbf{F}_q$, the *Frobenius morphism* $F_X : X \to X$ is defined as the identity map on points, together with the map $f \to f^q$ in the structure sheaf. This F_X acts like identity on the site $X_{\text{ét}}$ and, therefore, induces identity on the cohomology groups $H^i(X_{\text{ét}}, \mathbf{Z}/m\mathbf{Z})$. On $\bar{V} = V \times_k \bar{k}$ we have $F_{\bar{V}} = F_V \times F_{\bar{k}} = \varphi \times \sigma$, say, where $\varphi : V \to V$ is the usual Frobenius morphism, and where

σ is the canonical "generator" of $G(\bar{k}/k)$. Since $\varphi \times \sigma$ acts as identity on cohomology groups $H_l^i(\bar{V})$, we have $\varphi_{i,l} = \sigma_{i,l}^{-1}$, where $\varphi_{i,l}$ is the linear transformation of $H_l^i(\bar{V})$ induced by the $\bar{k}$-morphism $\varphi \times 1$, and where $\sigma_{i,l}$ is the linear transformation of $H_l^i(\bar{V})$ produced by the operation of σ as element of $G(\bar{k}/k)$.

The zeta function of the scheme V (see Serre's talk) is given by

$$\zeta(V, s) = \frac{P_1(q^{-s}) \cdots P_{2d-1}(q^{-s})}{P_0(q^{-s})P_2(q^{-s}) \cdots P_{2d}(q^{-s})}, \tag{11}$$

where $d = \dim V$; and where $P_i(t)$ is the characteristic polynomial of Frobenius operating on cohomology of dimension i, as in (10). Formula (11) results from Lefschetz' formula (9) for $\Lambda(\varphi^\nu)$ and the definition of ζ; see Weil [11]. Since the "reciprocal roots" α_{ij} of $P_i(t)$ have absolute value $q^{i/2}$, the zeros of $\zeta(V, s)$ are on the lines $Rs = 1/2, 3/2, \ldots, (2d-1)/2$, and its poles are on the lines $Rs = 0, 1, 2, \ldots, d$. The order of the pole at the point $s = i$ is equal to the number of times q^i occurs as a reciprocal root of $P_{2i}(t)$, or what is the same, as an eigenvalue of $\varphi_{2i,l}$. By the semisimplicity of $\varphi_{2i,l}$, this is the dimension of the space of $x \in H_l^{2i}(\bar{V})$ such that $\varphi_{2i,l}x = q^i x$, or $x = \sigma_{2i,l}q^i x$. Now σ operates as q on our twisting space, W, because σ raises l^nth roots of unity to the qth power. Thus for $y \in W^{\otimes i}$ we have $\sigma y = q^i y$ and $\sigma(x \otimes y) = \sigma_{2i,l}\, x \otimes q^i y = (\sigma_{2i,l} q^i\, x) \otimes y$. It follows that the dimension we are computing is that of the subspace of all $z \in H^{2i}(\bar{V})(i)$ such that $\sigma z = z$, that is, the dimension of $[H^{2i}(\bar{V})(i)]^{G(\bar{k}/k)}$. If (7) is true we have then

$$\operatorname{rank}\mathfrak{A}^i(V) = \text{order of pole of } \zeta(V, s) \text{ at } s = i, \tag{12}$$

assuming, as always, that (a), (b), (c), and (d) hold. Moreover, the inequality $\leq$ always holds under those assumptions, and equality in (12) for all (sufficiently large) finite extensions of k is equivalent to Conjecture 1.

I have tried to check (12) in case $V = V_{n,r,p}$ is the hypersurface in projective r-space defined by the equation

$$X_0^n + X_1^n + \cdots + X_r^n = 0 \tag{13}$$

over a large finite field k of characteristic p not dividing n. Weil [11] has computed the zeta function and hence the order of the pole; it is the determination of the rank of $\mathfrak{A}^i(V)$ which is difficult. There is only one nontrivial dimension i, namely that for which $r = 2i + 1$. I have succeeded in the verification of (12) only in two special cases (I) if $p^\nu \equiv -1 (\bmod n)$ for some ν and (II) if $p \equiv 1 (\bmod n)$, and $r = 3$, $i = 1$.

In case (I) the order of the pole turns out to be equal to the Betti number b_{2i}, so the problem is to prove that the algebraic cohomology classes span $H_l^{2i}(\bar{V})(i)$. For this we can replace n by its multiple $q + 1$, where $q = p^\nu$, because $V(q + 1, r, p)$ dominates $V(n, r, p)$ as the map $X_j \to X_j^{(q+1)/n}$ shows. This gives us the advantage that our hypersurface

$$X_0^{q+1} + X_1^{q+1} + \cdots + X_r^{q+1} = 0$$

has a large group of automorphisms, namely those induced by the group U of projective transformations

$$X_j \to \Sigma a_{ji} X_i,$$

where (a_{ji}) is a matrix in $\mathbf{F}_{q^2}$ which is unitary with respect to the conjugation $a \to \bar{a} = a^q$. John Thompson and I proved that the representation of U on $H_l^{2i}(\bar{V})$ is the direct sum of the trivial representation and an irreducible one, and the required result follows easily from this. Incidentally, the nontrivial irreducible representation in question, which is of degree $q \dfrac{q^r + 1}{q + 1}$, seems to be the irreducible representation of lowest degree > 1 of the group of $(r + 1) \times (r + 1)$ unitary matrices (a_{ij}) with $a_{ij} \in \mathbf{F}_{q^2}$, for r odd.

In case (II), the order of the pole turns out to be equal to the rank of $\mathfrak{A}^i(\bar{V})$ for the surface V in characteristic 0 defined by equation (13). Since the rank of $\mathfrak{A}^i$ can only increase under specialization (look at the intersection matrix), equality (12) must hold. The computation of the rank (Picard number) in characteristic 0 is made with the aid of the Lefschetz theorem; it turns out to be possible to count the dimension of the space of rational cohomology classes of type (1, 1) by regarding the cohomology as a representation space for the commutative group of automorphisms of the form $X_i \to \zeta_i X_i$, where $\zeta_i^n = 1$, $0 \leq i \leq r$. The point is that the spaces $H^{2,0}$, $H^{1,1}$, and $H^{0,2}$ have no common irreducible constituents. If we assume the Hodge conjecture, we can treat case (II) for arbitrary $r = 2i + 1$.

§4. CONNECTIONS WITH ZETAS (FINITELY GENERATED k)

Let us turn now to the case where k is finitely generated over the prime field, rather than finite. We can then construct a projective and smooth morphism $f : X \to Y$ of schemes of finite type over $\mathbf{Z}$, with Y regular and X irreducible, whose general fiber is our given morphism $V \to (\mathrm{Spec} k)$. (The case which has been studied classically is that in which k is an algebraic number field and Y is an open subset of the spectrum of the ring of integers of k such that V has "nondegenerate reduction" at all points of Y.) For each "closed" point $y \in Y$, we let V_y (rather that the conventional X_y) denote the fiber $f^{-1}(y)$, and we let $k(y)$ denote the residue field of y, which is finite with (definition) N_y elements, as Serre mentioned in his talk. Thus the scheme V_y over $k(y)$, and the corresponding "geometric fiber" $\bar{V}_y$ over $\overline{k(y)}$, are as discussed in the preceding section, with $q = Ny$. By expressing the zeta function of the scheme X as a product of the zetas of the closed fibers we have

$$\zeta(X, s) = \prod_{\substack{y \in Y \\ y \text{ closed}}} \zeta(V_y, s). \tag{14}$$

If we express the zeta functions of the fibers in the form of equation (11) we have then

$$\zeta(X, s) = \frac{\Phi_0(s)\Phi_2(s) \cdots \Phi_{2d}(s)}{\Phi_1(s) \cdots \Phi_{2d-1}(s)}, \tag{15}$$

where we have put, for $0 \leq i \leq 2d$,

$$\Phi_i(s) = \prod_{\substack{y \in Y \\ y \text{ closed}}} \frac{1}{P_{y,i}(Ny^{-s})}. \tag{16}$$

The $P_{y,i}(t)$ are of fixed degree (see below) with reciprocal roots α_{ij} of absolute value $(Ny)^{i/2}$ [recall that we *assume* conjecture (d) of §3]. Therefore, by Theorem 1 of Serre's talk the product (16) converges absolutely for $Rs > \dim Y + (i/2)$. It is conjectured that the Φ_i can be continued meromorphically in the whole s-plane (cf. Weil [13]). At present the continuability is known only in very special cases. From Poincaré duality, we have $\Phi_{2d-i}(s) = \Phi_i(s - d + i)$.

If we replace Y by a nonempty open subscheme in (16), we divide $\Phi_i(s)$ by a product which converges for $Rs > \dim Y + (i/2) - 1$. It follows that (insofar as Φ_i is extendible there) the zeros and poles of Φ_i in the strip

$$\dim Y + \frac{i}{2} - 1 < Rs \leq \dim Y + \frac{i}{2}$$

depend only on V/k and not on our choice of X/Y. It is therefore natural to try to relate the orders of the zeros and poles of Φ_i at critical places in that critical strip to other invariants of the variety V/k. The original idea in this direction is the following striking

Conjecture of B + S-D. The rank of the group of k-rational points on the Picard variety of V is equal to the order of the zero of $\Phi_1(s)$ at $s = \dim Y$ (and of $\Phi_{2d-1}(s) = \dim X - 1$, by duality).

This conjecture is due to Birch and Swinnerton-Dyer, at least in case V is an elliptic curve over a numberfield k. If $k = \mathbf{Q}$, and V is an elliptic curve of the form $y^2 = x^3 - Dx$, $D \in \mathbf{Z}$, their computers have produced overwhelming numerical evidence for the fact that $\Phi_1(1) = 0$ if and only if the curve has a rational point of infinite order [14]. In case of finite k, the conjecture is trivially true, amounting to $0 = 0$.

I would like now to discuss the following generalization of (12):

Conjecture 2. The rank of $\mathfrak{A}^i(V)$ is equal to the order of the pole of $\Phi_{2i}(s)$ at the point $s = \dim Y + i$ (and of $\Phi_{2d-2i}(s)$ at $s = \dim X - i$, by duality).

Notice that the position of the pole considered here is on the boundary of the half-plane of convergence of the product, so that conjecture 2 can be given meaning even without supposing analytic continuation. In this respect it is different from the conjecture of $B + S\text{-}D$, which presupposes analytic continuation a distance of ½ unit to the left of the line of convergence. On the other hand, the two conjectures are intimately related, at least insofar as the case $i = 1$ of Conjecture 2 is concerned. This is not surprising, because both of them relate the order of a function at $s = \dim X - 1$ to the rank of a group of divisor classes. For example, let $V \to W$ be a morphism of varieties of our type over k, whose general fiber $V_w/k(w)$ is also of our type. If k is finite, and W and V_w are curves, then it is easy to see, as I mentioned in Stockholm [9], that Conjecture 2 for V/k is equivalent to the conjecture of B+ S-D, for $V_w/k(w)$. To treat the general situation, let X be an irreducible regular scheme of finite type over **Z** whose zeta function $\zeta(X, s)$ can be meromorphically continued to the point $s = \dim X - 1$. Let $e(X)$ be the order of $\zeta(X, s)$ at that point, and put

$$z(X) = \operatorname{rank} H^0(X, \mathbf{O}_X^*) - \operatorname{rank} H^1(X, \mathbf{O}_X^*) - e(X).$$

If one removes from X a closed irreducible subscheme Z of codimension 1, then $z(X)$ does not change. Thus $z(X)$ is a birational invariant and depends only on the function field of X. Suppose now $f : X \to Y$ with general fiber V/k is as discussed at the beginning of §4 (so f projective and smooth, Y regular, and $\bar{V}$ irreducible.) Then it is easy to see that any two of the following statements imply the third:

(i) The Conjecture of Birch and Swinnerton-Dyer for V/k.
(ii) The Conjecture 2, for $i = 1$, for V/k.
(iii) The equality $z(X) = z(Y)$.

Since we have $z(X) = 0$, if X is the spectrum of a finite field or of the ring of integers in an algebraic number field, and since $z(X)$ is a birational invariant, we can conclude $z(X) = 0$ for all X if (i) and (ii) hold for all V. We are thus led to

Conjecture B + S-D + 2. If X is a regular scheme of finite type over **Z**, then the order of $\zeta(X, s)$ at the point $s = \dim X - 1$ is equal to $\operatorname{rank} H^0(X, \mathbf{O}_X^*) - \operatorname{rank} H^1(X, \mathbf{O}_X^*)$.

Conversely, this last conjecture implies conjecture B + S-D for curves V/k, because Conjecture 2 is trivial for curves. And B + S-D for curves implies the same for Jacobians, hence arbitrary abelian varieties, and hence finally for arbitrary V/k. Thus it seems that Conjecture B + S-D + 2 is equivalent to the union of Conjecture B + S-D and the case $i = 1$ of Conjecture 2.

Conjecture 2 has been verified in some special cases. If k is a number field and V the surface $X_0^n + X_1^n + X_2^n + X_3^n = 0$, then Weil [12] has computed $\Phi_2(s)$ as a product of Hecke L-series. Its pole at $s = 1$ turns out to be equal to the Picard number of $\bar{V}$ if k contains the $2n$th roots of unity. The corresponding statement is true for the hyper-surface $\Sigma_{i=0}^r X_i^n = 0$, r odd, if Hodge's conjecture is true for it.

Henry Pohlmann has verified Conjecture 2 for $i = 1$ in case V is an abelian variety of C.M. type in the sense of Shimura-Taniyama [7].

It is interesting to consider the case k a number field, $V = E^m$ the product of an elliptic curve E with itself m times over k. For each prime y where E has nondegenerate reduction, put

$$\zeta(E_y, s) = \frac{(1 - \varepsilon_y Ny^{1/2-s})(1 - \bar{\varepsilon}_y Ny^{1/2-s})}{(1 - Ny^{-s})(1 - Ny^{1-s})},$$

and let

$$\varepsilon_y = e^{i\theta(y)}, \quad 0 \leq \theta(y) \leq \pi.$$

Then we have

$$\Phi_i(s) = \prod_{0 \leq \nu \leq i/2} \left(L_{i-2\nu}\left(s - \frac{i}{2}\right)\right)^{\binom{m}{\nu}\binom{m}{i-\nu}} \tag{17}$$

where $L_0(s) = \prod_y \dfrac{1}{1 - Ny^{-s}}$,

and $L_\nu(s) = \prod_y \dfrac{1}{(1 - \varepsilon_y^\nu Ny^{-s})(1 - \bar{\varepsilon}_y^\nu Ny^{-s})}$ for $\nu > 0$. (18)

In case E has complex multiplication the $L_\nu(s)$ are Hecke L-series, we have $\operatorname{rank}\mathfrak{A}^i(\bar{V}) = \binom{m}{i}^2$, and Conjecture 2 is easily checked for all i.

Suppose now that E has no complex multiplication. Then we find

$$\operatorname{rank}\mathfrak{A}^i(V) = \operatorname{rank}\mathfrak{A}^i(\bar{V}) = \binom{m}{i}^2 - \binom{m}{i-1}\binom{m}{i+1}. \tag{19}$$

Let c_ν be the order of $L_\nu(s)$ at $s = 1$. By assuming Conjecture 2, we conclude from (17) and (19) that

$$c_0 = 1, \quad c_2 = -1, \quad \text{and } c_{2\nu} = 0 \qquad \text{for } \nu > 1.$$

On the other hand, arguing *formally* from (19) (I have not investigated the analytical subtleties—this is all heuristic) we find for $0 \leq a < b \leq \pi$ that the density of the set of primes y such that $a \leq \theta(y) \leq b$ is given by $\int_a^b f(t)\, dt$, where

$$f(t) = \frac{1}{\pi} \sum_{\nu=0}^{\infty} c_\nu \cos \nu t.$$

Assuming $f(t) = f(\pi - t)$, we conclude that $c_\nu = 0$ for ν odd, and consequently

$$f(t) = \frac{1}{\pi}(1 - \cos 2t) = \frac{2}{\pi}\sin^2 t.$$

I understand that M. Sato has found this $\sin^2$ distribution law experimentally with machine computations. Conjecture 2 seems to offer an explanation for it!

I should say partial explanation, because the assumption $f(t) = f(\pi - t)$ had no justification; it amounts to conjecturing, in this special case, that for *odd* i the function $\Phi_i(s)$ has no zero and no pole at $s = \dim Y + (i/2)$, that is, at the real point on its boundary of convergence. It is tempting to make that conjecture in general (after all, in odd dimensions there are no algebraic cycles to create poles). However, it is false; over a finite field with q^2 elements it is easy to make varieties (supersingular elliptic curves for example) for which q is a reciprocal root of P_1. Perhaps the conjecture is true over number fields. I have no idea what to expect in general.

Another question I would like to raise concerns algebraic cycles on abelian varieties. Let A be an abelian variety of dimension n over **C**. *Is the ring of rational cohomology classes on A of type (p, p), $0 \leq p \leq n$, generated over* $\mathbf{Q}$ *by those of type* $(1, 1)$? An affirmative answer would imply both the Hodge conjecture for A, and also that every algebraic cycle is homologically equivalent to a rational linear combination of intersections of divisors. Mattuck [3] has proved that the answer is yes "in general," and it was by treating the case $A = E^m$ (power of an elliptic curve) that I was able to compute the ranks of the groups $\mathfrak{A}^i(E^m)$ in the example discussed above. In terms of a period matrix for A, we have a completely down-to-earth question which could be explained to a bright freshman and which should be settled one way or the other.†

The last thing I wish to discuss is the relation between Conjectures 1 and 2. We have already seen their equivalence [modulo (a), (b), (c), (d)] in case k is finite. For infinite k, the relation involves Taniyama's idea of L-series attached to l-adic representations (cf. [8]).

† Footnote added during the correction of the proofs: Mumford has shown that the answer to the question is negative, by giving an example of an abelian variety of C.M.-type of dimension 4 having a rational cohomology class of type (2,2) which is not a linear combination of products of those of type (1,1).

As Mike Artin explained in his Woods Hole talk, it follows from the theorems of specialization and base change in étale cohomology that the cohomology groups $H_l^i(\bar{V}_y)$ are independent of y for $y \in Y_l$ (here the Y_l denotes the locus $l \neq 0$ in Y). To make the statement precise, we choose a "strict localization" $\bar{\mathbf{O}}_y \subset \bar{k}$ of the local ring $\mathbf{O}_y$ of y on Y and use the residue field of $\bar{\mathbf{O}}_y$ as the algebraic closure $\overline{k(y)}$ of $k(y)$. The decomposition subgroup

$$D_y = \{\sigma \in G(\bar{k}/k) \,|\, \sigma\bar{\mathbf{O}}_y = \bar{\mathbf{O}}_y\}$$

is then mapped homomorphically onto $G(\overline{k(y)}/k(y))$, the kernel being, by definition, the inertia subgroup I_y of y. As usual, everything is determined up to conjugation by y, but actually depends on the choice of $\bar{\mathbf{O}}_y$, which plays the role of a path from the general geometric point, spec$\bar{k}$, to the special one, spec$\overline{k(y)}$. This "path" determines an isomorphism

$$H_l^i(\bar{V}_y) \simeq H_l^i(\bar{V}) \tag{20}$$

which is compatible with the operation of D_y. In particular, the inertia group I_y operates trivially on $H_l^i(\bar{V})$ for all $y \in Y_l$, so that in its action on $H_l^i(\bar{V})$, $G(\bar{k}/k)$ operates through its quotient group, $\pi_1(Y_l)$, the fundamental group of Y_l.

For each closed $y \in Y_l$, let σ_y be the image in $\pi_1(Y_l)$ of an inverse image in D_y of the canonical generator $\tilde{\sigma}_y$ of $G(\overline{k(y)}/k(y))$. (Thus, σ_y is determined by y up to conjugation and in case k is a number field it is a "Frobenius substitution" in the classical sense.) The compatibility of (20), together with the fact that $\tilde{\sigma}_y^{-1}$ operates on $H_l^i(\bar{V})$ as φ_y does (see p. 101), shows that the polynomial $P_{y,i}(t)$ in (16) is given by

$$P_{y,i}(t) = \det(1 - t\sigma_{y,i,l}^{-1}) \tag{21}$$

where $\sigma_{y,i,l}$ denotes the endomorphism of $H_l^i(\bar{V})$ induced by the operation of σ_y. Thus, *the function* Φ_i *is completely determined by the scheme* Y, *together with the* l-adic *representations* $H_l^i(\bar{V})$ *of the fundamental groups* $\pi_1(Y_l)$. We are therefore led to the following generalization:

Let Y be a regular irreducible scheme of finite type over $\mathbf{Z}$ with function field k. Suppose for each prime $l \neq$ char$k$, we have a finite dimensional vector space H_l over $\mathbf{Q}_l$ on which $\pi_1(Y_l)$ operates continuously in such a way that the characteristic polynomial

$$P_y(t) = \det(1 - t(\sigma_y^{-1} \,|\, H_l)) \tag{22}$$

has coefficients in $\mathbf{Z}$, is independent of l for $y \in Y_l$, and has complex "reciprocal roots" of absolute value Ny^ρ, where ρ is a real number independent of y. We then say that $H = (H_l)$ is a *system of representations of weight* ρ *over* Y.

Given such a system, we put

$$L(Y, H; s) = \prod_{\substack{y \in Y \\ y \text{ closed}}} \frac{1}{P_y(Ny^{-s})}, \tag{23}$$

this product being absolutely convergent for $Rs > \rho + \dim Y$. Notice the analogy between this definition and Artin's definition of L-functions [cf. Serre's talk, formula (9)]. Comparison of (16), (21), (22), and (23) shows that

$$\Phi_i(s) = L(Y, H^i(\bar{V}); s), \tag{24}$$

is an L-series for the system of representations $(H_l^i(\bar{V}))$ of weight $i/2$ over Y. Twisting a system of representations by m decreases its weight by m, and translates the corresponding L-function m units:

$$L(Y, H(m); s) = L(Y, H; s - m). \tag{25}$$

Thus
$$\Phi_{2i}(s - i) = L(Y, H^{2i}(\bar{V})(i); s)$$

belongs to the representation system $H^{2i}(\bar{V})(i)$ of weight 0. Conjecture 2 states that the pole of this function at $s = \dim Y$ is of order $\operatorname{rank}\mathfrak{A}^i(V)$. Conjecture 1 states that $\operatorname{rank}\mathfrak{A}^i(V)$ is equal to the dimension of the subspace of $H^{2i}(\bar{V})(i)$, which is fixed under $\pi_1(Y)$. If we assume the $\pi_1(Y_l)$-modules $H_l^i(\bar{V})$ are semisimple (as Serre and Grothendieck believe), the equivalence of Conjectures 1 and 2 would follow from:

Conjecture 3. For some class of representation systems $H = (H_l)$ of weight 0 over Y, including at least those of the form

$$H = (H_l^{2i}(\bar{V})(i)),$$

the order of the pole of $L(Y, H; s)$ at $s = \dim Y$ is equal to the number of times the identity representation occurs in H_l (this being independent of l).

Of course, Conjecture 3 is true for ordinary Artin L-series (cf. Theorem 6 of Serre's talk), and for Hecke's L-series. I conclude this talk with the hope that it is true in far greater generality.

BIBLIOGRAPHY

1. Birch, B. J. and Swinnerton-Dyer, H. P. F. Notes on elliptic curves. II, *J. reine. u. angew. Math.* **218**(1965), 79–108.
2. Deuring, M., Die Typen der Multiplikatorenringe elliptischer Funk. tionenkörper. *Abh. Math. Sem. Hamburg*, **14**(1941), 197–272.
3. Hodge, W. V. D., The topological invariants of algebraic varieties- *Proceedings of the International Congress of Mathematicians*, Cambridge, Mass., 1950, 182–192.
4. Mattuck, A., Cycles on abelian varieties, *Proceedings A.M.S.*, **9**(1958), 88–98.
5. Serre, J.-P., Analogues Kählériens de certaines conjectures de Weil. *Ann. of Math.*, **71**(1960), 392–394.
6. Serre, J.-P., Sur les groupes de congruence des variétés abéliennes, *Izv. Akad. Nauk. SSSR*, **28**(1964), 3–20.
7. Serre, J.-P., *Groupes de Lie l-adiques attachés aux courbes elliptiques*, colloque de Clermont-Ferrand, April, 1964, publié par les soins de l'Institute des Hautes Etudes Scientific, Bures-sur-Yvette, France.
8. Shimura, G. and Taniyama, Y., Complex multiplication of abelian varieties and its application to number theory. *Publ. Math. Soc. Japan*, No. 6, 1961.
9. Taniyama, Y., $\mathfrak{L}$-functions of number fields and zeta functions of abelian varieties. *J. Math. Soc. Japan*, **9**(1957), 330–366.
10. Tate, J., Duality theorems in Galois cohomology. *Proceedings of the International Congress of Mathematicians*, Stockholm, 1962, 288–295.
11. Weil, A., *Variétés abéliennes et courbes algébriques*, Paris, Hermann, 1948.
12. Weil, A., Numbers of solutions of equations in finite fields, *Bull. Amer. Math. Soc.*, **55**(1949), 497–508.
13. Weil, A., Jacobi sums as "Grössencharaktere," *Trans. A.M.S.*, **73**(1952), 487–495.
14. Weil, A., Abstract versus classical algebraic geometry, *Proceedings of the International Congress of Mathematicians* (Volume III) Amsterdam, 1954, p. 550–558.

Resolution of Singularities of Arithmetical Surfaces

Shreeram S. Abhyankar

§1. INTRODUCTION

The aim of this paper is to prove the following:

Resolution Theorem. Let I be a pseudogeometric Dedekind domain such that I/P is perfect for every maximal ideal P in I, and let K be a function field over I such that $\operatorname{absdim}_I K = 2$. Then there exists a nonsingular projective model of K over I. Furthermore, given any finite number of complete models $V_1, \ldots, V_t$ of K over I there exists a nonsingular projective model V of K over I such that V dominates V_i for all i.

The precise definitions of the terms being used in the Introduction will be given in §2.

The above theorem was previously proved only in the geometric case, that is, when I is a field. Note that in the geometric case the assumptions are equivalent to saying that I is perfect and K is a finitely generated field extension of I of transcendence degree two. When I is the field of complex numbers, the first rigorous proof of the theorem was given by Walker [15]. When I is a field of characteristic zero, the theorem was proved by Zariski [16]. When I is a perfect field of nonzero characteristic, the theorem was proved in [1] and [3]; also see [5].

When I is a Dedekind domain which is not a field the assumptions are equivalent to saying that: (1) the integral closure of I in any finite algebraic extension of the quotient field k of I is a finite I-module, (2) I/P is perfect for every maximal ideal P in I, and (3) K is a finitely generated field extension of k of transcendence degree one. Note that conditions (1) and (2) are satisfied in the arithmetical case, that is, when I is the ring of ordinary integers; this is the novel case of particular interest.

We shall give a unified treatment of the above resolution theorem, that is, without separating the arithmetical case from the geometric case.

In Proposition 23 of §3 we shall prove the following:

Proposition. Let I be a pseudogeometric Dedekind domain and let K be a function field over I such that $\operatorname{absdim}_I K = 2$. Assume that for each valuation v of K over I there exists a regular local domain R with quotient field K such that R is a spot over I and v dominates R. Then there exists a nonsingular projective model of K over I. Furthermore, given any finite number of complete models $V_1, \ldots, V_t$ of K over I there exists a nonsingular projective model V of K over I such that V dominates V_i for all i.

The proof of the above proposition closely follows the proof given by Zariski [17] in the geometric case.

In view of the above proposition, the proof of the resolution theorem is reduced to the following:

Uniformization Lemma. Let I be a pseudogeometric Dedekind domain such that I/P is perfect for every maximal ideal P in I, and let K be a function field over I such that $\operatorname{absdim}_I K = 2$. Then for each valuation v of K over I there exists a regular local domain R with quotient field K such that R is a spot over I and v dominates R.

Several steps leading to the above lemma were given in [2], [6], [7], and [8]. In §4, we recall these steps and complete the proof. For a slightly more detailed version of the above lemma see Theorem 7 of §4. §4 depends on §3 only in the use of Definitions 5 and 6 and Propositions 6, 9, and 10. Also the part of §2 beginning with Definition 1 is not used in §4.

§2. TERMINOLOGY

By a ring we mean a commutative ring with identity. Given a ring R and a subset H of an R-module S, by HR we denote the submodule of S generated by H; in other words, HR is the set of all elements in S which can be expressed as $x_1y_1 + \cdots + x_ny_n$ with $x_i \in R$ and $y_i \in H$; H is said to be an R-basis (or simply, a basis) of S if $HR = S$; S is said to be a finite R-module if S has a finite R-basis; elements $y_1, \ldots, y_n$ in S are said to be linearly independent over R if $x_1y_1 + \cdots + x_ny_n = 0$ with $x_i \in R$ implies that $x_i = 0$ for all i; elements $y_1, \ldots, y_n$ in S are said to form a free R-basis of S if they form an R-basis of S and they are linearly independent over R.

A prime ideal in a ring R is assumed to be different from R. By a *domain* we mean an integral domain. A domain is said to be *normal* if it is integrally closed in its quotient field.

A *quasilocal ring* is a ring R having exactly one maximal ideal M; we may indicate this by saying that (R, M) is a quasilocal ring. A *local ring* (R, M) is a noetherian quasilocal ring; the dimension of R is denoted by $\dim R$, that is, $\dim R$ is the greatest integer n such that there exists a sequence $P_0 \subset P_1 \subset \cdots \subset P_n$ of distinct prime ideals in R; R is said to be *regular* if M has a basis consisting of n elements where $n = \dim R$.

Given a domain B and a subdomain A of B, by $\mathrm{trdeg}_A B$ we denote the transcendence degree of the quotient field L of B over the quotient field K of A, and by $[B : A]$ we denote the vector space dimension of L over K. Given a quasilocal ring (R, M) and a subring A of R we can identify $A/(M \cap A)$ with a subdomain of R/M and then by $\dim_A R$ we denote the transcendence degree of R/M over the quotient field of $A/(M \cap A)$.

Given quasilocal domains (R, M) and (S, N) we say that S *dominates* R if R is a subring of S and $N \cap R = M$.

Let A be a domain. An *affine ring* over A is a domain B which is a finitely generated ring extension of A, that is, A is a subring of B and there exists a finite number of elements $x_1, \ldots, x_n$ in B such that $B = A[x_1, \ldots, x_n]$. A *spot* over A is a quasilocal ring (R, M) which is the quotient ring B_P of an affine ring B over A with respect to a prime ideal P in B; note that then $P = M \cap B$. An *algebraic spot* over A is a spot (R, M) over A such that $\dim_A R = 0$; note that then $[R/M : A/(M \cap A)]$ is finite. Note that if R is a spot over A and S is a spot over R then S is a spot over A. A *function field* over A is a field which is the quotient field of an affine ring over A; that is, a function field over A is a field which is a spot over A.

By a *Dedekind domain* we mean a normal noetherian domain in which every nonzero prime ideal is maximal. Note that every field is then a Dedekind domain. For a function field K over a Dedekind domain I, by $\operatorname{absdim}_I K$ we denote the *absolute dimension* of K over I, that is, $\operatorname{absdim}_I K = \operatorname{trdeg}_I K$ if I is a field, and $\operatorname{absdim}_I K = 1 + \operatorname{trdeg}_I K$ if I is not a field.

Let v be a valuation of a field K. The valuation ring of v is denoted by R_v and the maximal ideal in R_v is denoted by M_v, that is, R_v (resp: M_v) is the set of all elements x in K such that $v(x) \geqq 0$ (resp: $v(x) > 0$). Given a subring R of K, we say that v is a valuation of K over R if $R \subset R_v$, and then we set: $\dim_R v = \dim_R R_v$. Given a quasilocal domain R, we say that v dominates R if R_v dominates R. Given an overfield L of K and a valuation w of L, we say that v is the restriction of w to K or that w is an extension of v to L if $R_w \cap K = R_v$; note that then $M_w \cap K = M_v$. v is said to be *real* if the value group of v is order isomorphic to an additive subgroup of the real numbers; note that this is equivalent to saying that if P is any nonzero prime ideal in R_v then $P = M_v$. Also note that if R' is any domain with quotient field K' then: R' is the valuation ring of a real valuation of K' if and only if there does not exist any subring of K' which contains R' and is different from K'. v is said to be *real discrete* if the value group of v is an infinite cyclic group. Note that for a ring R the following four conditions are equivalent: (1) R is a domain and R is the valuation ring of a real discrete valuation of the quotient field of R; (2) R is a local Dedekind domain which is not a field;

(3) R is a one-dimensional normal local domain; (4) R is a one-dimensional regular local ring.

A ring A is said to be *pseudogeometric* if A is noetherian, and for every prime ideal P in A we have that the integral closure of A/P in any finite algebraic extension of the quotient field of A/P is a finite (A/P)-module. In regard to this notion we note the following: every homomorphic image of a pseudogeometric ring is pseudogeometric; every field is pseudogeometric; a Dedekind domain I is pseudogeometric if and only if the integral closure of I is any finite algebraic extension of the quotient field of I is a finite I-module; in particular every Dedekind domain of characteristic zero is pseudogeometric. The following basic result concerning pseudogeometric domains is due to Nagata [14: (36.5) and (36.6)].

Proposition 1. Every spot over a pseudogeometric domain is pseudogeometric. Every affine ring over a pseudogeometric domain is pseudogeometric.

The *dimension formula* is said to hold in a noetherian domain A, if for every spot (R, M) over A we have that: $\dim R + \dim_A R = \dim A_{A\cap M} + \operatorname{trdeg}_A R$. By a *maximal chain* of prime ideals in a domain A, we mean a finite sequence $P_0 \subset P_1 \subset \cdots \subset P_d$ of distinct prime ideals in A such that: $P_0 = \{0\}$; P_d is a maximal ideal in A; and there does not exist any prime ideal P in A such that $P_{i-1} \subset P \subset P_i$ and $P_{i-1} \neq P \neq P_i$ for some i with $1 \leqq i \leqq d$. The *first chain condition* is said to hold in a noetherian domain A, if for every maximal chain of prime ideals $P_0 \subset P_1 \subset \cdots \subset P_d$ in A we have that $d = \dim A_{P_d}$. The *second chain condition* is said to hold in a noetherian domain A, if for every nonnegative integer n the first chain condition holds in $A[X_1, \ldots, X_n]$ where $X_1, \ldots, X_n$ are indeterminates (note that $A[X_1, \ldots, X_n] = A$ in case $n = 0$). By Nagata [14: (25.12) and (35.5)] we get the following.

Proposition 2. If A is any Dedekind domain then the second chain condition and the dimension formula hold in every spot over A, and the second chain condition and the dimension formula hold in every affine ring over A.

Definition 1. Given a quasilocal domain S and a set V of quasilocal domains, we say that S dominates V if S dominates some element in V. Given a valuation v and a set V of quasilocal domains, we say that v dominates V if R_v dominates V. Given two sets V and V' of quasilocal domains we say that V' dominates V if every element in V' dominates V. For any nonempty set V of local domains we set $\dim V = \max_{R \in V} \dim R$. A set V of local domains is said to be *nonsingular* if every element in V is regular.

Definition 2. For any domain A, by $\mathfrak{V}(A)$ we denote the set of all quotient rings of A with respect to the various prime ideals in A. For any domain A and any finite number of nonzero elements $x_0, \ldots, x_n$ in an overdomain of A we set

$$\mathfrak{W}(A; x_0, \ldots, x_n) = \bigcup_{i=0}^{n} \mathfrak{V}(A[x_0/x_i, \ldots, x_n/x_i]).$$

Definition 3. Let K be a field. By a *premodel* of K we mean a nonempty set of local domains with quotient field K. By an *irredundant premodel* of K we mean a premodel V of K such that no two distinct elements in V are dominated by the same valuation of K; in this case if R is any element in V and v is any valuation of K dominating R, then we say that R is the *center of v on V*. Note that if V an irredundant premodel of K and S is a local domain with quotient field K such that S dominates V, then S dominates exactly one element in V; namely, if v is any valuation of K dominating S and R is any element in V such that S dominates R, then R is the center of v on V. Elements in a premodel V of K may be called *points* in V; a point R in V is said to be a *closed point* in V if there does not exist any point S in V such that $S \neq R$ and $R \in \mathfrak{V}(S)$; note that if R is a point in V such that $\dim R = \dim V$, then R is a closed point in V (but not conversely).

Definition 4. Let K be a function field over a noetherian domain I. By a *premodel* (resp: *irredundant premodel*) *of K over I* we mean a premodel (resp: irredundant premodel) V of K such that every element of V is a spot over I. A premodel V of K is said to be an *affine model of K over I* if there exists an affine ring A over I such $V = \mathfrak{V}(A)$; note that then V is an irredundant premodal of K over I. By a *model of K over I* we mean an irredundant premodel V of K such that V is the union of a finite number of affine models of K over I; note that then V is an irredundant premodel of K over I; also note that a point R in V is a closed point in V if and only if there does not exist any point S in V such that $S \subset R$ and $S \neq R$. By a *complete premodel* (resp: *complete irredundant premodel, complete model*) *of* K *over* I we mean a premodel (resp: irredundant premodel, model) V of K over I such that every valuation of K over I dominates V. A premodel V of K is said to be a *projective model of* K *over* I if there exists a finite number of nonzero elements $x_0, \ldots, x_n$ in K such that $V = \mathfrak{W}(I; x_0, \ldots, x_n)$; by [19: pp. 119–120] it follows that V is then a complete model of K over I.

Proposition 3. Let L be a field, let K be a subfield of L such that L is a pure transcendental extension of K and $\mathrm{trdeg}_K L$ is finite, and let v be a valuation of K. Then there exists an extension w of v to L such that $R_w/M_w = R_v/M_v$.

Proof. By a straightforward induction, the general case follows from the case when $\mathrm{trdeg}_K L = 1$. So assume that $L = K(x)$ where x is a transcendental over K. Let R be the set of all elements in L which can be expressed in the form $f(x)/g(x)$, where $f(x)$ and $g(x)$ are polynomials in x with coefficients in K such that $g(0) \neq 0$ and $f(0)/g(0) \in R_v$. It is easily checked that R is a domain with quotient field L, and if y is any element in L such that $y \notin R$, then $1/y \in R$. Therefore, $R = R_w$ where w is a valuation of L. Clearly, $R_w \cap K = R_v$ and $R_w/M_w = R_v/M_v$.

Proposition 4. Let L be a field, let K be a subfield of L such that $\mathrm{trdeg}_K L$ is finite, and let v be a valuation of K. Then there exists an extension w of v to L such that R_w/M_w is algebraic over R_v/M_v.

Proof. Follows from Proposition 3.

Proposition 5. Let I be a Dedekind domain and let K be a function field over I. If V is any premodel of K over I then $\dim V \leqq \mathrm{absdim}_I V$. If V is any complete premodel of K over I then $\dim V = \mathrm{absdim}_I V$.

Proof. Given any spot (R, M) over I with quotient field K let $P = I \cap R$ and $A = I_P$; then A is a local Dedekind domain, R is a spot over A, R dominates A, and $\dim A + \mathrm{trdeg}_A K \leqq \mathrm{absdim}_I K$; consequently by Proposition 2 we get that $\dim R + \dim_A R = \dim A + \mathrm{trdeg}_A R$ and hence $\dim R \leqq \mathrm{absdim}_I K$. Therefore, $\dim V \leqq \mathrm{absdim}_I K$ for every premodel V of K over I. Let Q be a maximal ideal in I and let $B = I_Q$. Then $B = R_v$ where v is a valuation of the quotient field of I, and $\dim B + \mathrm{trdeg}_B K = \mathrm{absdim}_I K$. By Proposition 4 there exists an extension w of v to K such that R_w/M_w is algebraic over R_v/M_v. Given any complete premodel V of K over I, there exists $R' \in V$ such that w dominates R'; clearly, R' is then a spot over B, R' dominates B, and $\dim_B R' = 0$; consequently by Proposition 2 we get that $\dim R' + \dim_B R' = \dim B + \operatorname{trdeg}_B R'$ and hence $\dim R' = \operatorname{absdim}_I K$; therefore, $\dim V = \operatorname{absdim}_I K$.

§3. QUADRATIC TRANSFORMS

Definition 5. Let (R, M) be a positive dimensional local domain with quotient field K. By *an immediate* (or *a first*) *quadratic transform of* R we mean a quasilocal domain S such that S dominates R and $S \in \mathfrak{V}(R[Mx^{-1}])$ for some nonzero element x in M, where $R[Mx^{-1}]$ denotes the smallest subring of K which contains R and contains every element of the form y/x with $y \in M$; note that if $(x_1, \ldots, x_n)$ is any finite basis of M then $R[Mx^{-1}] = R[x_1/x, \ldots, x_n/x]$ and hence S is a spot over R, and in particular S is a positive dimensional local domain with quotient field K. By $\mathfrak{Q}(R)$ we denote *the set of all immediate quadratic transforms of* R. If $R_0 = R$ and R_i is an immediate quadratic transform of R_{i-1} for $i = 1, \ldots, j$ where j is a nonnegative integer, then we say that R_j is *a* jth *quadratic transform of* R. A local domain R' is said to be *a quadratic transform of* R if R' is a jth quadratic transform of R for some nonnegative integer j.

Proposition 6. Let (R, M) be a positive dimensional local domain with quotient field K, let v be a valuation of K dominating R, let $(x, x_1, \ldots, x_n)$ be any finite basis of M such that $x \neq 0$ and $v(x) \leqq v(x_i)$ for $i = 1, \ldots, n$, let $A = R[x_1/x, \ldots, x_n/x]$, let $P = M_v \cap A$, and let $S = A_P$. Then S is the unique element in $\mathfrak{Q}(R)$ which is dominated by v.

Proof. Clearly v dominates S, and S dominates R; also $A = R[Mx^{-1}]$ and hence $S \in \mathfrak{Q}(R)$. Let S' be any element in $\mathfrak{Q}(R)$ such that v dominates S'. Then there exists $0 \neq y \in M$ such that $B \subset R_v$ and $S' = B_Q$, where $B = R[My^{-1}]$ and $Q = M_v \cap B$. Now $y/x \in A \subset R_v$ and $x/y \in B \subset R_v$, and hence y/x and x/y are units in R_v. Since $y/x \in A \subset S$, y/x is a unit in R_v, and v dominates S, we get that y/x is a unit in S and hence $x/y \in S$. For any $z \in M$ we have that $z/y = (z/x)(x/y)$ and $z/x \in A \subset S$; since $x/y \in S$ we get that $z/y \in S$.

Therefore, $B \subset S$. Now $Q = M_v \cap B = (M_v \cap S) \cap B = N \cap B$ where N is the maximal ideal in S, and hence $S' = B_Q \subset S$. Since $x/y \in B \subset S'$, x/y is a unit in R_v, and v dominates S', we get that x/y is a unit in S' and hence $y/x \in S'$. For any $z \in M$ we have that $z/x = (z/y)(y/x)$ and $z/y \in B \subset S'$; since $y/x \in S'$ we get that $z/x \in S'$. Therefore, $A \subset S'$. Now $P = M_v \cap A = (M_v \cap S') \cap A = N' \cap A$, where N' is the maximal ideal in S', and hence $S = A_P \subset S'$. Therefore, $S' = S$.

Definition 6. Let R be a positive dimensional local domain with quotient field K, and let v be a valuation of K dominating R. By the above proposition there exists a unique element S in $\mathfrak{Q}(R)$ such that v dominates S; S is called *the immediate* (or *the first*) *quadratic transform of R along v*. If $R_0 = R$ and R_i is the immediate quadratic transform of R_{i-1} along v for $i = 1, \ldots, j$ where j is a nonnegative integer, then we say that R_j is *the* jth *quadratic transform of R along v*. A local domain R' is said to be *a quadratic transform of R along v* if R' is the jth quadratic transform of R along v for some nonnegative integer j. Note that a local domain R' is a quadratic transform (resp: the jth quadratic transform) of R along v if and only if R' is a quadratic transform (resp: a jth quadratic transform) of R and v dominates R'.

Proposition 7. Let (R, M) be a positive dimensional local domain and let $(x_0, \ldots, x_n)$ be any finite basis of M such that $x_i \neq 0$ for $i = 0, \ldots, n$. Then $\mathfrak{Q}(R) =$ the set of all elements in $\mathfrak{W}(R; x_0, \ldots, x_n)$ which dominate R.

Proof. Given $S \in \mathfrak{Q}(R)$, take a valuation v of K dominating S and take i such that $v(x_i) \leqq v(x_j)$ for $j = 0, \ldots, n$; then by Proposition 6 we get that $S \in \mathfrak{V}(R[x_0/x_i, \ldots, x_n/x_i])$ and hence $S \in \mathfrak{W}(R; x_0, \ldots, x_n)$. Conversely, given $S \in \mathfrak{W}(R; x_0, \ldots, x_n)$ such that S dominates R, we can take i such that $S \in \mathfrak{V}(R[x_0/x_i, \ldots, x_n/x_i])$, and then $R[x_0/x_i, \ldots, x_n/x_i] = R[Mx_i^{-1}]$ and hence $S \in \mathfrak{Q}(R)$.

Proposition 8. For a positive dimensional local domain (R, M) the following three conditions are equivalent: (1) $Q(R) = \{R\}$; (2) $R \in \mathfrak{Q}(R)$; (3) R is a one-dimensional regular local domain.

Proof. Obviously (1) implies (2). Suppose that $R \in \mathfrak{Q}(R)$; then there exists $0 \neq x \in M$ such that $R \in \mathfrak{V}(R[Mx^{-1}])$; in particular $R[Mx^{-1}] \subset R$, that is, $y/x \in R$ for all $y \in M$; consequently $M = xR$, and hence R is a one-dimensional regular local domain. Suppose that R is a one-dimensional regular local domain; then there exists $0 \neq x \in M$ such that $M = xR$; clearly, $\mathfrak{W}(R; x) = \mathfrak{V}(R)$, and hence by Proposition 7 we get that $\mathfrak{Q}(R) = \{R\}$.

Definition 7. Let (R, M) be a positive dimensional regular local domain with quotient field K. We get a real discrete valuation of K dominating R by taking the value of x/y to be $a - b$, where x and y are any nonzero elements in R, and a and b are the greatest integers such that $x \in M^a$ and $y \in M^b$. This valuation is denoted by ord_R.

Proposition 9. Let (R, M) be a positive dimensional regular local domain with quotient field K, let (R^*, M^*) be the valuation ring of ord_R, let S be any element in $\mathfrak{Q}(R)$, and let v be any valuation of K dominating S. Then $R^* \in \mathfrak{V}(S)$, S is regular, and $\dim R - \dim S = \dim_R v - \dim_S v \geqq 0$; in particular, if $\dim_R v = 0$ then $\dim S = \dim R$. Furthermore, R^* is the only one-dimensional element in $\mathfrak{Q}(R)$.

Proof. Let $n = \dim R$. For $n = 1$ our assertions follow from Proposition 8. Now assume that $n > 1$. Let $(x_1, \ldots, x_n)$ be a basis of M which is labeled so that $v(x_1) \leqq v(x_i)$ for $i = 1, \ldots, n$. Let $A = R[x_2/x_1, \ldots, x_n/x_1]$ and $P = M_v \cap A$. Then by Proposition 6 we get that $S = A_P$, and by [2: Lemma 10] or [4: Lemma 3.20 on p. 73] we get that S is regular and $\dim R - \dim S = \dim_R v - \dim_S v \geqq 0$; in particular, if $\dim_R v = 0$ then $\dim S = \dim R$. Clearly, $A \subset R^*$. Let $Q = M^* \cap A$. Then Q is a prime ideal in A and $A_Q \subset R^*$. Clearly, $x_1 \in Q$. Let z be any nonzero element in Q; since $0 \neq z \in A$, there exists a nonzero polynomial $f(X_2, \ldots, X_n)$ in indeterminates $X_2, \ldots, X_n$ with coefficients in R such that $z = f(x_2/x_1, \ldots, x_n/x_1)$; let d be the degree of $f(X_2, \ldots, X_n)$ in $X_2, \ldots, X_n$; then $x_1^d z \in R$ and $\text{ord}_R(x_1^d z) = d + \text{ord}_R(z) \geqq d + 1$, because $z \in M^*$; therefore, there exists a homogeneous polynomial $g(Y_1, \ldots, Y_n)$ of degree $d + 1$ in indeterminates $Y_1, \ldots, Y_n$ with coefficients in R such that $x_1^d z = g(x_1, \ldots, x_n)$; now $z = x_1 z'$ where $z' = x_1^{-(d+1)} g(x_1, \ldots, x_n) = g(1, x_2/x_1, \ldots, x_n/x_1) \in A$, and hence $z \in x_1 A$. Therefore, $Q = x_1 A$ and hence A_Q is a one-dimensional regular local domain with quotient field K; since $A_Q \subset R^*$ we must have $A_Q = R^*$. Since R^* dominates R and $A = R[Mx_1^{-1}]$, we conclude that $R^* \in \mathfrak{Q}(R)$. Also $Q = x_1 A = MA \subset P$ and hence $A_Q \in \mathfrak{V}(A_P)$. Therefore, $R^* \in \mathfrak{V}(S)$. Let R' be any one-dimensional element in $\mathfrak{Q}(R)$; since $R' \in \mathfrak{Q}(R)$, by what we have just proved we get that $R^* \in \mathfrak{Q}(R')$; since $\dim R^* = 1 = \dim R'$, we must have $R' = R^*$.

Proposition 10. Let $R_0, R_1, R_2, \ldots$ be an infinite sequence of two-dimensional regular local domains with a common quotient field K such that $R_i \in \mathfrak{Q}(R_{i-1})$ for all $i > 0$. Then $\bigcup_{i=1}^{\infty} R_i = R_v$ where v is a valuation of K such that v dominates R_i and $\dim_{R_i} v = 0$ for all $i \geqq 0$. Furthermore, if v^* is any valuation of K which dominates R_i for all $i \geqq 0$ then $v^* = v$.

Proof. By Proposition 8 we get that $R_i \neq R_{i-1}$ for all $i > 0$. Therefore, our assertion follows from [2: Lemma 12] or [4: Lemma 4.5 on p. 79].

Remark. In the proof of [4: Lemma 4.5 on p. 79] which was a restatement of [2: Lemma 12], we used [4: Proposition 4.1 on p. 75] which was a restatement of [2: Lemma 7]. We take this opportunity to make the following corrections to [4: Proposition 4.1] and [2: Lemma 7]. In the statements of [4: Proposition 4.1] and [2: Lemma 7] the phrase "Then there exist infinitely many valuations w of K which have . . ." should be changed to "Then there exists a valuation w of K which has . . . ." The last five sentences in the proof of [4: Proposition 4.1] which now read "Let p be any . . . required type" should be changed to read "Let P be the kernel of H. By 2.22 there exists a valuation w of K having center P in $R[x]$. Clearly, w has the required properties." The last six sentences in the proof of [2: Lemma 7] which now read "The canonical . . . required type" should be changed to read "The canonical homomorphism h of R onto D can be uniquely extended to a homomorphism H of $R[x]$ onto $D[X]$ for which $H(x) = X$, where X is a transcendental over D; see pp. 26–27 of [14]. Let P be the kernel of H. By the theorem of existence of valuations, there exists a valuation w of K having center P in $R[x]$. Clearly, w has the required properties."

Definition 8. Let V be a premodel of a field K and W be a set of positive dimensional points in V. We define:

$$\mathfrak{Q}(V; W) = (V - W) \cup \Big(\bigcup_{R \in W} \mathfrak{Q}(R) \Big).$$

A premodel V' of K is said to be *a quadratic transform of V with center W* if there exists a finite number of premodels $V_0, \ldots, V_n$ of K and a finite set W_i of positive dimensional closed points in V_i for

$i = 0, \ldots, n-1$, such that $V_0 = V$, $W_0 = W$, $V_n = V'$, $V_{i+1} = \mathfrak{Q}(V_i; W_i)$ for $i = 0, \ldots, n-1$, and $W_{i+1} \subset \bigcup_{R \in W_i} \mathfrak{Q}(R)$ for $i = 0, \ldots, n-2$.

Proposition 11. Let V be a premodel of a field K, let W be a finite set of positive dimensional closed points in V, and let V' be a quadratic transform of V with center W. Then V' dominates V. If V is an irredundant premodel of K, then V' is an irredundant premodel of K. If W is nonsingular, then the set of all nonregular elements in V coincides with the set of all nonregular elements in V'. If K is a function field over a noetherian domain I and V is a complete premodel of K over I then V' is a complete premodel of K over I.

Proof. Follows from Propositions 6 and 9.

Proposition 12. Let A be a noetherian domain with quotient field K, and let $x_0, \ldots, x_n$ be any finite number of nonzero elements in A such that $(x_0, \ldots, x_n)A = A$. Then $\mathfrak{W}(A; x_0, \ldots, x_n) = \mathfrak{V}(A)$.

Proof. Now $\mathfrak{W}(A; x_0, \ldots, x_n)$ is a projective model of K over A, and hence $\mathfrak{W}(A; x_0, \ldots, x_n)$ is a complete model of K over A. Also, clearly, $\mathfrak{V}(A)$ is a complete model of K over A. Therefore, it suffices to show that if v is any valuation of K over A, and (R, M) and (S, N) are the centers of v on $\mathfrak{V}(A)$ and $\mathfrak{W}(A; x_0, \ldots, x_n)$, respectively, then $R = S$. Since $(x_0, \ldots, x_n)A = A$ and $A \subset R_v$, there exists i such that $x_i \notin M_v$. Let $B = A[x_0/x_i, \ldots, x_n/x_i]$. Then $B \subset R_v$ and hence $S = B_Q$, where $Q = M_v \cap B$. Let $P = M_v \cap A$. Then $R = A_P$. Now $A \subset S$ and $P = M_v \cap A = (M_v \cap S) \cap A = N \cap A$, and hence $R = A_P \subset S$. Also $x_i \notin M_v \cap A = P$, and hence $B \subset A_P = R$. Therefore, $Q = M_v \cap B = (M_v \cap R) \cap B = M \cap B$, and hence $S = B_Q \subset R$. Therefore, $R = S$.

Proposition 13. Let A be a noetherian domain with quotient field K, let (R, M) be a positive dimensional closed point in $\mathfrak{V}(A)$, let $P = M \cap A$, and let $x_0, \ldots, x_n$ be a finite number of nonzero elements in A such that $(x_0, \ldots, x_n)A = P$. Then P is a maximal ideal in A and $\mathfrak{W}(A; x_0, \ldots, x_n) = \mathfrak{Q}(\mathfrak{V}(A); \{R\})$.

Proof. Since R is a closed point in $\mathfrak{V}(A)$, we get that P is a maximal ideal in A. Now $\mathfrak{W}(A; x_0, \ldots, x_n)$ is a projective model of K over A, and hence $\mathfrak{W}(A; x_0, \ldots, x_n)$ is a complete model of K

over A. Clearly, $\mathfrak{V}(A)$ is a complete model of K over A, and hence by Proposition 11 we get that $\mathfrak{Q}(\mathfrak{V}(A); \{R\})$ is a complete irredundant premodel of K over A. Therefore, it suffices to show that if v is any valuation of K over A and (S', N') and (S, N) are the centers of v on $\mathfrak{Q}(\mathfrak{V}(A); \{R\})$ and $\mathfrak{W}(A; x_0, \ldots, x_n)$ respectively, then $S' = S$. Let (R', M') be the center of v on $\mathfrak{V}(A)$. Clearly, $\mathfrak{Q}(\mathfrak{V}(A); \{R\})$ and $\mathfrak{W}(A; x_0, \ldots, x_n)$ dominate $\mathfrak{V}(A)$, and hence S' and S dominate R'. Take i such that $v(x_i) \leqq v(x_j)$ for $j = 0, \ldots, n$. Let $B = A[x_0/x_i, \ldots, x_n/x_i]$. Then $B \subset R_v$, and hence $S = B_Q$ where $Q = M_v \cap B$. Let $P' = M' \cap A$. Then $R' = A_{P'}$.

First suppose that $P' \neq P$. Then $R' \neq R$, and hence $R' \in \mathfrak{Q}(\mathfrak{V}(A); \{R\})$. Therefore, $S' = R'$. Also $(x_0, \ldots, x_n)A = P \not\subset P' = M_v \cap A$, and hence $(x_0, \ldots, x_n)R_v = R_v$; since $v(x_i) \leqq v(x_j)$ for $j = 0, \ldots, n$, we must have $x_i \notin M_v$. Therefore, $x_i \notin P'$ and hence $B \subset A_{P'} = R'$. Consequently, $Q = M_v \cap B = (M_v \cap R') \cap B = M' \cap B$, and hence $S = B_Q \subset R'$. Therefore, $S = R'$ and hence $S' = S$.

Next suppose that $P' = P$. Then $R' = R$, and by Proposition 6 we get that $S' = B_{Q'}$, where $B' = R[x_0/x_i, \ldots, x_n/x_i]$ and $Q' = M_v \cap B'$. Now $B \subset B'$ and $Q = Q' \cap B$. Therefore, $S = B_Q \subset B'_{Q'} = S'$. Also $R \subset S$ and hence $B' \subset S$. Now $N \cap B' = (M_v \cap S) \cap B' = M_v \cap B' = Q'$, and hence $S' = B'_{Q'} \subset S$. Therefore, $S' = S$.

Proposition 14. Let K be a function field over a noetherian domain I, let V be a model of K over I, let W be a finite set of positive dimensional closed points in V, and let $R \in W$. Then $W - \{R\}$ is a finite set of positive dimensional closed points in $\mathfrak{Q}(V; \{R\})$, and $\mathfrak{Q}(V; W) = \mathfrak{Q}(\mathfrak{Q}(V; \{R\}); W - \{R\})$.

Proof. Obvious.

Proposition 15. Let K be a function field over a noetherian domain I and let V be a model of K over I. If W is any finite set of positive dimensional closed points in V and V' is any quadratic transform of V with center W then V' is a model of K over I.

Proof. In view of Proposition 14 it suffices to show that if R is any positive dimensional closed point in V, then $\mathfrak{Q}(V; \{R\})$ is a model of K over I. Now $V = \bigcup_{i=1}^m \mathfrak{V}(A_i)$, where $A_1, \ldots, A_m$ are a finite number of affine rings over I with quotient field K. Clearly, $\mathfrak{Q}(V; \{R\}) = \bigcup_{i=1}^m \mathfrak{Q}(\mathfrak{V}(A_i); \{R\} \cap \mathfrak{V}(A_i))$, and hence by Propositions

12 and 13 we conclude that $\mathfrak{Q}(V; \{R\})$ is the union of a finite number of affine models of K over I. By Proposition 11, $\mathfrak{Q}(V; \{R\})$ is an irredundant premodel of K over I and hence $\mathfrak{Q}(V; \{R\})$ is a model of K over I.

Proposition 16. Let K be a function field over a noetherian domain I and let V be a projective model of K over I. If W is any finite set of positive dimensional closed points in V and V' is any quadratic transform of V with center W then V' is a projective model of K over I.

Proof. In view of Proposition 14 it suffices to show that if (R, M) is any positive dimensional closed point in V then $\mathfrak{Q}(V; \{R\})$ is a projective model of K over I. Now $V = \mathfrak{W}(I; x_0, \ldots, x_n)$, where $x_0, \ldots, x_n$ are a finite number of nonzero elements in K. Let $A_i = I[x_0/x_i, \ldots, x_n/x_i]$. Upon relabeling $x_0, \ldots, x_n$, we may assume that $R \in \mathfrak{V}(A_i)$ for $i \leqq n'$ and $R \notin \mathfrak{V}(A_i)$ for $i > n'$, where n' is an integer such that $0 \leqq n' \leqq n$. Then in particular $A_0 \subset R$, and hence $x_i/x_0 \in R$ for $i \leqq n$. For $i \leqq n'$ we have that $A_i \subset R$, $M \cap A_i$ is a nonzero maximal ideal in A_i, and R is the quotient ring of A_i with respect to $M \cap A_i$. For $i \leqq n'$ we thus have $x_i/x_0 \in A_0 \subset R$ and $x_0/x_i \in A_i \subset R$. Therefore, x_i/x_0 and x_0/x_i are units in R for $i \leqq n'$. Conversely, if i is such that $A_i \subset R$, then upon taking a valuation v of K dominating R and taking R' to be the quotient ring of A_i with respect to $M_v \cap A_i$ we get that v dominates R' and $R' \in \mathfrak{V}(A_i) \subset V$; since V is an irredundant premodel of K, we must have $R' = R$ and hence $i \leqq n'$. If i is such that $x_i/x_0 \notin M$ then $x_0/x_i \in R$, and hence $x_j/x_i = (x_j/x_0)(x_0/x_i) \in R$ for $j = 0, \ldots, n$, and hence $A_i \subset R$. Therefore, $x_i/x_0 \in M$ for $i > n'$.

Let H be the set of all homogeneous polynomials $f(Y_0, \ldots, Y_n)$ in indeterminates $Y_0, \ldots, Y_n$ with coefficients in I such that $f(1, x_1/x_0, \ldots, x_n/x_0) \in M$; (we consider the zero polynomial to be homogeneous). Note that since $M \cap A_0$ is a nonzero ideal in A_0, there exists $h(Y_0, \ldots, Y_n) \in H$ such that $h(1, x_1/x_0, \ldots, x_n/x_0) \neq 0$, and then $h(x_0, \ldots, x_n) = x_0^r h(1, x_1/x_0, \ldots, x_n/x_0) \neq 0$, where r is the degree of $h(Y_0, \ldots, Y_n)$ in $Y_0, \ldots, Y_n$. Since $I[Y_0, \ldots, Y_n]$ is noetherian, there exists a finite number of nonzero elements $f_1(Y_0, \ldots, Y_n), \ldots, f_t(Y_0, \ldots, Y_n)$ in H which form a basis of the ideal in $I[Y_0, \ldots, Y_n]$ generated by H. Upon relabeling $f_1(Y_0, \ldots, Y_n), \ldots, f_t(Y_0, \ldots, Y_n)$, we may assume that $f_k(x_0, \ldots, x_n) \neq 0$ for $k \leqq s$ and $f_k(x_0, \ldots, x_n) = 0$

for $k > s$, where s is an integer such that $1 \leqq s \leqq t$. Let $d(k)$ be the degree of $f_k(Y_0, \ldots, Y_n)$ in $Y_0, \ldots, Y_n$. Let d be a positive integer such that $d \geqq d(k)$ for $k \leqq s$. Let $m = s(n+1) - 1$. Let $g_{us+k-1}(Y_0, \ldots, Y_n) = Y_u^{d-d(k)} f_k(Y_0, \ldots, Y_n)$ for $0 \leqq u \leqq n$ and $1 \leqq k \leqq s$. Then for $j = 0, \ldots, m$, we have that $g_j(Y_0, \ldots, Y_n)$ is a nonzero homogeneous polynomial of degree d in $Y_0, \ldots, Y_n$ with coefficients in I, $g_j(x_0, \ldots, x_n) \neq 0$, and $g_j(Y_0, \ldots, Y_n) \in H$; in particular, $g_j(1, x_1/x_0, \ldots, x_n/x_0) \in M$. Let $y_j = g_j(x_0, \ldots, x_n)$ and $y_{ij} = g_j(x_0/x_i, \ldots, x_n/x_i)$. Then $0 \neq y_j \in K$, $0 \neq y_j/x_i^d = y_{ij} \in A_i$, and $y_{ib}/y_{ij} = (x_i^d y_{ib})/(x_i^d y_{ij}) = y_b/y_j$ for $0 \leqq i \leqq n$, $0 \leqq b \leqq m$, and $0 \leqq j \leqq m$.

We claim that if $f(Y_0, \ldots, Y_n)$ is any element in H then $f(x_0/x_i, \ldots, x_n/x_i) \in (y_{i0}, \ldots, y_{im})A_i$ for $0 \leqq i \leqq n$. Namely, since $f(Y_0, \ldots, Y_n) \in H$, there exist elements $F_k(Y_0, \ldots, Y_n)$ in $I[Y_0, \ldots, Y_n]$ such that

$$f(Y_0, \ldots, Y_n) = \sum_{k=1}^{t} F_k(Y_0, \ldots, Y_n) f_k(Y_0, \ldots, Y_n).$$

Upon multiplying both sides by Y_i^d, we get that

$$g(Y_0, \ldots, Y_n) = \sum_{j=0}^{m} G_j(Y_0, \ldots, Y_n) g_j(Y_0, \ldots, Y_n) + \sum_{k=s+1}^{t} F'_k(Y_0, \ldots, Y_n) f_k(Y_0, \ldots, Y_n),$$

where
$$g(Y_0, \ldots, Y_n) = Y_i^d f(Y_0, \ldots, Y_n),$$
$$F'_k(Y_0, \ldots, Y_n) = Y_i^d F_k(Y_0, \ldots, Y_n) \quad \text{for } s < k \leqq t,$$
$$G_{is+k-1}(Y_0, \ldots, Y_n) = Y_i^{d(k)} F_k(Y_0, \cdots Y_n) \quad \text{for } 1 \leqq k \leqq s,$$
and
$$G_{us+k-1}(Y_0, \ldots, Y_n) = 0 \quad \text{for } 1 \leqq k \leqq s \text{ and } 0 \leqq u \leqq n \text{ with } u \neq i.$$

Now
$$f_k\left(\frac{x_0}{x_i}, \ldots, \frac{x_n}{x_i}\right) = x_i^{-d(k)} f_k(x_0, \ldots, x_n) = 0 \quad \text{for } s < k \leqq t,$$
$$g_j\left(\frac{x_0}{x_i}, \ldots, \frac{x_n}{x_i}\right) = y_{ij} \quad \text{for } 0 \leqq j \leqq m,$$
and
$$g\left(\frac{x_0}{x_i}, \ldots, \frac{x_n}{x_i}\right) = f\left(\frac{x_0}{x_i}, \ldots, \frac{x_n}{x_i}\right).$$

Therefore, upon substituting $x_0/x_i, \ldots, x_n/x_i$ for $Y_0, \ldots, Y_n$, we get that

$$f\left(\frac{x_0}{x_i}, \ldots, \frac{x_n}{x_i}\right) = \sum_{j=0}^{m} G_j\left(\frac{x_0}{x_i}, \ldots, \frac{x_n}{x_i}\right) y_{ij}.$$

Since $G_j(x_0/x_i, \ldots, x_n/x_i) \in A_i$ for $0 \leqq j \leqq m$, we conclude that $f(x_0/x_i, \ldots, x_n/x_i) \in (y_{i0}, \ldots, y_{im})A_i$.

We claim that for $i > n'$, we have that $(y_{i0}, \ldots, y_{im})A_i = A_i$. Namely, take $f'(Y_0, \ldots, Y_n) = Y_i$; then $f'(1, x_1/x_0, \ldots, x_n/x_0) = x_i/x_0 \in M$, and hence $f'(Y_0, \ldots, Y_n) \in H$; consequently $1 = f'(x_0/x_i, \ldots, x_n/x_i) \in (y_{i0}, \ldots, y_{in})A_i$. Therefore, $(y_{i0}, \ldots, y_{im})A_i = A_i$ and hence by Proposition 12 we get that $\mathfrak{W}(A_i; y_{i0}, \ldots, y_{im}) = \mathfrak{V}(A_i)$.

Next we claim that for $i \leqq n'$, we have that $(y_{i0}, \ldots, y_{im})A_i = M \cap A_i$. Namely, for $0 \leqq j \leqq m$ we get that $y_{ij} = y_j/x_i^d = (y_j/x_0^d)(x_0/x_i)^d$, $(x_0/x_i)^d \in R$, and $y_j/x_0^d = x_0^{-d}g_j(x_0, \ldots, x_n) = g_j(1, x_1/x_0, \ldots, x_n/x_0) \in M$; consequently $y_{ij} \in M \cap A_i$ for $0 \leqq j \leqq m$. Conversely, let y be any nonzero element in $M \cap A_i$; since $0 \neq y \in A_i$, we can find a nonzero homogeneous polynomial $f^*(Y_0, \ldots, Y_n)$ of some degree e in $Y_0, \ldots, Y_n$ with coefficients in I such that $y = f^*(x_0/x_i, \ldots, x_n/x_i)$; since $y \in M$ and $x_i/x_0 \in R$ we get that $(x_i/x_0)^e y \in M$; clearly, $f^*(1, x_1/x_0, \ldots, x_n/x_0) = (x_i/x_0)^e y$ and hence $f^*(Y_0, \ldots, Y_n) \in H$; consequently, $f^*(x_0/x_i, \ldots, x_n/x_0) \in (y_{i0}, \ldots, y_{im})A_i$ and hence $y \in (y_{i0}, \ldots, y_{im})A_i$. Therefore, $(y_{i0}, \ldots, y_{im})A_i = M \cap A_i$ and hence by Proposition 13 we get that $\mathfrak{W}(A_i; y_{i0}, \ldots, y_{im}) = \mathfrak{Q}(\mathfrak{V}(A_i); \{R\})$.

Clearly,

$$\begin{aligned}\mathfrak{Q}(V; \{R\}) &= \bigcup_{i=0}^{n} \mathfrak{Q}(\mathfrak{V}(A_i); \{R\} \cap \mathfrak{V}(A_i)) \\ &= \left(\bigcup_{i=0}^{n'} \mathfrak{Q}(\mathfrak{V}(A_i); \{R\})\right) \cup \left(\bigcup_{i=n'+1}^{n} \mathfrak{V}(A_i)\right).\end{aligned}$$

Therefore, by what we have proved in the above two paragraphs we get that

$$\mathfrak{Q}(V; \{R\}) = \bigcup_{i=0}^{n} \mathfrak{W}(A_i; y_{i0}, \ldots, y_{im}).$$

Let $z_{ij} = x_i y_j$. Then $0 \neq z_{ij} \in K$. Let A_{ij} be the smallest subring of K which contains I and contains the element z_{ab}/z_{ij} for $0 \leqq a \leqq$

n and $0 \leqq b \leqq m$. Let $p = (m+1)(n+1) - 1$ and let $z_0, \ldots, z_p$ be a labeling of the elements z_{ij} for $0 \leqq i \leqq n$ and $0 \leqq j \leqq m$. Then, clearly,

$$\mathfrak{W}(I; z_0, \ldots, z_p) = \bigcup_{i=0}^{n} \bigcup_{j=0}^{m} \mathfrak{V}(A_{ij}).$$

For $0 \leqq i \leqq n$, $0 \leqq a \leqq n$, $0 \leqq j \leqq m$, and $0 \leqq b \leqq m$, we have that $z_{aj}/z_{ij} = x_a/x_i$, $z_{ib}/z_{ij} = y_b/y_j = y_{ib}/y_{ij}$, and $z_{ab}/z_{ij} = (x_a/x_i)(y_b/y_j) = (x_a/x_i)(y_{ib}/y_{ij})$. Therefore, $A_{ij} = A_i[y_{i0}/y_{ij}, \ldots, y_{im}/y_{ij}]$ for $0 \leqq i \leqq n$ and $0 \leqq j \leqq m$. Consequently,

$$\mathfrak{W}(A_i; y_{i0}, \ldots, y_{im}) = \bigcup_{j=0}^{m} \mathfrak{V}(A_{ij}) \qquad \text{for } 0 \leqq i \leqq n,$$

and hence $\mathfrak{W}(I; z_0, \ldots, z_p) = \bigcup_{i=0}^{n} \mathfrak{W}(A_i; y_{i0}, \ldots, y_{im})$.

Therefore, by what we have proved in the above paragraph we get that $\mathfrak{Q}(V; \{R\}) = \mathfrak{W}(I; z_0, \ldots, z_p)$. Therefore, $\mathfrak{Q}(V; \{R\})$ is a projective model of K over I.

Definition 9. Let V and V' be premodels of a field K. A point R in V is said to be *fundamental for* V' if R does not dominate V'. By $\mathfrak{F}(V, V')$ [resp: $\mathfrak{F}'(V, V')$] we denote the set of all regular (resp: normal) points in V which are fundamental for V'. Note that $\mathfrak{F}(V, V') \subset \mathfrak{F}'(V, V')$.

Proposition 17. Let I be a pseudogeometric Dedekind domain, let K be a function field over I such that $\text{absdim}_I K = 2$, let V be a model of K over I, and let V' be a complete model of K over I. Then $\mathfrak{F}'(V, V')$ is a finite set and every point in $\mathfrak{F}'(V, V')$ is two-dimensional.

Proof. If R is any normal point in V such that $\dim R \neq 2$ then $\dim R \leqq 1$ by Proposition 5 and hence $R = R_v$ where v is a valuation of K over I; let R' be the center of v on V'; then R dominates R' and hence R dominates V'; therefore, R is not fundamental for V'. Since V is the union of a finite number of affine models of K over I, to prove that $\mathfrak{F}'(V, V')$ is a finite set, without loss of generality, we may assume that $V = \mathfrak{V}(A)$, where A is an affine ring over I with quotient field K. Let B be the integral closure of A in K. By Proposition 1, B is a finite A-module, and hence B is an affine ring over I. Now every normal point in $\mathfrak{V}(A)$ is contained in $\mathfrak{V}(B)$ and hence $\mathfrak{F}'(\mathfrak{V}(A), V')$

$\subset \mathfrak{F}'(\mathfrak{V}(B), V')$. Therefore, it suffices to show that $\mathfrak{F}'(\mathfrak{V}(B), V')$ is a finite set.

Let H be the set of all prime ideals P in B such that B_P is fundamental for V'. Let $D = \bigcap_{P \in H} P$. Then D is an ideal in B and the radical of D is D. If $D = B$ then $\mathfrak{F}'(\mathfrak{V}(B), V')$ is empty. Now assume that $D \neq B$. Then $D = Q_1 \cap \cdots \cap Q_t$, where $Q_1, \ldots, Q_t$ are a finite number of prime ideals in B. Suppose if possible that $\mathfrak{F}'(\mathfrak{V}(B), V')$ is an infinite set. Then H is an infinite set, and hence there exists $P' \in H$ such that $Q_i \neq P'$ for $i = 1, \ldots, t$. Now $D \subset P'$ and hence $Q_i \subset P'$ for some i; let $Q = Q_i$ and $S = B_Q$. By Proposition 5, $\dim B_{P'} \leqq 2$; since $Q \subset P'$ and $Q \neq P'$, we get that $\dim S \leqq 1$. Now S is normal because B is normal. Therefore, $S = R_w$ where w is a valuation of K over I. Let S' be the center of w on V'. Then there exists a finite number of elements $x_1, \ldots, x_n$ in K such that $S' \in \mathfrak{V}(A') \subset V'$ where $A' = I[x_1, \ldots, x_n]$. Since $x_i \in S' \subset R_w = B_Q$ for $i = 1, \ldots, n$, there exist elements $y_1, \ldots, y_n, z$ in B such that $z \notin Q$ and $x_i = y_i/z$ for $i = 1, \ldots, n$. If P is any prime ideal in B such that $z \notin P$ then $A' \subset B_P$ and hence B_P dominates $\mathfrak{V}(A')$; consequently, B_P dominates V' and hence $P \notin H$. Therefore, $z \in P$ for all $P \in H$, and hence $z \in D$. Since $D \subset Q$, we get that $z \in Q$. This is a contradiction.

The following proposition is a very special case of Tychonoff's theorem.

Proposition 18. Let Z be the set of all nonnegative integers, let Z' be the set of all positive integers, let X be a set, for each $i \in Z$ let X_i be a nonempty finite subset of X, and for each $i \in Z'$ let g_i be a map of X_i into X_{i-1}. Then there exists a map h of Z into X such that $h(i) \in X_i$ for all $i \in Z$ and $g_i(h(i)) = h(i-1)$ for all $i \in Z'$.

Proof. For any nonempty set Y, let $P(Y)$ denote the set of all subsets of Y, let $Q(Y)$ denote the set of all nonempty subsets A of $P(Y)$ such that $\bigcap_{M \in B} M$ is nonempty for every nonempty finite subset B of A, and let $R(Y)$ denote the set of all elements A in $Q(Y)$ such that there does not exist any element A' in $Q(Y)$ for which $A \subset A'$ and $A \neq A'$. Note that: (1) if $A \in R(Y)$ and B is any nonempty finite subset of A then $\bigcap_{M \in B} M \in A$; consequently: (2) if $A \in R(Y)$ and $N \in P(Y)$ such that $M \cap N$ is nonempty for all $M \in A$ then $N \in A$. Clearly: (3) if Y is finite and $A \in Q(Y)$ then $\bigcap_{M \in A} M$ is nonempty. By applying Zorn's lemma to $Q(Y)$ we get that: (4) given $A' \in Q(Y)$ there exists $A \in R(Y)$ such that $A' \subset A$. If t is a map of Y into a set Y' then for any $M \in P(Y)$, as usual, by $t(M)$ we denote the set of all $y' \in Y'$ such that $y' = t(y)$ for some $y \in M$, and similarly for any $A \in P(P(Y))$ by $t(A)$ we denote the set of all $M' \in P(Y')$ such that $M' = t(M)$ for some $M \in A$. Note that: (5) if t is a map of Y into a set Y' then $t(A) \in Q(Y')$ for all $A \in Q(Y)$.

Now let Y denote the set of all maps u of Z into X such that $u(i) \in X_i$ for all $i \in Z$. For each $i \in Z'$ let Y_i denote the set of all elements u in Y such that $g_i(u(i)) = u(i-1)$. Then $\bigcap_{0<i\leqq j} Y_i$ is nonempty for all $j \in Z'$. Therefore, by (4) there exists $A \in R(Y)$ such that $Y_i \in A$ for all $i \in Z'$. For each $i \in Z$ let t_i be the map of Y into X_i given by taking $t_i(u) = u(i)$ for all $u \in Y$; then $t_i(A) \in Q(X_i)$ by (5) and hence $\bigcap_{N \in t_i(A)} N$ is nonempty by (3); therefore, there exists $x_i \in X_i$ such that $x_i \in t_i(M)$ for all $M \in A$. For each $i \in Z$ let D_i be the set of all $u \in Y$ such that $u(i) = x_i$; then $M \cap D_i$ is nonempty for all $M \in A$ and hence $D_i \in A$ by (2). For each $i \in Z'$ we thus have that Y_i, D_i, D_{i-1} are elements in A and hence there exists $v_i \in Y_i \cap D_i \cap D_{i-1}$; since $v_i \in Y_i$ we get that $g_i(v_i(i)) = v_i(i-1)$; since $v_i \in D_i \cap D_{i-1}$ we set that $v_i(i) = x_i$ and $v_i(i-1) = x_{i-1}$; therefore, $g_i(x_i) = x_{i-1}$. Let h be the map of Z into X such that $h(i) = x_i$ for all $i \in Z$. Then $h(i) \in X_i$ for all $i \in Z$ and $g_i(h(i)) = h(i-1)$ for all $i \in Z'$.

Proposition 19. Let I be a pseudogeometric Dedekind domain, let K be a function field over I such that $\operatorname{absdim}_I K = 2$, let V be a model of K over I, and let V' be a complete model of K over I. Then $\mathfrak{F}(V, V')$ is a finite set of two-dimensional closed points in V, and there exists a quadratic transform V^* of V with center $\mathfrak{F}(V, V')$ such that $\mathfrak{F}(V^*, V')$ is empty.

Proof. Let $V_0 = V$, and for all positive integers i define V_i by the recurrence equation: $V_i = \mathfrak{Q}(V_{i-1}, \mathfrak{F}(V_{i-1}, V'))$. Then clearly

$$\mathfrak{F}(V_i, V') \subset \bigcup_{R \in \mathfrak{F}(V_{i-1}, V')} \mathfrak{Q}(R)$$

for all $i > 0$. Therefore, by Propositions 5, 15, and 17, for all $i \geqq 0$ we get that: $\mathfrak{F}(V_i, V')$ is a finite set of two-dimensional closed points in V_i, V_i is a model of K over I, and V_i is a quadratic transform of V with center $\mathfrak{F}(V, V')$. We shall show that $\mathfrak{F}(V_i, V')$ is empty for some i and then it would suffice to take $V^* = V_i$. Suppose if possible that $\mathfrak{F}(V_i, V')$ is nonempty for all $i \geqq 0$. For any $i > 0$ and any element R in $\mathfrak{F}(V_i, V')$ there exists a unique element S in $\mathfrak{F}(V_{i-1}, V')$

such that $R \in \mathfrak{Q}(S)$; define $g_i(R)$ to be S. Then g_i is a map of $\mathfrak{F}(V_i, V')$ into $\mathfrak{F}(V_{i-1}, V')$ for all $i > 0$. By Proposition 18 there exists an infinite sequence $R_0, R_1, R_2, \ldots,$ such that $R_i \in \mathfrak{F}(V_i, V')$ for all $i \geqq 0$ and $g_i(R_i) = R_{i-1}$ for all $i > 0$. By Proposition 10 there exists a valuation v of K such that $\bigcup_{i=0}^{\infty} R_i = R_v$, and v dominates R_i for all $i \geqq 0$. Let R' be the center of v on V'. Then there exists a finite number of elements $x_1, \ldots, x_n$ in K such that $A \subset R_v$ and $R' = A_P$ where $A = I[x_1, \ldots, x_n]$ and $P = M_v \cap A$. Since $\bigcup_{i=0}^{\infty} R_i = R_v$, there exists i such that $A \subset R_i$. It follows that then R_i dominates R' and hence R_i dominates V'. This is a contradiction.

Proposition 20. Let I be a pseudogeometric Dedekind domain, let K be a function field over I such that $\text{absdim}_I K = 2$, let V be a nonsingular projective model of K over I, and let $V_1, \ldots, V_t$ be a finite number of complete models of K over I. Then there exists a nonsingular projective model V^* of K over I such that V^* dominates V and V^* dominates V_i for all i.

Proof. The general case follows from the case when $t = 1$ by a straightforward induction. So assume that $t = 1$. By Proposition 19, $\mathfrak{F}(V, V_1)$ is a finite set of two-dimensional closed points in V, and there exists a quadratic transform V^* of V with center $\mathfrak{F}(V, V_1)$ such that $\mathfrak{F}(V^*, V_1)$ is empty. By Propositions 11 and 16 we get that V^* is a nonsingular projective model of K over I and V^* dominates V. Since V^* is nonsingular and $\mathfrak{F}(V^*, V_1)$ is empty, we conclude that V^* dominates V_1.

Proposition 21. Let I be a pseudogeometric Dedekind domain, let K be a function field over I such that $\text{absdim}_I K = 2$, and let $V_1, \ldots, V_t$ be a finite number of projective models of K over I. Then there exists a projective model V of K over I having the following property: if v is any valuation of K over I such that the center of v on V_i is regular for some i then the center of v on V is regular.

Proof. The general case follows from the case when $t = 2$ by a straightforward induction. So assume that $t = 2$. By Proposition 19, $\mathfrak{F}(V_1, V_2)$ is a finite set of two-dimensional closed points in V_1, and there exists a quadratic transform V' of V with center $\mathfrak{F}(V_1, V_2)$ such that $\mathfrak{F}(V', V_2)$ is empty. By Proposition 16, V' is a projective model of K over I. Again by Proposition 19, $\mathfrak{F}(V_2, V')$ is a finite set of two-dimensional closed points in V_2, and there exists a quadratic transform V^* of V_2 with center $\mathfrak{F}(V_2, V')$ such that $\mathfrak{F}(V^*, V')$ is empty. By Proposition 16, V^* is a projective model of K over I. By [19: Lemma 6 on p. 120] there exists a unique projective model V of K over I that has the following two properties: (1) V dominates V' and V^*; (2) if S is any quasilocal ring with quotient field K such that S dominates V' and V^* then S dominates V; (V is called the *join* of V' and V^*). Given any valuation v of K over I let R_1, R_2, R', R^*, and R be the centers of v on V_1, V_2, V', V^*, and V, respectively. Note that by (1), R dominates R' and R^*.

First suppose that R_2 is regular. Then R^* is regular by Proposition 11. Since $\mathfrak{F}(V^*, V')$ is empty, we get that R^* dominates V', and hence R^* dominates R'. Therefore, by (2) we get that R^* dominates V, and hence R^* dominates R. Since R dominates R^*, we must have $R = R^*$. Therefore, R is regular.

Next suppose that R_2 is nonregular and R_1 is regular. Since R_2 is nonregular, by Proposition 11 we get that $R_2 \in V^*$ and hence $R^* = R_2$. Since R_1 is regular, by Proposition 11 we get that R' is regular. Since $\mathfrak{F}(V', V_2)$ is empty, we get that R' dominates V_2. Therefore, R' dominates R_2 and hence R' dominates R^*. Consequently, by (2) we get that R' dominates V, and hence R' dominates R. Since R dominates R', we must have $R = R'$. Therefore, R is regular.

Proposition 22. Let I be a pseudogeometric Dedekind domain and let K be a function field over I. Assume that for each valuation v of K over I there exists a regular local domain R with quotient field K such that R is a spot over I and v dominates R. Then there exists a finite number of projective models $V_1, \ldots, V_t$ of K over I such that if v is any valuation of K over I then the center of v on V_i is regular for some i.

Proof. Let X be the set of all valuations of K over I. Let T be the set of all subrings A of K such that A is an affine ring over I. For each A in T let $E(A)$ denote the set of all $v \in X$ such that $A \subset R_v$. Let T' be the set of all subsets Y of X such that $Y = E(A)$ for some $A \in T$. By [19: pp. 110–114], T' is a basis of a topology T^* on X and X is quasicompact in T^*. Given $v \in X$, by assumption there exists a regular local domain R with quotient field K such that R is a spot over I and v dominates R; we can take $B \in T$ such that $R \in \mathfrak{V}(B)$; let V' be the set of all regular points in $\mathfrak{V}(B)$; by [12: Theorem 1 on p. 429], V' is a model of K over I and hence there exists $A(v) \in T$ such that $R \in \mathfrak{V}(A(v)) \subset V'$; since $A(v) \in T$, there exists a finite number of nonzero elements $x_1, \ldots, x_n$ in K such that $A(v) = I[x_1, \ldots, x_n]$; let $W(v) = \mathfrak{W}(I; 1, x_1, \ldots, x_n)$; then $W(v)$ is a projective model of K over I and $\mathfrak{V}(A(v)) \subset W(v)$. Thus for each $v \in X$ we have found $A(v) \in T$ and a projective model $W(v)$ of K over I such that $\mathfrak{V}(A(v)) \subset W(v)$, $v \in E(A(v))$, and $\mathfrak{V}(A(v))$ is nonsingular. Clearly, $\cup_{v \in X} E(A(v)) = X$. Since X is quasicompact in T^*, there exists a finite number of elements $v_1, \ldots, v_t$ in X such that $\cup_{i=1}^{t} E(A(v_i)) = X$. Let $V_i = W(v_i)$. Then $V_1, \ldots, V_t$ are a finite number of projective models of K over I having the required property.

Proposition 23. Let I be a pseudogeometric Dedekind domain and let K be a function field over I such that $\text{absdim}_I K = 2$. Assume that for each valuation v of K over I there exists a regular local domain R with quotient field K such that R is a spot over I and v dominates R. Then there exists a nonsingular projective model of K over I. Furthermore, given any finite number of complete models $V_1, \ldots, V_t$ of K over I there exists a nonsingular projective model V of K over I such that V dominates V_i for all i.

Proof. Follows from Propositions 20, 21, and 22.

§4. UNIFORMIZATION

Before proceeding to the proof of the Uniformization Lemma, we introduce some more terminology in Definition 10 and give some auxiliary results in Lemmas 1 to 12.

Definition 10. Given quasilocal domains (R, M) and (S, N), we say that S *lies above* R if the quotient field L of S is a finite algebraic extension of the quotient field of R and $S = T_P$, where T is the integral closure of R in L and P is a maximal ideal in T; note that then $P = N \cap T$ and $M = N \cap R$. Let R be a quasilocal domain with quotient field K, L a finite algebraic extension of K, v a valuation of K, and w an extension of v to L; note that if there exists a quasilocal domain S with quotient field L such that S lies above R and w dominates S then v dominates R; conversely if v dominates R, then there exists a unique quasilocal domain S with quotient field L such that S lies above R and w dominates S.

If K is a field, L is a finite algebraic extension of K, and $(x_1, \ldots, x_n)$ is a free K-basis of L, then the *discriminant* of $(x_1, \ldots, x_n)$ relative to the field extension L over K is denoted by $\mathfrak{D}_{L/K}(x_1, \ldots, x_n)$; for definition see [18: p. 92]. If R is a normal domain with quotient field K and L is a finite algebraic extension of K, then by $\mathfrak{D}(R, L)$ we denote the ideal in R generated by the discriminants $\mathfrak{D}_{L/K}(x_1, \ldots, x_n)$ of all the free K-bases $(x_1, \ldots, x_n)$ of L over K such that the elements $x_1, \ldots, x_n$ are integral over R.

Let R be a normal quasilocal domain with quotient field K, let L be a Galois extension (i.e., a finite algebraic separable normal extension) of K, and let (S, N) be a quasilocal domain with quotient field L such that S lies above R. Recall that the *inertia group* of S over R is the set of all elements g in the Galois group of L over K such that $x - g(x) \in N$ for all $x \in S$; and the *inertia field* of S over R is the fixed field of the inertia group of S over R. If $R = R_v$ and $S = R_w$, where v and w are valuations of K and L, respectively, then the inertia group (resp: inertia field) of S over R is also called the inertia group (resp: inertia field) of w over v.

Let v be a valuation of a field K and let w be an extension of v to an overfield L of K. Then the value group G_v of v can be regarded as a subgroup of the value group G_w of w; the order of the factor group G_w/G_v is called the *reduced ramification index* of w over v, and it is denoted by $\mathfrak{r}(w : v)$. Note that if v and w are real discrete then $\mathfrak{r}(w : v)$ is the positive integer e such that $M_vR_w = (M_w)^e$.

We shall need the following Diskriminantensatz of Krull; for a proof see [11] or [4: §6].

Lemma 1. Let P be a prime ideal in a normal domain A, let $R = A_P$ and $M = PR$, let K be the quotient field of A, let L be a finite algebraic extension of K, let $(S_1, N_1), \ldots, (S_q, N_q)$ be the quasilocal domains with quotient field L lying above R, and let d_i be the vector space dimension over R/M of the maximal separable algebraic extension of R/M in S_i/N_i. Then $d_1 + \cdots + d_q \leqq [L : K]$, and equality holds if and only if $\mathfrak{D}(A, L) \not\subset P$. Furthermore if $\mathfrak{D}(A, L) \not\subset P$ then S_i/N_i is separable over R/M and $MS_i = N_i$ for $i = 1, \ldots, q$.

Lemma 2. Let A be a normal domain with quotient field K and let L be a finite algebraic extension of K. Then L is separable over K if and only if $\mathfrak{D}(A, L) \neq \{0\}$.

Proof. Follows by taking $\{0\}$ for P in Lemma 1. Alternatively see [18: §11 of Chapter II].

The following result is due to Cohen; see [9: Theorem 8 on p. 68].

Lemma 3. Let (R, M) and (S, N) be complete local rings such that S dominates R. If MS is primary for N and $[S/N : R/M]$ is finite then S is a finite R-module. If $MS = N$ and $S/N = R/M$ then $S = R$.

Lemma 4. Let (R, M) and (S, N) be local domains such that the completion of R is a domain, S is regular, S dominates R, $\dim R = \dim S$, $MS = N$, and S/N is a finite algebraic separable extension of R/M. Then R is regular.

Proof. Let $(\mathfrak{R}, \mathfrak{M})$ and $(\mathfrak{S}, \mathfrak{N})$ be the completions of R and S, respectively. By [7: Proposition 15], R is a subspace of S, and hence we may regard $\mathfrak{R}$ to be a subring of $\mathfrak{S}$ and then we have that $\mathfrak{S}$ dominates $\mathfrak{R}$, $\mathfrak{M}\mathfrak{S} = \mathfrak{N}$, and $\mathfrak{S}/\mathfrak{N}$ is a finite algebraic separable extension of $\mathfrak{R}/\mathfrak{N}$. By Lemma 3 we then get that $\mathfrak{S}$ is a finite $\mathfrak{R}$-module. Now $\mathfrak{S}$ is regular because S is regular. In particular $\mathfrak{S}$ is a normal domain. Therefore, the quotient field L of $\mathfrak{S}$ is a finite algebraic extension of the quotient field K of $\mathfrak{R}$, and $\mathfrak{S}$ is the integral closure of $\mathfrak{R}$ in L. Since $\mathfrak{S}/\mathfrak{N}$ is separable over $\mathfrak{R}/\mathfrak{M}$, by Lemma 1 we get that $[\mathfrak{S}/\mathfrak{N} : \mathfrak{R}/\mathfrak{M}] \leqq [L : K]$. Therefore, by [7: Proposition 26], $\mathfrak{R}$ is regular and hence R is regular.

We shall need the following four known results on the inertia field.

Lemma 5. Let (R, M) be a normal quasilocal domain with quotient field K, let L be a Galois extension of K, let (S, N) be a quasilocal domain with quotient field L lying above R, let L' be the inertia field of S over R, let $S' = S \cap L'$, and let $N' = N \cap L'$. Then (S', N') is a quasilocal domain with quotient field L' lying above R, $MS' = N'$, S'/N' is a Galois extension of R/M, S is the integral closure of S' in L, and S/N is purely inseparable over S'/N'.

Proof. See [4: Theorem 1.48].

Lemma 6. Let R' and R^* be normal quasilocal domains with a common quotient field K, let L be a Galois extension of K, let S' be a quasilocal domain with quotient field L lying above R', let L' be the inertia field of S' over R', let S^* be a quasilocal domain with quotient field L lying above R^*, and let L^* be the inertia field of S^* over R^*. If $S' \subset S^*$ then $L' \subset L^*$.

Proof. By [4: Proposition 1.29], $R' = S' \cap K$, and $R^* = S^* \cap K$. Therefore, our assertion follows from [4: Proposition 1.50].

Lemma 7. Let R be a normal quasilocal domain with quotient field K, let L be a Galois extension of K, let S be a quasilocal domain with quotient field L lying above R, let L' be the inertia field of S over R, let K' be a subfield of L containing K, let $R' = S \cap K'$, and let K'' be the inertia field of S over R'. Then K'' is the compositum of K' and L' in L.

Proof. See [4: Proposition 1.49].

Lemma 8. Let v be a real discrete valuation of a field K, let L be a Galois extension of K, let w be an extension of v to L, let L' be the inertia field of w over v, let K' be a subfield of L containing K, and let v' be the restriction of w to K'. Then $K' \subset L'$ if and only if $R_{v'}/M_{v'}$ is separable over R_v/M_v and $\mathfrak{r}(v' : v) = 1$.

Proof. Let w' be the restriction of w to L'. Then by Lemma 5 we get that: (1) R_w/M_w is purely inseparable over $R_{w'}/M_{w'}$ and w is the only extension of w' to L; and (2) $R_{w'}/M_{w'}$ is separable over R_v/M_v and $\mathfrak{r}(w' : v) = 1$. Let K'' be the compositum of K' and L' in L and let v'' be the restriction of w to K''. Then by Lemma 7, K'' is the inertia field of w over v', and hence by Lemma 5 we get that: (3) $R_{v''}/M_{v''}$ is separable over $R_{v'}/M_{v'}$ and $\mathfrak{r}(v'' : v') = 1$. Since $L' \subset K'' \subset L$, by (1) we get that $R_{v''}/M_{v''}$ is purely inseparable over $R_{w'}/M_{w'}$ and v'' is the only extension of w' to K''. Since K'' is separable over L' and v'' is the only extension of w' to K'', by [18: Corollary on p. 287] we get that

$$[K'' : L'] = \mathfrak{r}(v'' : w')[R_{v''}/M_{v''} : R_{w'}/M_{w'}];$$

since $R_{v''}/M_{v''}$ is purely inseparable over $R_{w'}/M_{w'}$, we thus get that: (4) $K'' = L'$ if and only if $R_{v''}/M_{v''}$ is separable over $R_{w'}/M_{w'}$ and $\mathfrak{r}(v'' : w') = 1$. Clearly: (5) $K' \subset L'$ if and only if $K'' = L'$. Our assertion now follows from (2), (3), (4), (5).

Lemma 9. Let A be a Dedekind domain with quotient field K and let L be a finite algebraic extension of K. Then $\mathfrak{D}(A, L) = A$ if and only if the following condition holds: (1) L is separable over K and for every real discrete valuation w of L over A we have that R_w/M_w is separable over R_v/M_v and $\mathfrak{r}(w:v) = 1$ where v is the restriction of w to K.

Proof. First suppose that $\mathfrak{D}(A, L) = A$. Then L is separable over K by Lemma 2. If w is any real discrete valuation of L over A and v is the restriction of w to K then upon letting $P = M_v \cap A$ we get that P is a maximal ideal in A, $R_v = A_P$, and R_w lies above R_v. Now $\mathfrak{D}(A, L) \not\subset P$ and hence by Lemma 1 we get that R_w/M_w is separable over R_v/M_v and $M_vR_w = M_w$, that is, $\mathfrak{r}(w:v) = 1$.

Conversely, suppose that condition (1) is satisfied. Since L is separable over K, by Lemma 2 we get that $\mathfrak{D}(A, L) \neq \{0\}$. Therefore, to prove $\mathfrak{D}(A, L) = A$, it suffices to show that if P is any nonzero prime ideal in A then $\mathfrak{D}(A, L) \not\subset P$. Now $A_P = R_v$ and $PR_v = M_v$, where v is a real discrete valuation of K. Let $w_1, \ldots, w_q$ be the extensions of v to L. Then $R_{w_1}, \ldots, R_{w_q}$ are the quasi-local domains with quotient field L lying above R_v, and since L is separable over K by [18: Corollary on p. 287] we get that

$$\sum_{i=1}^{q} \mathfrak{r}(w_i : v)[R_{w_i}/M_{w_i} : R_v/M_v] = [L : K].$$

By assumption R_{w_i}/M_{w_i} is separable over R_v/M_v and $\mathfrak{r}(w_i : v) = 1$ for $i = 1, \ldots, q$. Therefore, by Lemma 1 we get that $\mathfrak{D}(A, L) \not\subset P$.

Lemma 10. Let A be a Dedekind domain with quotient field K, let L be a finite algebraic extension of K, and let $L_1, \ldots, L_n$ be a finite number of subfields of L containing K such that L is the compositum of $L_1, \ldots, L_n$ in L. Then $\mathfrak{D}(A, L) = A$ if and only if $\mathfrak{D}(A, L_i) = A$ for $i = 1, \ldots, n$.

Proof. If $\mathfrak{D}(A, L) = A$ then by Lemma 9 it follows that $\mathfrak{D}(A, L_i) = A$ for $i = 1, \ldots, n$. Now assume that $\mathfrak{D}(A, L_i) = A$ for $i = 1, \ldots, n$. Then by Lemma 2 we get that L_i is separable over K for $i = 1, \ldots, n$, and hence L is separable over K. Therefore, in view of Lemma 9, to prove $\mathfrak{D}(A, L) = A$ it suffices to show that if w is any real discrete valuation of L over A then R_w/M_w is separable over R_v/M_v and $\mathfrak{r}(w:v) = 1$, where v is the restriction of w to K. Let w_i be the restriction of w to L_i. Let L' be a Galois extension of K containing L, let w' be an extension of w to L', and let K' be the inertia field of w' over v. By assumption $\mathfrak{D}(A, L_i) = A$

and hence by Lemma 9 we get that R_{w_i}/M_{w_i} is separable over R_v/M_v and $\mathfrak{r}(w_i : v) = 1$; therefore, by Lemma 8 we get that $L_i \subset K'$. This being so far $i = 1, \ldots, n$, we get that $L \subset K'$. Therefore, again by Lemma 8 we get that R_w/M_w is separable over R_v/M_v and $\mathfrak{r}(w : v) = 1$.

Lemma 11. Let A be a Dedekind domain with quotient field K, let L' be an overfield of K, let K' and L be subfields of L' containing K such that L' is the compositum of K' and L, and let A' be a normal domain with quotient field K' such that $A \subset A'$. Assume that L is a finite algebraic extension of K and $\mathfrak{D}(A, L) = A$. Then L' is a finite algebraic separable extension of K', and $\mathfrak{D}(A', L') = A'$.

Proof. First we shall consider the *special case* when K' is a finite algebraic separable extension of K and A' is the integral closure of A in K'. Since $\mathfrak{D}(A, L) \neq \{0\}$, by Lemma 2 we get that L is separable over K. Therefore, L' is a finite algebraic separable extension of K and hence also of K'. Let L'' be a Galois extension of K containing L'. Let w' be any real discrete valuation of L' over A'. Let v, v', and w be the restrictions of w' to K, K', and L, respectively. Let w'' be an extension of w' to L''. Let H and H' be the inertia fields of w'' over v and v', respectively. Since $\mathfrak{D}(A, L) = A$, by Lemma 9 we get that R_w/M_w is separable over R_v/M_v and $\mathfrak{r}(w : v) = 1$; consequently, by Lemma 8 we get that $L \subset H$. By Lemma 7, H' is the compositum of K' and H in L'', and hence we get that $L' \subset H'$. Therefore, again by Lemma 8 we get that $R_{w'}/M_{w'}$ is separable over $R_{v'}/M_{v'}$ and $\mathfrak{r}(w' : v') = 1$. This being so for any real discrete valuation w' of L' over A', by Lemma 9 we conclude that $\mathfrak{D}(A', L') = A'$.

Now we shall consider the *general case*. Since $\mathfrak{D}(A, L) \neq \{0\}$, by Lemma 2 we get that L is separable over K and hence there exists a primitive element z of L over K. Then $L' = K'(z)$ and hence L' is a finite algebraic separable extension of K'. Let $f(Z) = Z^n + f_1Z^{n-1} + \cdots + f_n$ be the minimal monic polynomial of z over K', where $f_1, \ldots, f_n$ are elements in K', and Z is an indeterminate. Let $K^* = K(f_1, \ldots, f_n)$ and let L^* be the compositum of K^* and L in L'. Then K^* is a subfield of K', $L^* = K^*(z)$, L' is the compositum of K' and L^* in L', and $[L' : K'] = n = [L^* : K^*]$. Let $z_1, \ldots, z_n$ be elements in an overfield of L' such that $f(Z) = (Z - z_1) \cdots (Z - z_n)$. Then $f_j \in K(z_1, \ldots, z_n)$ for $j = 1,$

$\ldots, n$ and hence $K^* \subset K(z_1, \ldots, z_n)$. Let $g(Z)$ be the minimal monic polynomial of z over K. Since z is separable over K, we get that $g(Z)$ is a separable polynomial. Now $f(Z)$ divides $g(Z)$ in $K'[Z]$, and hence $g(z_i) = 0$ for $i = 1, \ldots, n$. Therefore, $g(Z)$ is the minimal monic polynomial of z_i over K, and hence z_i is separable over K for $i = 1, \ldots, n$. Therefore, $K(z_1, \ldots, z_n)$ is a finite algebraic separable extension of K. Since $K^* \subset K(z_1, \ldots, z_n)$, we conclude that K^* is a finite algebraic separable extension of K. Therefore, by the special case proved above we get that $\mathfrak{D}(A^*, L^*) = A^*$, where A^* is the integral closure of A in K^*. Clearly, $A^* \subset A'$. Let P' be any prime ideal in A' and let $P^* = P' \cap A^*$. Then P^* is a prime ideal in A^* and hence $\mathfrak{D}(A^*, L) \not\subset P^*$. Therefore, there exists a free K^*-basis $(x_1, \ldots, x_n)$ of L^* such the elements $x_1, \ldots, x_n$ are integral over A^* and $\mathfrak{D}_{L^*/K^*}(x_1, \ldots, x_n) \notin P^*$. Now $\mathfrak{D}_{L^*/K^*}(x_1, \ldots, x_n) \in A^*$, and hence $\mathfrak{D}_{L^*/K^*}(x_1, \ldots, x_n) \notin P'$. Since $A^* \subset A'$, the elements $x_1, \ldots, x_n$ are integral over A'. Since $[L' : K'] = [L^* : K^*]$, we get that $(x_1, \ldots, x_n)$ is a free K'-basis of L' and $\mathfrak{D}_{L'/K'}(x_1, \ldots, x_n) = \mathfrak{D}_{L^*/K^*}(x_1, \ldots, x_n)$. Therefore, $\mathfrak{D}(A', L') \not\subset P'$. This being so for every prime ideal P' in A', we conclude that $\mathfrak{D}(A', L') = A'$.

Lemma 12. Let (A, P) be a local Dedekind domain such that A/P is perfect. Let K be the quotient field of A. Let H be an algebraically closed overfield of K. Let L be the compositum of all the finite algebraic extensions K^* of K in H such that $\mathfrak{D}(A, K^*) = A$. Let A^* be the integral closure of A in L and let P^* be a prime ideal in A^* such that $P^* \cap A = P$. Let $B = A^*_{P^*}$ and $Q = P^*B$. Then we have the following: (1) (B, Q) is a local Dedekind domain, B/Q is algebraically clo:ed, $\dim B = \dim A$, $PB = Q$, $B \cap K = A$, and $Q \cap K = P$. (2) If K^* is any finite algebraic extension of K in L then $\mathfrak{D}(A, K^*) = A$. (3) If A is pseudogeometric then B is pseudogeometric.

Proof. If A is a field then our assertion follows from Lemma 2. So henceforth assume that A is not a field. Then $A = R_v$ and $P = M_v$, where v is a real discrete valuation of K. Now A^* is integral over A, P is a maximal ideal in A, and P^* is a prime ideal in A^* such that $P^* \cap A = P$; therefore, P^* must be a maximal ideal in A^*, and hence by [19: Corollary 2 on p. 27] we get that $B = R_w$ and $Q = M_w$, where w is an extension of v to L. Since w is an extension of v to L, we get that $B \cap K = A$ and $Q \cap K = P$. Since w is an extension of v to L, v is real, and L is algebraic over K, we get that w is real. If K^* is any finite algebraic extension of K in L, then there exists a finite number of finite algebraic extensions $K_1, \ldots, K_m$ of K in H such that $\mathfrak{D}(A, K_i) = A$ for $i = 1, \ldots, m$, and $K^* \subset K^{**}$, where K^{**} is the compositum of $K_1, \ldots, K_m$ in H; now $\mathfrak{D}(A, K^{**}) = A$ by Lemma 10, and hence $\mathfrak{D}(A, K^*) = A$ by Lemma 9. Given any element z in Q, let $K^* = K(z)$, and let v^* be the restriction of w to K^*; then by what we have just proved we get that $\mathfrak{D}(A, K^*) = A$ and hence by Lemma 9 we get that $\mathfrak{r}(v^* : v) = 1$, and hence $PR_{v^*} = M_{v^*}$; thus $z \in M_{v^*} = PR_{v^*} \subset PB$; since z was an arbitrary element in Q, we conclude that $PB = Q$. Therefore, w is real discrete and $\mathfrak{r}(w : v) = 1$. In particular, (B, Q) is a local Dedekind domain and $\dim B = 1 = \dim A$. Let $h : B \to B/Q$ be the natural epimorphism, and let Z be an indeterminate. To prove that B/Q is algebraically closed it suffices to show that if $f(Z)$ is any monic polynomial of some positive degree n in Z with coefficients in $h(A)$ such that $f(Z)$ is irreducible in $(h(A))[Z]$, then there exist elements $z_1, \ldots, z_n$ in A^* such that

$$f(Z) = (Z - h(z_1)) \cdots (Z - h(z_n)).$$

Take elements $F_1, \ldots, F_n$ in A such that $f(Z) = Z^n + h(F_1)Z^{n-1} + \cdots + h(F_n)$. Let $F(Z) = Z^n + F_1Z^{n-1} + \cdots + F_n$. Since H is algebraically closed, there exist elements $z_1, \ldots, z_n$ in H such that $F(Z) = (Z - z_1) \cdots (Z - z_n)$. Let D and d be the Z-discriminants of $F(Z)$ and $f(Z)$ respectively. Then $D \in A$ and $d = h(D)$. Since $h(A)$ is perfect and $f(Z)$ is irreducible in $(h(A))[Z]$, we get that $d \neq 0$, and hence $D \notin P$. Since A is normal and $f(Z)$ is irreducible in $(h(A))[Z]$, we get that $F(Z)$ is irreducible in $K[Z]$. Therefore, $F(Z)$ is the minimal monic polynomial of z_i over K, and hence $D = \mathfrak{D}_{K(z_i)/K}(1, z_i, \ldots, z_i^{n-1}) \in \mathfrak{D}(A, K(z_i))$. Since $D \notin P$, we conclude that $\mathfrak{D}(A, K(z_i)) = A$, and hence $K(z_i) \subset L$. Therefore, $z_i \in A^*$. This being so for $i = 1, \ldots, n$, we conclude that $z_1, \ldots, z_n$ are elements in A^* and $f(Z) = (Z - h(z_1)) \cdots (Z - h(z_n))$. This completes the proof of (1) and (2).

Now assume that A is pseudogeometric. To prove that B is pseudogeometric, what we have to show is that if L' is any finite algebraic extension of L and B' is the integral closure of B in L', then B' is a finite B-module. Let $w_1, \ldots, w_t$ be the distinct extensions of w to L'. Since B/Q is algebraically closed, by [18: Theorem 21 on p. 285] we get that B' is a finite B-module if and only if $\mathfrak{r}(w_1 : w) + \cdots + \mathfrak{r}(w_t : w) = [L' : L]$. Let L'' be the maximal separable extension of L in L', and let W_i be the restriction of w_i to L''. Then $W_1, \ldots, W_t$ are exactly all the distinct extensions of w to L'', and $\mathfrak{r}(w_i : w) = \mathfrak{r}(w_i : W_i)\mathfrak{r}(W_i : w)$ for $i = 1, \ldots, t$. Since B/Q is algebraically closed, by [18: Theorem 21 on p. 285] we get that $\mathfrak{r}(W_1 : w) + \cdots + \mathfrak{r}(W_t : w) = [L'' : L]$ and $\mathfrak{r}(w_i : W_i) \leqq [L' : L'']$ for $i = 1, \ldots, t$. Since $[L' : L] = [L' : L''][L'' : L]$, we conclude that B' is a finite B-module if and only if $\mathfrak{r}(w_i : W_i) = [L' : L'']$ for $i = 1, \ldots, t$. If $L' = L''$, then we have nothing to show. So now assume that $L' \neq L''$. Then L is of characteristic $p \neq 0$, and L' is purely inseparable over L''. We can find a finite number of elements $Y_1, \ldots, Y_r$ in L' and a positive integer s such that upon letting $q = p^s$ and $y_i = Y_i^q$, we have that $L' = L''(Y_1, \ldots, Y_r)$ and $y_i \in L''$ for $i = 1, \ldots, r$. Take an element x_i in R_{W_i} such that $x_i R_{W_i} = M_{W_i}$. Let $K'' = K(x_1, \ldots, x_t, y_1, \ldots, y_r)$, and $K' = K''(Y_1, \ldots, Y_r)$. Let v_i and V_i be the restrictions of w_i to K' and K'', respectively. Since $x_i \in K''$, we get that $\mathfrak{r}(W_i : V_i) = 1$, and hence $\mathfrak{r}(v_i : V_i) \leqq \mathfrak{r}(w_i : W_i)$. Let A'' be the integral closure of A in K''. Now K'' is a finite algebraic extension of K, and A is pseudogeometric; therefore, A'' is pseudogeometric. Also R_{V_i} is the quotient ring of A'' with respect to the prime ideal $M_{V_i} \cap A''$ in A'', and hence R_{V_i} is pseudogeometric. Now R_{V_i}/M_{V_i} is a finite algebraic extension of A/P, and A/P is perfect; therefore, R_{V_i}/M_{V_i} is perfect. Clearly, K' is a finite purely inseparable extension of K'' and hence R_{v_i}/M_{v_i} is a finite purely inseparable extension of R_{V_i}/M_{V_i}. Therefore, we must have $R_{v_i}/M_{v_i} = R_{V_i}/M_{V_i}$. Since R_{V_i} is pseudogeometric, we get that the integral closure of R_{V_i} in K' is a finite (R_{V_i})-module. Finally, since K' is purely inseparable over K'', we get that v_i is the only extension of V_i to K'. Therefore, by [18: Theorem 21 on p. 285] we conclude that $\mathfrak{r}(v_i : V_i) = [K' : K'']$. Clearly, L' is the compositum of K' and L'' in L', and hence $[L' : L''] \leqq [K' : K'']$. Thus $\mathfrak{r}(w_i : W_i) \leqq [L' : L''] \leqq [K' : K''] = \mathfrak{r}(v_i : V_i) \leqq \mathfrak{r}(w_i : W_i)$, and hence $\mathfrak{r}(w_i : W_i) = [L' : L'']$. This being so for $i = 1, \ldots, t$, we conclude that B' is a finite B-module.

Now we proceed to prove the Uniformization Lemma. In [8: Theorem 11], [8: Theorem 12], and [8: Lemma 22] we proved the following three results respectively.

Theorem 1. Let (S, N) be a two-dimensional regular local domain such that S is a spot over a pseudogeometric domain I, S is of nonzero characteristic, and S/N is algebraically closed. Let L be the quotient field of S, let K be a finite algebraic purely inseparable extension of L, and let v be a valuation of K dominating S such that $\dim_S v = 0$. Assume that if v is real discrete then the completion of any normal algebraic spot over S which dominates S is a normal domain. Then there exists a two-dimensional regular local domain R with quotient field K such that v dominates R and R is a spot over S.

Theorem 2. Let (S, N) be a two-dimensional regular local domain such that S/N is algebraically closed. Assume that S is an algebraic spot over a pseudogeometric domain I such that the second chain condition holds in I, and the completion of any normal algebraic spot over I is a domain. Let L be the quotient field of S, let K be a finite algebraic extension of L, and let v be a valuation of K dominating S such that $\dim_S v = 0$. Assume that there exists a finite chain of subfields $L = L_0 \subset L_1 \subset \ldots \subset L_m = K$ of K such that L_i is a Galois extension of L_{i-1} and the Galois group of L_i over L_{i-1} is solvable for $i = 1, \ldots, m$. Then there exists a two dimensional regular local domain R with quotient field K such that v dominates R and R is a spot over S.

Theorem 3. Let L be a field and let K be a finite algebraic extension of K. Let I be a subring of L such that I is a pseudogeometric domain, the second chain condition holds in I, and the completion of any normal algebraic spot over I is a domain. Let (R', M') be a two-dimensional regular local domain with quotient field K such that R' is an algebraic spot over I, R'/M' is algebraically closed, and R'/M' = the quotient field of $(R' \cap L)/(M' \cap L)$. Let v be a valuation of K dominating R' such that $\dim_{R'} v = 0$. Assume that $[K : L]$ is not divisible by the characteristic of R'/M', and there exists a finite chain of subfields $L = L_0 \subset L_1 \subset \ldots \subset L_m = K$ of K such that L_i is a Galois extension of L_{i-1} and the Galois group of L_i over L_{i-1} is solvable for $i = 1, \ldots, m$. Then there exists a two-dimensional regular local domain S with quotient field L and a two-dimensional normal local domain R with quotient field K such that S is an algebraic spot over I, R lies above S, R is a spot over R', and v dominates R.

Using the above three theorems we shall now prove the following.

Theorem 4. Let (S, N) be a two-dimensional regular local domain such that S/N is algebraically closed. Assume that S is an algebraic spot over a pseudogeometric domain I such that the second chain condition holds in I, and the completion of any normal algebraic spot over I is a domain. Let L be the quotient field of S, let K be a finite algebraic extension of L, and let v be a valuation of K dominating S such that $\dim_S w = 0$. Assume that if v is real discrete and L is not separable over K, then the completion of any normal algebraic spot over I is a normal domain. Then there exists a two-dimensional regular local domain R with quotient field K such that v dominates R and R is a spot over S.

Proof. Let K^* be the maximal separable extension of L in K. Let L'' be a Galois extension of L containing K^*. Let v^* be the restriction of v to K^*, let w be the restriction of v^* to L, and let w'' be an extension of v^* to L''. Let p be the characteristic of S/N. Then p is the characteristic of R_w/M_w. Let $q = p$ if $p \neq 0$, and let $q = 1$ if $p = 0$. Let L' be the inertia field of w'' over w, let K' be the compositum of K^* and L' in L'', let w' be the restriction of w'' to L', and let v' be the restriction of w'' to K'. By Lemma 7 we get that K' is the inertia field of w'' over v^*. Let G be the Galois group of L'' over L'. Then by definition, G is the inertia group of w'' over w, and hence by a result of Krull (see [10] or [19: §12 of Chapter VI]) there exists a normal subgroup G_1 of G such that the order of G_1 is a power of q and the factor group G/G_1 is an abelian group whose order is not divisible by p; (in [19], G_1 is called the large ramification group of w'' over w). Let L_1 be the fixed field of G_1. Then L_1 is a Galois extension of L' and the Galois group of L_1 over L' is abelian, because it is isomorphic to G/G_1. Let G' be the Galois group of L'' over K'. Then G' is a subgroup of G. Let $H = G' \cap G_1$, let L^* be the fixed field of H, and let w^* be the restriction of w'' to L^*. Then H is a normal subgroup of G' and the factor group G'/H is isomorphic to a subgroup of G/G_1. Therefore, L^* is a Galois extension of K' and the Galois group of L^* over K' is an abelian group whose order is not divisible by p. Now H is a subgroup of G_1 and the order of G_1 is a power of q; therefore, there exists a finite chain of subgroup $H = H_m \subset H_{m-1} \subset \ldots \subset H_1 = G_1$ of G_1 such that H_i is a normal subgroup of H_{i-1} and the order of H_{i-1}/H_i is q for $i = 2, \ldots, m$, (for instance, see the corollaries on pages 110 and 111 of [20]). Let L_i be the fixed field of H_i. Then $L_1 \subset L_2 \subset \ldots \subset L_m = L^*$ and for $i = 2, \ldots, m$ we have that L_i is a Galois extension of L_{i-1} and the Galois group of L_i over L_{i-1} is a cyclic group of order q.

Since L' is the inertia field of w'' over w, by [8: Lemma 14] there exists a quadratic transform (S_0, N_0) of S along w such that upon letting T = the integral closure of S_0 in L'', $P = M_{w''} \cap T$, $S_0'' = T_P$, and $N_0'' = PS_0''$, we have that (S_0'', N_0'') is a local domain with quotient field L'', S_0'' lies above S_0, and L' is the inertia field of S_0'' over S_0. Let $S_0' = S_0'' \cap L'$ and $N_0' = N_0'' \cap L'$. Then by Lemma 5 we get that (S_0', N_0') is a local domain with quotient field L', S_0' lies above S_0, and $N_0S_0' = N_0'$. Now S_0 is a two-dimensional regular local domain and hence so is S_0'. Clearly, S_0' is an algebraic spot over I, S_0'/N_0' is algebraically closed, w^* dominates S_0', and $R_{w^*}/M_{w^*} = S_0'/N_0'$. Let $L_0 = L'$. Then $L' = L_0 \subset L_1 \subset \ldots \subset L_m = L^*$ and for $i = 1, \ldots, m$ we have that L_i is a Galois extension of L_{i-1} and the Galois group of L_i over L_{i-1} is solvable. Therefore, by Theorem 2 there exists a two-dimensional regular local domain (S^*, N^*) with quotient field L^* such that w^* dominates S^* and S^* is a spot over S_0'. Clearly, S^* is an algebraic spot over I, S^*/N^* is algebraically closed, and S^*/N^* = the quotient field of $(S^* \cap K')/(N^* \cap K')$. Also L^* is a Galois extension of K' and the Galois group of L^* over K' is a solvable group whose order is not divisible by the characteristic of S^*/N^*. Therefore, by Theorem 3 there exists a two-dimensional regular local domain (R_1', M_1') with quotient field K' and a two-dimensional normal local domain (S_1^*, N_1^*) with quotient field L^* such that R_1' is an algebraic spot over I, S_1^* lies above R_1', S_1^* is a spot over S^*, and w^* dominates S_1^*. Clearly, v' dominates R_1' and $R_{v'}/M_{v'} = R_1'/M_1'$. Therefore, by [7: Theorem 3] there exists a quadratic transform (R', M') of R_1' along v' such that upon letting $R^* = R' \cap K^*$ and $M^* = M' \cap K'$ we have that (R^*, M^*) is a two-dimensional normal local domain with quotient field K^*, R^* is an algebraic spot over I, and R' lies above R^*. Clearly, v^* dominates R^*, R^*/M^* is algebraically closed, and $R_{v^*}/M_{v^*} = R^*/M^* = R'/M'$.

Let T' be the integral closure of R^* in L'', let $P' = M_{w''} \cap T'$, and let $S'' = T'_{P'}$. Then S'' is a local domain with quotient field L'', S'' lies above R^*, $R' = S'' \cap K'$, and w'' dominates S''. Let K'' be the inertia field of S'' over R^*. Since K' is the inertia field of w'' over v^* and v^* dominates R^*, by Lemma 6 we get that $K'' \subset K'$. Let $R_0^* = S_0'' \cap K^*$. Then R_0^* is a local domain with quotient field K^*, and R_0^* lies above S_0. Since L' is the inertia field of S_0'' over S_0, and K' is the compositum of K^* and L' in L, by Lemma 7 we get that K' is the inertia field of S_0'' over R_0^*. Now $S_0 \subset S_0' \subset S^* \subset S_1^*$, $R_1' = K' \cap S_1^*$, $R_1' \subset R' \subset S''$, and $R^* = S'' \cap K^*$; therefore, $S_0 \subset R^*$. Now v^* dominates R^*, v^* dominates R_0^*, R_0^* lies above S_0, and $S_0 \subset R^*$; therefore, R^* dominates R_0^*. Since S'' lies above R^*, S_0'' lies above R_0^*, w'' dominates S'', w'' dominates S_0'', and R^* dominates R_0^*, we get that S'' dominates S_0''. Since S'' lies above R^*, S_0'' lies above R_0^*, R^* dominates R_0^*, S'' dominates S_0'', and K' is the inertia field of S_0'' over R_0^*, by Lemma 7 we get that $K' \subset K''$. Therefore, $K'' = K'$; that is, K' is the inertia field of S'' over R^*, and hence by Lemma 5 we get $M^*R' = M'$. Since $I \subset S \subset S_0 \subset R^*$ and R^* is a spot over I, we get that R^* is a spot over S.

Let $(\mathfrak{R}^*, \mathfrak{M}^*)$ and $(\mathfrak{R}', \mathfrak{M}')$ be the completions of R^* and R', respectively. Now R' is regular and hence $\mathfrak{R}'$ is regular. Since R^* is a normal algebraic spot over I, we get that $\mathfrak{R}^*$ is a domain. Also R' dominates R^*, $\dim R' = \dim R^*$, $R'/M' = R^*/M^*$, and $M^*R' = M'$. Therefore, by [7: Proposition 15] we get R^* is a subspace of R'. Consequently, we may regard $\mathfrak{R}^*$ to be a subring of $\mathfrak{R}'$. Then $\mathfrak{R}'$ dominates $\mathfrak{R}^*$, $\mathfrak{R}'/\mathfrak{M}' = \mathfrak{R}^*/\mathfrak{M}^*$, and $\mathfrak{M}^*\mathfrak{R}' = \mathfrak{M}'$. Therefore, by Lemma 3 we get that $\mathfrak{R}^* = \mathfrak{R}'$. Consequently, $\mathfrak{R}^*$ is regular and hence R^* is regular.

If $K = K^*$, then we are done by taking $R = R^*$. So now assume that $K \neq K^*$. Then K is a finite algebraic purely inseparable extension of K^*, v dominates R^*, and $\dim_{R^*} v = 0$. Since R^* is an algebraic spot over I, we get that if R_1 is any algebraic spot over R^* such that R_1 dominates R^* then R_1 is an algebraic spot over I. If v is real discrete then by assumption the completion of any normal algebraic spot over I is a normal domain. Therefore, by Theorem 1 there exists a two-dimensional regular local domain R with quotient field K such that v dominates R and R is a spot over R^*. Clearly, R is then a spot over S.

Theorem 5. Let (A, P) be a pseudogeometric local Dedekind domain such that A/P is algebraically closed. Let K be a function field over A such that $\dim A + \text{trdeg}_A K = 2$. Let v be a valuation of K such that v dominates A and $\dim_A v = 0$. Then there exists a two-dimensional regular local domain R with quotient field K such that v dominates R and R is a spot over A.

Proof. Suppose we have shown that: (1) there exists a two-dimensional regular local domain (S, N) with quotient field L such that S is a spot over A, v dominates S, and K is a finite algebraic extension of L. Since A/P is algebraically closed, it then follows that S/N is algebraically closed, $\dim_S v = 0$, and S is an algebraic spot over A. By [14: (37.5)] the completion of any normal spot over A is a normal domain, and by Proposition 2 the second chain condition holds in A. Therefore, by Theorem 4 there exists a two-dimensional regular local domain R with quotient field K such that v dominates R and R is a spot over S. It then follows that R is a spot over A. To prove (1) we shall divide the argument into two cases.

Case when A is a field. Then $\text{trdeg}_A K = 2$. Let (x', y') be a transcendence basis of K over A. Now $R_v/M_v = A$, and hence if $x' \in R_v$ then there exists $a \in A$ such that $x' - a \in M_v$, and if $y' \in R_v$ then there exists $b \in A$ such that $y' - b \in M_v$. Let $x = x' - a$ if $x' \in R_v$, and let $x = 1/x'$ if $x' \notin R_v$. Let $y = y' - b$ if $y' \in R_v$, and let $y = 1/y'$ if $y' \notin R_v$. Then (x, y) is a transcendence basis of K over A, and $x \in M_v$ and $y \in M_v$. Let $B = A[x, y]$, $Q = M_v \cap B$, $S = B_Q$, and $Q' = xB$. Then clearly $Q = (x, y)B$, and Q' is a nonzero prime ideal in B such that $Q' \subset Q$ and $Q' \neq Q$. Therefore, S is a two-dimensional regular local domain. Clearly, S is a spot over A and v dominates S. Since K is finitely generated over A, it follows that K is a finite algebraic extension of the quotient field of S.

Case when A is not a field. Then $\dim A = 1$, $\text{trdeg}_A K = 1$, and $P = xA$ where $0 \neq x \in A$. Let y' be a transcendence basis of K over the quotient field k of A. Now $R_v/M_v = A/P$, and hence if $y' \in R_v$ then there exists $b \in A$ such that $y' - b \in M_v$. Let $y = y' - b$ if $y' \in R_v$, and let $y = 1/y'$ if $y' \notin R_v$. Then y is a transcendence basis of K over k, and $y \in M_v$. Let $B = A[y]$, $Q = M_v \cap B$, $S = B_Q$, and $Q' = xB$. Then clearly $Q = (x, y)B$, and Q' is a nonzero prime ideal in B such that $Q' \subset Q$ and $Q' \neq Q$. Therefore, S is a two-dimensional regular local domain. Clearly, S is a spot over A and v dominates S. Since K is a finitely generated field extension of k, it follows that K is a finite algebraic extension of the quotient field of S.

Theorem 6. Let (A, P) be a pseudogeometric local Dedekind domain such that A/P is perfect. Let K be a function field over A such that $\dim A + \mathrm{trdeg}_A K = 2$. Let v be a valuation of K such that v dominates A and $\dim_A v = 0$. Then there exists a two-dimensional regular local domain R with quotient field K such that v dominates R and R is a spot over A.

Proof. Let H be an algebraically closed overfield of K, k the quotient field of A, and k^* the compositum of all the finite algebraic extensions k^{**} of k in H such that $\mathfrak{D}(A, k^{**}) = A$. Let L be the compositum of k^* and K in H, w an extension of v to L, and A^* the integral closure of A in k^*; then $A^* \subset R_w$. Let $P^* = M_w \cap A^*$, $B = A^*_{P^*}$, and $Q = P^*B$; then P^* is a prime ideal in A^* and $P^* \cap A = P$. Therefore, by Lemma 12 we get that (B, Q) is a pseudogeometric local Dedekind domain with quotient field k^*, B/Q algebraically closed, $\dim B = \dim A$, B dominating A, and $\mathfrak{D}(A, k') = A$ for every finite algebraic extension k' of k in k^*. Clearly, w dominates B, $\dim_B w = 0$, L is a function field over B, and $\dim B + \mathrm{trdeg}_B L = 2$. Therefore, by Theorem 5 there exists a two-dimensional regular local domain S^* with quotient field L such that w dominates S^* and S^* is a spot over B. Clearly $\dim_{S^*} w = 0$. Since K is a function field over A, there exists a finite number of elements $y_1, \ldots, y_n$ in K such that K is the quotient field of $A[y_1, \ldots, y_n]$. Let $x_i = y_i$ if $y_i \in R_v$, and let $x_i = 1/y_i$ if $y_i \notin R_v$. Then $x_i \in R_w$ for $i = 1, \ldots, n$ and hence by Proposition 10 there exists a quadratic transform (S, N) of S^* along w such that $x_i \in S$ for $i = 1, \ldots, n$. Then (S, N) is a two-dimensional regular local domain with quotient field L, w dominates S, $\dim_S w = 0$, S is an algebraic spot over B, and S dominates B. Let (x, y) be a basis of N. Let $E_1 = A[x, y, x_1, \ldots, x_n]$, let K'' be the quotient field of E_1, and let E'' be the integral closure of E_1 in K''. Then E_1 is an affine ring over A, and K'' is a finite algebraic extension of K in L. Since A is pseudogeometric, by Proposition 1 we get that E'' is a finite E_1-module and hence E'' is an affine ring over A. Also $E_1 \subset S$ and S is normal; therefore, $E'' \subset S$. Let $J'' = N \cap E''$, $R' = E''_{J''}$, and $M'' = J''R''$. Then (R'', M'') is a normal local domain with quotient field K'', S dominates R'', R'' is an algebraic spot over

A, R'' dominates A, and $\dim A + \operatorname{trdeg}_A R'' = 2$. Therefore, by Proposition 2 we get that $\dim R'' = 2$. Also x and y are in M''. Let $E_2 = B[x, y, x_1, \ldots, x_n]$. Then L is the quotient field of E_2. Let E be the integral closure of E_2 in L. Since E_2 is an affine ring over B and B is pseudogeometric, by Proposition 1 we get that E is a finite E_2-module, and hence E is an affine ring over B. Also $E_2 \subset S$ and S is normal; therefore, $E \subset S$. Let $J = N \cap E$, $S' = E_J$, and $N' = JS'$. Then (S', N') is a normal local domain with quotient field L, S dominates S', S' is an algebraic spot over B, S' dominates B, and $\dim B + \operatorname{trdeg}_B S' = 2$. Therefore, by Proposition 2 we get that $\dim S' = 2 = \dim S$. Now x and y are in N', and hence $N'S = N$. Also $S/N = B/Q = S'/N'$. Finally, since S' is a normal spot over the pseudogeometric Dedekind domain, by [14: (37.5)] we get that the completion of S' is a domain. Therefore, by [7: Proposition 14] we conclude that $S = S'$. Let $E_3 = A^*[x, y, x_1, \ldots, x_n]$ and let E^* be the integral closure of E_3 in L. Then $E_3 \subset E_2$ and hence $E^* \subset E$. Let $J^* = J \cap E^*$. Then $E^*_{J^*} \subset E_J$. Also $J^* \cap A^* = M_w \cap A^* = P^*$ and hence $B = A^*_{P^*} \subset E^*_{J^*}$. Therefore, $E_2 \subset E^*_{J^*}$. Now $E^*_{J^*}$ is normal and hence $E \subset E^*_{J^*}$. Finally, $(J^*E^*_{J^*}) \cap E = (J \cap E^*_{J^*}) \cap E = J$, and hence $E_J \subset E^*_{J^*}$. Since we have shown that $S = E_J$, we conclude that $S = E^*_{J^*}$. Let $z_1, \ldots, z_m$ be a basis of M''. Since $M'' \subset N$ and $S = E^*_{J^*}$, there exist elements a_i, b_i, c_i in E^* such that $c_i \notin N$ and $c_i z_i = a_i x + b_i y$. We can take a finite algebraic extension k' of k in k^* such that upon letting K' to be the compositum of k' and K in L we have that $K'' \subset K'$ and the elements a_i, b_i, c_i are in K' for $i = 1, \ldots, m$. Now $\mathfrak{D}(A, k') = A$ and clearly K' is the compositum of k' and K'' in L. Therefore, by Lemma 11 we get that K' is a finite algebraic separable extension of K'', and $\mathfrak{D}(R'', K') = R''$. Let E' be the integral closure of R'' in K'. Then $E' \subset S$. Let $J' = N \cap E'$, $R' = E'_{J'}$, and $M' = J'R'$. Then J' is a prime ideal in E' and $J' \cap R = N \cap R = M$. Therefore, (R', M') is a two-dimensional normal local domain with quotient field K', R' lies above R'', S dominates R', and R' is an algebraic spot over A. Since $\mathfrak{D}(R'', K') = R''$, by Lemma 1 we get that $M''R' = M'$ and hence $M' = (z_1, \ldots, z_m)R'$. Also x and y are in M'. Clearly, E_3 is integral over E_1, and hence E^* is integral over E_1. In particular, the elements a_i, b_i, c_i are integral over E_1, and hence they are integral over R' because $E_1 \subset R'$. Since R' is a normal domain with quotient field K'

and the elements a_i, b_i, c_i are in K', we conclude that the elements a_i, b_i, c_i are in R'. Also $c_i \notin N$ and $M' \subset N$. Therefore, $c_i \notin M'$. Since $c_i z_i = a_i x + b_i y$, we get $z_i \in (x, y)R'$ for $i = 1, \ldots, m$. Therefore, $M' = (x, y)R'$, and hence R' is regular. Let v' be the restriction of w to K'. Then v' dominates R' and $\dim_{R'} v' = 0$.

Thus K' is a finite algebraic extension of K, k' is a finite algebraic extension of the quotient field k of A such that $\mathfrak{D}(A, k') = A$ and K' is the compositum of k' and K in K', v' is an extension of v to K', and R' is a two-dimensional regular local domain with quotient field K' such that R' is an algebraic spot over A, v' dominates R', and $\dim_{R'} v' = 0$. Now by [7: Theorem 3] there exists a quadratic transform (R_1, M_1) of R' along v' such that upon letting $R = R_1 \cap K$ and $M = M_1 \cap K$ we have that (R, M) is a two-dimensional normal local domain with quotient field K, R is an algebraic spot over A, and R_1 lies above R. Since $A \subset R$ and $\mathfrak{D}(A, k') = A$, by Lemma 11 we get that $\mathfrak{D}(R, K') = R$. Therefore, by Lemma 1 we get that $MR_1 = M_1$ and R_1/M_1 is a finite algebraic separable extension of R/M. Since R is a normal spot over the pseudogeometric Dedekind domain A, by [14: (37.5)] we get that the completion of R is a domain. Therefore, since R_1 is regular, by Lemma 4 we conclude that R is regular. Clearly v dominates R.

Remark. Compare the proofs of Lemma 12 and Theorem 6 with [3]. In [3: Theorem 8] we have proved the following somewhat stronger result for the geometric case: Given a field k and a function field K over k such that $\text{trdeg}_k K = 2$, there exists a finite algebraic purely inseparable extension k' of k such that upon letting K' to be a free join of k' and K we have that there exists a nonsingular projective model of K' over k'. (In the statement of [3: Theorem 8] the phrase "if k'' is any finite algebraic" should be replaced by the phrase "if k'' is any").

The following lemma is well known.

Lemma 13. Let k be a field, let K be a function field over k such that $\text{trdeg}_k K = 1$, and let v be a valuation of K such that $k \subset R_v \neq K$. Then $\dim_k v = 0$, R_v is a one-dimensional regular local domain, and R_v is a spot over k.

Proof. Take $y \in K$ such that y is transcendental over k. Let $x = y$ if $y \in R_v$, and let $x = 1/y$ if $y \notin R_v$. Let $I = k[x]$, $Q = M_v \cap I$,

$A = I_Q$, and $P = QA$. Then (A, P) is a local domain with quotient field $k(x)$, R_v dominates A, and the quotient field K of R_v is a finite algebraic extension of $k(x)$; since R_v is normal and $R_v \neq K$, we must have $A \neq k(x)$ and hence $Q \neq \{0\}$. Consequently, $Q = f(x)I$ where $f(Z)$ is a monic irreducible polynomial of positive degree in an indeterminate Z with coefficients in k; therefore, (A, P) is a one-dimensional regular local domain and $\dim_k A = 0$. Let I' be the integral closure of A in K. Now A is a spot over the field k; therefore, by Proposition 1 we get that A is pseudogeometric, and hence I' is a finite A-module. Let $Q' = M_v \cap I'$ and $A' = I'_{Q'}$. Then $Q' \cap A = P$ and hence A' lies above A. Therefore, A' is a one-dimensional regular local domain with quotient field K, A' is a spot over A, A' dominates A, and $\dim_A A' = 0$. Since A is a spot over k and $\dim_k A = 0$, we get that A' is a spot over k and $\dim_k A' = 0$. Since $A' \subset R_v \subset K$, $R_v \neq K$, and A' is a one-dimensional regular local domain with quotient field K, we get that $R_v = A'$.

Theorem 7. Let I be a pseudogeometric Dedekind domain, let K be a function field over I such that $\operatorname{absdim}_I K = 2$, let v be a valuation of K such that $I \subset R_v \neq K$, and let $Q = M_v \cap I$. Then we have the following: (1) If Q is not a maximal ideal in I then $\dim_I v = 0$, R_v is a one-dimensional regular local domain, and R_v is a spot over I. (2) If $\dim_I v \neq 0$ then $\dim_I v = 1$, R_v is a one-dimensional regular local domain, and R_v is a spot over I. (3) If $\dim_I v = 0$, Q is a maximal ideal in I, and I/Q is perfect, then there exists a two-dimensional regular local domain R with quotient field K such that v dominates R and R is a spot over I.

Proof. First, suppose that Q is not a maximal ideal in I. Let k be the quotient field of I. Then $Q = \{0\}$, $k \subset R_v$, K is a function field over k, and $\operatorname{trdeg}_k K = 1$. Therefore, by Lemma 13 we get that $\dim_k v = 0$, R_v is a one-dimensional regular local domain, and R_v is a spot over k. Clearly, $\dim_I v = \dim_k v$ and hence $\dim_I v = 0$. Also k is a spot over I and hence R_v is a spot over I.

Secondly, suppose that $\dim_I v \neq 0$ and I is a field. Then there exists $x \in R_v$ such that $h(x)$ is transcendental over $h(I)$, where $h : R_v \to R_v/M_v$ is the natural epimorphism. Clearly, x is transcendental over I and $M_v \cap I[x] = \{0\}$. Therefore, $I(x) \subset R_v$. Now K is a function field over $I(x)$ and $\operatorname{trdeg}_{I(x)} K = 1$. Consequently, by Lemma 13 we get that $\dim_{I(x)} v = 0$, R_v is a one-dimensional regular local domain, and R_v is a spot over $I(x)$. It follows that $\dim_I v = 1$, and R_v is a spot over I.

Thirdly, suppose that $\dim_I v \neq 0$ and I is not a field. By (1) we get that Q is a maximal ideal in I. Let $A = I_Q$, $P = QA$, and $k =$ the quotient field of A. Then (A, P) is a one-dimensional regular local domain, v dominates A, $\dim_A v = \dim_I v \neq 0$, K is a function field over k, and $\operatorname{trdeg}_k K = 1$. Since (A, P) is a one-dimensional regular local domain, there exists $0 \neq y \in A$ such that $P = yA$. Since $\dim_A v \neq 0$, there exists $x \in R_v$ such that $h(x)$ is transcendental over $h(A)$ where $h : R_v \rightarrow R_v/M_v$ is the natural epimorphism. Let $B' = A[x]$, $Q' = M_v \cap B'$, $A' = B'_{Q'}$, $P' = Q'A'$, and $K' =$ the quotient field of A'. Then (A', P') is a local domain, $PB' \subset Q'$, v dominates A', A' dominates A, and $\dim_I A' = \dim_A A' = 1$. Also A' is a spot over A, and A is a spot over I; therefore, A' is a spot over I, and hence by Proposition 1 we get that A' is pseudogeometric. Since v dominates A and $h(x)$ is transcendental over $h(A)$, we get that if $f(Z)$ is any polynomial in an indeterminate Z with coefficients in A such that at least one of the coefficients of $f(Z)$ is not in P, then $h(f(x)) \neq 0$, that is, $f(x) \notin Q'$; therefore, $Q' = PB'$, and hence $P' = PA' = yA'$. Thus (A', P') is a local domain and P' is a nonzero principal ideal; therefore, A' is a one-dimensional regular local domain. Let $g(Z)$ be any nonzero polynomial in an indeterminate Z with coefficients in k; since $P = yA$, we can write $g(Z) = y^n f(Z)$, where n is an integer and $f(Z)$ is a polynomial in Z with coefficients in A such that at least one of the coefficients of $f(Z)$ is not in P; since v dominates A and $h(x)$ is transcendental over $h(A)$, we then have $h(f(x)) \neq 0$; consequently, $f(x) \neq 0$, and hence $g(x) \neq 0$. This shows that x is transcendental over k, and hence K is a finite algebraic extension of K'. Let B^* be the integral closure of A' in K. Then $B^* \subset R_v$. Let $Q^* = M_v \cap B^*$, $A^* = B^*_{Q^*}$, and $P^* = Q^*A^*$. Since A' is pseudogeometric, we get that B^* is a finite A'-module. Therefore, (A^*, P^*) is a normal local domain with quotient field K, and A^* is a spot over A' and hence A^* is a spot over I. Also $Q^* \cap A' = M_v \cap A' = P'$; consequently A^* lies above A' and hence $\dim A^* = \dim A = 1$. Therefore, A^* is a one-dimensional regular local domain with quotient field K; since $A^* \subset R_v \subset K$ and $R_v \neq K$, we must then have $R_v = A^*$. Since A^* lies above A', we also get A^* dominates A' and $\dim_{A'} A^* = 0$; therefore, $\dim_I A^* = 1$. Thus we have shown that R_v is a one-dimensional regular local domain, R_v is a spot over I, and $\dim_I v = 1$.

Finally, suppose that $\dim_I v = 0$, Q is a maximal ideal in I, and I/Q is perfect. Let $A = I_Q$ and $P = QA$. Then (A, P) is a pseudogeometric local Dedekind domain, A/P is perfect, $\dim A + \operatorname{trdeg}_A K = 2$, v dominates A, and $\dim_A v = 0$. Therefore, by Theorem 6 there exists a two-dimensional regular local domain R with quotient field K such that v dominates R and R is spot over A. Now A is a spot over I, and hence R is a spot over I.

REFERENCES

1. Abhyankar, S., Local uniformization on algebraic surfaces over ground fields of characteristic $p \neq 0$, *Annals Math.*, **63**(1956), 491–526. Corrections, *Annals Math.*, **78**(1963), 202–203.
2. ———, On the valuations centered in a local domain, *Amer. Jour. Math.*, **78**(1956), 321–348.
3. ———, On the field of definition of a nonsingular birational transform of an algebraic surface, *Annals Math.*, **65**(1957), 268–281.
4. ———, *Ramification Theoretic Methods in Algebraic Geometry*, Princeton University Press, Princeton, 1959.
5. ———, Uniformization in p-cyclic extensions of algebraic surfaces over ground fields of characteristic p, *Math. Annalen*, **153**(1964), 81–96.
6. ———, Reduction to multiplicity less than p in a p-cyclic extension of a two dimensional regular local ring (p = characteristic of the residue field), *Math. Annalen*, **154**(1964), 28–55.
7. ———, Uniformization of Jungian local domains, *Math. Annalen*, **160**(1965), 1–43.
8. ———, Uniformization in a p-cyclic extension of a two dimensional regular local domain of residue field characteristic p, forthcoming.
9. Cohen, I. S., On the structure and ideal theory of complete local rings, *Trans. Amer. Math. Soc.*, **57**(1946), 54–106.
10. Krull, W., Allgemeine Bervertungstheorie, *Jour. für die reine und angewandte Math.*, **167**(1932), 160–196.
11. ———, Die allgemeine Diskriminantensatz, *Math. Zeit.*, **45**(1939), 1–19.
12. Nagata, M., A general theory of algebraic geometry over Dedekind domains, III: Absolutely irreducible models, simple spots, *Amer. Jour. Math.*, **81**(1959), 401–435.

13. ———, Note on a chain condition for prime ideals, *Memoirs of the College of Science, University of Kyoto*, **32**(1959), 85–90.
14. ———, *Local Rings*, Interscience Publishers, N.Y., 1962.
15. Walker, R. J., Reduction of singularities of an algebraic surface, *Annals Math.*, **36**(1935), 336–365.
16. Zariski, O., The reduction of singularities of an algebraic surface, *Annals Math.*, **40**(1939), 639–689.
17. ———, A simplified proof for the reduction of singularities of an algebraic surface, *Annals Math.*, **43**(1942), 583–593.
18. Zariski, O., and P. Samuel, *Commutative Algebra*, vol. I, Van Nostrand, Princeton, 1958.
19. ———, *Commutative Algebra*, vol. II, Van Nostrand, Princeton, 1960.
20. Zassenhaus, H., *The Theory of Groups*, Chelsea, N.Y., 1949.

On the Equivalence of Singularities, I

Heisuke Hironaka

Introduction. Let Γ be a plane curve defined by an equation $f(x, y) = 0$. Let p be a point of Γ. For simplicity, let us assume that the base field is the field of complex numbers **C**, that the curve is analytically irreducible at the point p, that p is the origin of the complex two plane $\mathbf{C}^2$, and that the line $x = 0$ is not tangent to Γ at p. In this case, we can solve the equation $f(x, y) = 0$ by exhibiting y as a Puiseux expansion in x. Namely,

$$y = \sum_{i=1}^{k_0} a_{0,i}x^i + \sum_{i=0}^{k_1} a_{1,i}x^{(\mu_1+i)/\nu_1} + \cdots + \sum_{i=0}^{k_p} a_{p,i}x^{(\mu_p+i)/\nu_1\nu_2\cdots\nu_p}$$
$$+ \cdots + \sum_{i=0}^{\infty} a_{g,i}x^{(\mu_g+i)/\nu_1\nu_2\cdots\nu_g} \quad (0.1)$$

THIS RESEARCH WAS PARTIALLY SUPPORTED BY THE ALFRED P. SLOAN FOUNDATION AND ALSO, IN THE FINAL COURSE OF PREPARATION, BY THE NATIONAL SCIENCE FOUNDATION, CONTRACT GP-1904.

where (1) the exponents are strictly monotone increasing in the written order of terms, (2) ν_p and μ_p are relatively prime integers greater than 1 for $1 \leq p \leq g$, and (3) $a_{p,0} \neq 0$ for $1 \leq p \leq g$. The g pairs of integers (μ_p, ν_p) are called *the characteristc pairs of the singularity* of Γ at p. The integer $\nu = \nu_1\nu_2 \ldots \nu_g$ is equal to the order of $f(x, y)$ as a power series in x and y, that is *the multiplicity of the curve* Γ at p. The system of characteristic pairs determines the local topological structure of the embedding of Γ into $\mathbf{C}^2$, and conversely. (Here any two embeddings of Γ into $\mathbf{C}^2$ are locally analytically equivalent at the point p.) In fact, it is known that the characteristic pairs determine the knot type obtained by intersection of Γ with a 3-sphere of sufficiently small radius about the origin in $\mathbf{C}^2$, and that Alexander polynomial of the knot type is enough to determine the characteristic pairs. Thus, in so far as the topological structure of the singularity is concerned, only the g terms with the exponents $\mu_1/\nu_1, \mu_2/\nu_1\nu_2, \ldots, \mu_g/\nu_1\nu_2 \ldots \nu_g$, in the Puiseux expansion are important, and the coefficients in the other terms are irrelevant.

However, if the analytic structure of the singularity (i.e., the structure of singularity up to analytic isomorphism) is questioned, some of those coefficients in the other terms can become essential. For instance, a singularity of a plane curve having the only one characteristic pair (7, 3) is analytically equivalent to either one (not both) of the following two: $y = x^{7/3}$ and $y = x^{7/3} + x^{8/3}$. In fact, such a singularity is equivalent to $y = x^{7/3}$, resp. $y = x^{7/3} + x^{8/3}$, if its Puiseux expansion as in (0.1) does not (resp. does) have the term $x^{8/3}$ with nonzero coefficient. In general, when (μ, ν) is the only characteristic pair of a singularity, the analytic structure of the singularity remains unchanged by dropping off those terms in the Puiseux expansion as in (0.1) whose exponents are of the form $a\nu + b\mu/\nu$ with non-negative integers a and b. Although these are not in general all the irrelevant terms, the immediate implication is that there are only a finite number of essential terms up to analytical equivalence. In fact, we can prove:

Theorem A. The system of characteristic pairs $\{(\mu_1, \nu_1), (\mu_2, \nu_2), \ldots, (\mu_g, \nu_g)\}$ being given, there exists an integer t such that any two singularities of plane curves are locally analytically isomorphic to each other if they have the given characteristic pairs and their

Puiseux expansions as in (0.1) coincide up to the term of exponent $t/\nu_1\nu_2 \ldots \nu_g$.

It is important that there exists such t depending only upon the system of characteristic pairs. It follows from the theorem that the totality of all plane curve singularities with fixed characteristic pairs can be parametrized (not effectively in almost all cases) by a finite number of variables and, in particular, the totality is connected in the sense of deformation of one to another. A proof of the theorem may be obtained as follows:

Proof. Let $R = \mathbf{C}\{x, y\}/(f)$ be the analytic local ring of a curve Γ at p, where the singularity has the given system of characteristic pairs. Let $\nu = \nu_1\nu_2 \ldots \nu_g$ which is the multiplicity at p. Then the integral closure of R in its field of fractions is equal to $\mathbf{C}\{\sqrt[\nu]{x}\}$. Let $\tilde{R} = \mathbf{C}\{\sqrt[\nu]{x}\}$. Let $\mathfrak{c}$ be the conductor of $\tilde{R}$ in R. Then *there exists an integer t such that $\mathfrak{c} = (\sqrt[\nu]{x})^t\tilde{R}$, and this integer t has the property stated in theorem A.* Here we should refer to a theorem of Gorenstein, which says that t is exactly twice of the order of singularity $\delta_p(\Gamma) = \dim_C(\tilde{R}/R)$, where R and $\tilde{R}$ are viewed as $\mathbf{C}$-modules, and also to a classical formula, due to Italian Geometers, which expresses the order of singularity only in terms of characteristic pairs.

Not only for plane curve singularities, but also for singularities of curves in arbitrary spaces, no matter what is the characteristic of the base field, and no matter whether curves are irreducible or not, there exists a theorem of the same type. Namely,

Theorem B. Let k be any algebraically closed field, Γ a reduced algebraic curve over the field k (not necessarily irreducible), and p a point of Γ. Let $\delta = \delta_p(\Gamma)$ be the order of singularity of the curve Γ at p, that is, $\delta = \dim_C(\tilde{R}/R)$ with the local ring R of Γ at p and its integral closure $\tilde{R}$ in the total ring of fractions of R. Then there exists a pair of integers (t, r), for instance with $t = 3\,\delta + 1$ and $r = 3\,\delta$, which has the following property. Let Γ' be any reduced algebraic curve over the field k, and p' a point of Γ'. Let R' be the local ring of Γ' at p', and M (resp. M') the maximal ideal of R (resp. R'). If ϕ_ν with an integer $\nu \geqq t$ is an isomorphism $R/M^{\nu+1} \underset{\rightarrow}{\approx} R'/M'^{\nu+1}$, then there exists an isomorphism $\hat{\phi} : \hat{R} \underset{\rightarrow}{\approx} \hat{R}'$ with the M-adic (resp. M'-adic) completion $\hat{R}$ (resp. $\hat{R}'$), of R (resp. R'), such that ϕ_ν and $\hat{\phi}$ induce the same isomorphism $R/M^{\nu-r+1} \underset{\rightarrow}{\approx} R'/M'^{\nu-r+1}$.

Most probably, $(3\delta + 1, 3\delta)$ would not be the best possible pair of integers (t, r) having the property of the theorem. However, the interesting point is again the fact that there exists such a pair (t, r) depending only upon the order of singularity. We can get a slightly better example of (t, r) than $(3\delta + 1, 3\delta)$ as follows:

Let $\mathfrak{c}$ be the conductor of R in $\tilde{R}$, and let a (resp. b) be the largest (resp. the smallest) integer such that $M^a \supseteqq \mathfrak{c}$(resp. $\mathfrak{c}^3 \supseteqq M^b$). Then $(t, r) = (b + 1, b - a)$ has the property of the theorem.

The proof is based on the following facts: (1) the normalization (i.e., the desingularization) of an algebraic curve is equal to the birational blowing-up of the conductor; namely if c is a general k–linear combination of a base of $\mathfrak{c}$, then $\tilde{R} = R[c^{-1}\mathfrak{c}]$, (2) the completion of the semilocal ring $\tilde{R}$ is a direct sum of copies of the formal power series ring of one variable over the field k, the structure of which is uniquely determined by the number of copies, and (3) if $\mathfrak{c}' \supset M'^{\nu+1}$ and $\phi_\nu(\mathfrak{c}/M^{\nu+1}) = \mathfrak{c}'/M'^{\nu+1}$ and if $c' \varepsilon \mathfrak{c}'$ and ϕ_ν $(c \bmod M^{\nu+1}) = c' \bmod M'^{\nu+1}$, then an isomorphism $R/M^{\alpha+1}\mathfrak{c}^2 \overset{\approx}{\to} R'/M'^{\alpha+1}\mathfrak{c}'^2$ with $\alpha = \nu - b$, induced by ϕ_ν, extends uniquely to an isomorphism $R[c^{-1}\mathfrak{c}/M^{\alpha+1}\mathfrak{c} \overset{\approx}{\to} R'[c'^{-1}\mathfrak{c}']/M'^{\alpha+1}\mathfrak{c}'$, which induces back an isomorphism $R/M^{\alpha+1} \overset{\approx}{\to} R'/M'^{\alpha+1}$.

The primary purpose of this work is to generalize the theorems as above to the higher dimensional cases including those of schemes over the ring of integers or arithmetic schemes. Before we state our first main theorem in this direction, let us introduce the following *notion of* TR-*index*, which is the central theme of this work.

Definition (0.2). Let Y be a noetherian scheme and y_0 a closed point of Y. Let $\mathfrak{C}$ be a category of schemes over Y. (For instance, take the category of Y-schemes of finite type.) Let us consider a triple (π, X, ϵ) such that

a. X is a Y-scheme with morphism $\pi : X \to Y$, and $\varepsilon : Y \to X$ is a Y-morphism so that $\pi \circ \varepsilon = id_Y$, all belonging to $\mathfrak{C}$.
b. X is flat over Y.
c. For every point y in some neighborhood of y_0 in Y, the fibre $\pi^{-1}(y)$ is reduced, equidimensional, and its dimension is independent of y.
d. There is given a coherent sheaf of ideals $\boldsymbol{H}$ on X, such that $\boldsymbol{H}$ is contained in the sheaf of ideals of $\varepsilon(Y)$ and that $\pi : X \to Y$ is

formally smooth at every point of X outside the closed subscheme X_0 defined by $\boldsymbol{H}$.

Then a pair of nonnegative integers (t, r) will be called *an* $\boldsymbol{H}$*-adic* TR-*index of* $(Y, y_0, \pi, X, \varepsilon)$ *with respect to the category* $\mathcal{C}$, or shortly (whenever so permissible) *an* $\boldsymbol{H}$*-adic* TR-*index of the* Y*-scheme* X *at the point* $\varepsilon(y_0)$, if the integers t and r have the following property. Let ν be any integer with $\nu \geqq t$. Let (π', X', ε') be any triple satisfying the conditions (a), (b), and (c), and let $\boldsymbol{H}'$ be any coherent sheaf of ideals on X'. Let us denote X_α (resp. X'_α) the closed subscheme of X (resp. X') defined by the ideal sheaf $\boldsymbol{H}^{\alpha+1}$ (resp. $\boldsymbol{H}'^{\alpha+1}$), for each nonnegative integer α. Suppose $\dim\pi^{-1}(y_0) = \dim\pi'^{-1}(y_0)$, and there is given a Y-isomorphism $\phi_\nu : X_\nu \rightarrow X'_\nu$ within a neighborhood of the point $\varepsilon(y_0)$ in X, which induces Y-isomorphism $\phi_\mu : X_\mu \rightarrow X'_\mu$ for every integer μ with $0 \leqq \mu \leqq \nu$. Then the Y-isomorphism $\phi_{\nu-r} : X_{\nu-r} \rightarrow X'_{\nu-r}$, induced by ϕ_ν, extends to a Y-isomorphism $\hat{\phi} : \hat{X} \rightarrow \hat{X}'$ within a neighborhood of $\varepsilon(y_0)$ in X where $\hat{X}$ (resp. $\hat{X}'$) denotes the $\boldsymbol{H}$-adic (resp. $\boldsymbol{H}'$-adic) completion of X (resp. X').

Here, of course, "$\phi_{\nu-r}$ *extends* to $\hat{\phi}$" means "$\hat{\phi}$ induces $\phi_{\nu-r}$." In general, r cannot be zero. It should be noted that if (t, r) is an $\boldsymbol{H}$-adic TR-index of $(Y, y_0, \pi, X, \epsilon)$ then so is (t', r') with any integers $t' \geqq t$ and $r' \geqq r$. Intuitively speaking, an integer t as above may be described by saying that *the structure of the* Y-scheme X at the point $\varepsilon(y_0)$ is determined by that of Y-scheme X_t up to formal equivalence.
We have the following.

Main Theorem I. Let $(Y, y_0, \pi, X, \varepsilon)$ and $\boldsymbol{H}$ be the same as in Definition (0.2), satisfying the assumptions (a), (b), (c), and (d), where $\mathcal{C}$ is the category of Y-schemes of finite type. Then there exists an $\boldsymbol{H}$-adic TR-index of $(Y, y_0, \pi, X, \varepsilon)$.

For simplicity, take the situation in which $Y = \text{Spec}(k)$ with a field k and $\boldsymbol{H}$ is the ideal sheaf of the point $\varepsilon(y_0)$ on X. In this case, an $\boldsymbol{H}$-adic TR-index of $(Y, y_0, \pi, X, \varepsilon)$ may be called simply *a* TR-*index of the algebraic scheme* X *at the point* $x_0 = \varepsilon(y_0)$. When we restrict ourselves to this simpler situation, we can think of at least two different approaches towards the existence proof of a TR-index.

First Approach. For instance, suppose k has characteristic zero, so that the techniques in the resolution of singularities are available.

Here $X - \{x_0\}$ is a nonsingular algebraic scheme, and hence there exists a primary ideal E in the local ring R of X at x_0 belonging to the maximal ideal M, such that if $p : \tilde{X} \to X$ is the birational blowing-up of the ideal sheaf generated by E on X, then $\tilde{X}$ is nonsingular. Let X' be another algebraic scheme over the same field k, which is reduced, equidimensional, and of the same dimension as X. Let x_0' be a point of X', R' the local ring of X' at x_0', and M' the maximal ideal of R'. Suppose we are given an isomorphism $\phi_\nu : R/M^{\nu+1} \overset{\approx}{\to} R'/M'^{\nu+1}$ with some ν, sufficiently large but depending only upon X and p. Say $M^\nu \subset E$. Then we get an ideal E' in R' such that $E' \supset M'^{\nu+1}$ and $\phi_\nu(E/M^{\nu+1}) = E'/M'^{\nu+1}$. Let $p' : \tilde{X}' \to X'$ be the birational blowing-up of the ideal sheaf generated by E'. Then a close observation on the construction of birational blowing-up provides us with the fact that there exists an integer α, depending only upon $p : \tilde{X} \to X$, such that an isomorphism ϕ_ν as above induces an isomorphism $\tilde{\phi}_{\nu-\alpha} : \tilde{X}_{\nu-\alpha} \overset{\approx}{\to} \tilde{X}'_{\nu-\alpha}$, where $\tilde{X}_{\nu-\alpha}$ (resp. $\tilde{X}'_{\nu-\alpha}$) denotes the closed subscheme of $\tilde{X}$ (resp. $\tilde{X}'$) defined by the ideal sheaf generated by $M^{\nu-\alpha+1}$ (resp. $M'^{\nu-\alpha+1}$).

Notice that the nonsingularity of $\tilde{X}$ implies the same of $\tilde{X}'$ at least within a neighborhood of $X'_{\nu-\alpha}$, provided $\nu - \alpha \geqq 1$. There are cohomological obstructions to the extension of $\tilde{\phi}_{\nu-\alpha}$ to an isomorphism of formal schemes $\lim_{\mu\to\infty} \tilde{X}_\mu \overset{\approx}{\to} \lim_{\mu\to\infty} \tilde{X}'_\mu$, which disappears if ν is taken sufficiently large, depending only upon $p : \tilde{X} \to X$. Here the point is that the nonsingularity of the schemes in question makes much simpler the local infinitesimal calculus which produces the cohomological obstructions. The local infinitesimal calculus is simplified further if we choose the birational blowing-up $p : \tilde{X} \to X$ so that, in addition to the nonsingularity of $\tilde{X}$, $p^{-1}(x_0)$ has only normal crossings. It is easy to bring down the formal isomorphism of the blown-up schemes to such of the original schemes of X and X'.

Second Approach. Let us first consider the case of complete intersections. Let k be any field, and let k^N denote the affine N-space or $\mathrm{Spec}(k[T_1, \ldots, T_N])$ with N indeterminates T_j. Let X be a reduced closed subscheme of k^N which contains the origin, which has dimension n, $0 < n < N$, and whose ideal in $k[T] = k[T_1, \ldots, T_N]$ is generated by $m = N - n$ polynomials $(f_1(T), \ldots, f_m(T))$, at least locally at the origin. Let H be the ideal in $k[T]$ generated by the f_j, $1 \leqq j \leqq m$, and by the $m \times m$-minors of the Jacobian

$\partial(f_1, \ldots, f_m)/\partial(T_1, \ldots, T_N)$. Notice that H is an ideal defining the singular locus of the scheme X, at least locally at the origin. Let us consider the $k[T]$–linear map

$$\sigma : \prod^{N+m^2} k[T] \rightarrow \prod^{m} k[T]$$

($\prod^{p}$ denotes the product of p copies), which is defined as follows:

For $\xi \in \prod^{N+m^2} k[T]$, $\sigma(\xi) = (\sigma_1(\xi), \ldots, \sigma_m(\xi))$

with

$$\sigma_i(\xi) = \sum_{a=1}^{N} \frac{\partial f_i}{\partial T_a}(T)\xi_a + \sum_{b=1}^{m} f_b(T)\xi_{N+m(i-1)+b}.$$

It is then shown that there exists an integer $s \geqq 0$ such that $Im(\sigma)$ contains $H^s(\prod^m k[T])$. Let s be the smallest integer with this property. Let X_∞ denote the H-adic completion of X. From now on, I exclude the case in which X is nonsingular at the origin. Hence X_∞ has the same dimension at the origin as X. (Note that X_∞ is also reduced.) There exists an integer $s' \geqq 0$ such that if X'_∞ is any formal subscheme of X_∞ which is different from X_∞, even locally at the origin but is reduced, equidimensional of the same dimension as X_∞; then the ideals of X_∞ and X'_∞ at the origin are not congruent modulo $H^{s'-s+1}$. (The s' may be zero, if X_∞ is locally irreducible at the origin.) Let s' be the smallest integer having the property. Then we have the next theorem.

Theorem C. Let $t = \max\{s+2, 2s, s'\}$ and $r = s$. Then (t, r) is an $\boldsymbol{H}$-adic TR-index of the scheme X at the origin.

This is based on the following.

Lemma (0.3). Let $t_1 = \max\{s+2, 2s\}$. Let ν be any integer $\geqq t_1$. Let $\hat{A}$ be the $\boldsymbol{H}$-adic completion of $k[T] = k[T_1, \ldots, T_N]$. Let $g_j \in \hat{A}$, $1 \leqq j \leqq m$, and suppose $g_j \equiv f_j \mod \hat{H}^{\nu+1}$ with $\hat{H} \equiv H\hat{A}$. Then there exists $\xi = (\xi_1, \ldots, \xi_N) \in \prod^N \hat{H}^{\nu-s+1}$ such that if $f_j^* = f_j(T_1 + \xi_1, \ldots, T_N + \xi_N)$ for $1 \leqq j \leqq m$, then $(f_1^*, \ldots, f_m^*)\hat{A} = (g_1, \ldots, g^m)\hat{A}$.

Proof. A proof of this lemma is easily obtained by means of the following $\hat{A}$-linear mapping

$$\sigma_{(g)} : \prod^{N+m^2} \hat{A} \rightarrow \prod^{m} \hat{A}$$

defined as follows: For $\xi \in \prod^{N+m^2} \hat{A}$,

$$\sigma_{(g)}(\xi) = (\sigma_{(g)j}(\xi), j = 1, 2, \ldots, m) \text{ with}$$

$$\sigma_{(g)j}(\xi) = \sum_{a=1}^{N} \frac{\partial f_j}{\partial T_a}(T)\xi_a + \sum_{b=1}^{m} g_b(T)\xi_{N+m(j-1)+b}.$$

It should be observed here that $Im(\sigma_{(g)})$ contains $H^s(\prod^m \hat{A})$ with the same integer s as above.

Remark (0.4). The arguments as above can be carried out in the same way if we replace the polynomial ring $k[T]$ by a formal power series ring $k[[T]]$. By this means, it can be easily shown that *every formal complete intersection with an isolated singular point can be obtained from an algebraic scheme by completing at an isolated singular point.*

The second approach described in the case of a complete intersection gives me a suggestion that there must be a good homology-algebraic technique which generalizes the proof in the special case (without using the techniques of birational blowing-ups, as in the first approach). For instance, say X is given as a closed subscheme of a nonsingular algebraic scheme Z. Let x_0 be a closed point of X, R the local ring of Z at x_0, and $\mathbf{O}$ the local ring of X at x_0. Say the base field k is algebraically closed. Then there exists a canonical R-linear homomorphism

$$\beta : \mathrm{Der}_k(R, R) \to \mathrm{Ext}^1_R(\mathbf{O}, \mathbf{O})$$

Namely, let J be the ideal of X in R, and then the exact sequence $0 \to J \to R \to \mathbf{O} \to 0$ gives us a canonical homomorphism $\mathrm{Hom}_R(J, \mathbf{O}) \to \mathrm{Ext}^1_R(\mathbf{O}, \mathbf{O})$. Moreover, the k-derivations of R into itself, applied to $J \subset R$, produce an R-homomorphism $\mathrm{Der}_k(R, R) \to \mathrm{Hom}_R(J, \mathbf{O})$. By composing these two, we get the said homomorphism β as above. We can see that the support of Coker (β) is contained in the singular locus of X at x_0. For instance, if x_0 is an isolated singular point of X, then Coker (β) is a finite k-module. This module Coker (β), or its length, seems to have some role relating to the TR-indices of X at x_0.

In this article, I prefer to take a combination of two approaches mentioned above. Although available results on desingularization problems are unsatisfactory up to the present moment, I apply a suitable monoidal transformation to the given scheme X, or rather to some nonsingular ambient scheme of X, so that after the transformation the techniques for complete intersections are available. Let me describe some of the ideas in this direction below.

Let Z be a *nonsingular irreducible* algebraic scheme over an algebraically closed field k. Let X be a closed subscheme of Z which is *reduced and equidimensional*, and let x_0 be a closed point of X. I shall localize the situation freely about the point x_0, whenever it is convenient to do so. For instance, I assume always that Z is affine. Let us take a base of the ideal of X on Z, say $(f_1, \ldots, f_m)$. Let $N = \dim Z$ and $n = \dim X$, so that $m \geqq d = N - n$. Take a base of all linear relations among the f_j, say $\Sigma_{j=1}^m \nu_{ij} f_j = 0$ for $i = 1, 2, \ldots, m'$, where $\nu_{ij} \in \Gamma(Z, \mathbf{O}_Z)$. Let R be the ideal on Z generated by all the $(m - d) \times (m - d)$–minors of the matrix $((\nu_{ij}))$. This R depends only upon X and the embedding $X \to Z$. Let I be the Jacobian ideal of X on Z, that is, the ideal generated by the f_j and the $d \times d$–minors of the Jacobian $\partial(f_1, \ldots, f_m)/\partial(x_1, \ldots, x_N)$, where $(x) = (x_1, \ldots, x_N)$ is a regular system of parameters of Z at x_0. (Here localize Z about x_0 if necessary.) Let us choose a pair of ideals E and H on Z, subject to the following conditions:

1. Some positive power of E is a product of R and some other ideal on Z.
2. E generates the unit ideals in the local rings of X within a dense open subset.
3. $H \subseteqq E \cap I \cap$ (the ideal of x_0 on Z).
4. Let $p : \tilde{Z} \to Z$ be the birational blowing-up of the ideal E, and $\tilde{X} = p^{-1}(X)$ the subscheme of $\tilde{Z}$ defined by the ideal sheaf generated by that of X on Z. Let $\tilde{X}(\infty)$ be the H-adic completion of $\tilde{X}$ (with reference to the morphism p). Then every pair of distinct irreducible components of $\tilde{X}(\infty)$ have no common points, unless one of them is contained (point-set-theoretically) in the subscheme defined by H.

Now, let us observe that (1) implies that the ideal of $\tilde{X}$ on $\tilde{Z}$ is generated by d elements, and in fact d elements among the f_j $(1 \leqq j \leqq m)$, at least locally everywhere. Take a covering of $\tilde{Z}$ by a finite number of open affine schemes,

$$\tilde{Z} = \bigcup_{i=1}^{e} \operatorname{Spec}(\tilde{A}_i) \tag{0.5}$$

such that, for each i, the ideal of $\tilde{X}$ in $\tilde{A}_i$ is generated by d elements among the f_j, $1 \leqq j \leqq m$. In choosing once for all such a covering and such d elements for each i, $1 \leqq i \leqq e$, I define the $\tilde{A}_i$-linear map, for each i,

$$\sigma^{(i)} : \prod^{N+d^2} \tilde{A}_i \rightarrow \prod^{d} \tilde{A}_i \tag{0.6}$$

defined in the same way as before. To be precise, we have chosen $(x) = (x_1, \ldots, x_N)$, a regular system of parameters of Z at x_0, for which $\partial f_j / \partial x_k$ makes sense. To simplify the notation, given i, I relabel the f_j so that $(f_1, \ldots, f_d)$ is the chosen ideal base of $\tilde{X}$ in $\tilde{A}_i$. Then $\sigma^{(i)}$ is defined by

$$\sigma_p^{(i)}(\xi) = \sum_{a=1}^{N} \frac{\partial f_p}{\partial x_a} \xi_a + \sum_{b=1}^{d} f_b \xi_{N+d(p-1)+b}$$

for $1 \leqq p \leqq d$. There exists an integer $s \geqq 0$ such that

$$H^s(\Pi^d \tilde{A}_i) \subseteqq Im(\sigma^{(i)}) \tag{0.7}$$

for all i, $1 \leqq i \leqq e$. This integer s plays an important role. Let us fix any (or the smallest) such s.

Let us choose a base $(e_0, e_1, \ldots, e_\alpha)$ of the ideal E. Let $\tilde{Z}(\infty)$ be the H-adic completion of $\tilde{Z}$ (with respect to the morphism p), and $\tilde{\boldsymbol{H}}(\infty)$ the ideal sheaf on $\tilde{Z}(\infty)$ generated by H. Consider the following homomorphism of coherent sheaves of $\boldsymbol{O}_{\tilde{Z}(\infty)}$-modules:

$$\Delta : \prod^{N} \boldsymbol{O}_{\tilde{Z}(\infty)} \rightarrow \prod^{(\alpha+1)^2} \boldsymbol{O}_{\tilde{Z}(\infty)} \tag{0.8}$$

defined by

$$\Delta_{p,q}(\xi) = \sum_{j=1}^{N} \Delta_{p,q}^{(j)} \xi_j$$

for $0 \leqq p,\ q \leqq \alpha$, where $\Delta_{p,q}^{(j)} = e_q \left(\dfrac{\partial e_p}{\partial x_j}\right) - e_p \left(\dfrac{\partial e_q}{\partial x_j}\right)$. We define a coherent sheaf of $\boldsymbol{O}_{\tilde{Z}(\infty)}$-modules $\boldsymbol{G}_\nu$, for each integer $\nu \geqq 0$, by

$$\boldsymbol{G}_\nu = [\prod^{N} \tilde{\boldsymbol{H}}(\infty)^{\nu+1}] \cap \Delta^{-1}[E^2 \prod^{(\alpha+1)^2} \tilde{\boldsymbol{H}}(\infty)^{\nu+1}] \tag{0.9}$$

We then define a coherent subsheaf $G^X_{\nu,\mu}$, $\mu \geqq \nu \geqq 0$, of G_ν as follows:

$$G^X_{\nu,\mu} = G_\nu \cap \tau^{-1}[\prod^m (\tilde{H}(\infty)^{\mu+1} + \tilde{K}(\infty))], \qquad (0.10)$$

where $\tilde{K}(\infty)$ is the ideal sheaf of $\tilde{X}(\infty)$ on $\tilde{Z}(\infty)$ (i.e., the ideal sheaf generated by those f_j, $1 \leq j \leqq m$) and τ is the homomorphism

$$\tau : \prod^N O_{\tilde{Z}(\infty)} \to \prod^m O_{\tilde{Z}(\infty)} \qquad (0.11)$$

defined by

$$\tau_i(\xi) = \sum_{a=1}^N \frac{\partial f_i}{\partial x_a} \xi_a$$

for $1 \leqq i \leqq m$.

Remark (0.12). The sheaves G_ν has a certain geometric interpretation as will be seen in Theorem (3.16), §3. Namely, if $2 \leqq \nu \leqq \mu \leqq 2(\nu - 1)$, then the factor sheaf G_ν/G_μ, when viewed as a sheaf of additive groups, is isomorphic to a sheaf of multiplicative groups of certain automorphisms of $\tilde{Z}(\mu)$ which induce the identity in $\tilde{Z}(\nu)$, where $\tilde{Z}(a)$ denotes the subscheme of $\tilde{Z}$ (as well as $\tilde{Z}(\infty)$) defined by the ideal H^{a+1} (with respect to $p : \tilde{Z} \to Z$). This sheaf of automorphisms of $\tilde{Z}(\mu)$, isomorphic to G_ν/G_μ, will be denoted by G^*_ν/G^*_μ and its precise description will be found in §3, in particular Theorem (3.16). Along the interpretation of G_ν/G_μ as automorphisms, the factor sheaf $G^X_{\nu,\mu}/G_\mu$ corresponds to the sheaf of automorphisms of $\tilde{Z}(\mu)$, belonging to G^*_ν/G^*_μ, which induce automorphisms of the subscheme $\tilde{X}(\mu)$. Here, as before, $\tilde{X}(\mu)$ denotes the subscheme of $\tilde{X}$ defined by $H^{\mu+1}$ with respect to p. We have the following inclusion relations:

$$\prod^N \tilde{H}(\infty)^{\nu+1} \supset G_\nu \supset G^X_{\nu,\mu} \supset G_\mu \supset \prod^N \tilde{H}(\infty)^{\mu+2}$$

for every pair of integers (ν, μ) with $\mu \geqq \nu \geqq 0$, and

$$G_\mu \cap G^X_{\nu,\gamma} = G^X_{\mu,\gamma} \qquad \text{for all } (\gamma, \mu, \nu) \text{ with } \gamma \geqq \mu \geqq \nu.$$

Remark (0.13). It is easy to see that $\tilde{H}(\infty)^\gamma G_\nu \subseteqq G_{\nu+\gamma}$ and $\tilde{H}(\infty)^\gamma G^X_{\nu,\mu} \subseteqq G^X_{\nu+\gamma,\mu+\gamma}$, for all $\mu \geqq \nu \geqq 0$ and $\gamma \geqq 0$. We can prove that there exists an integer ν_0 such that

$$\tilde{H}(\infty)^\mu G_\nu = G_{\nu+\mu} \qquad \text{for all } \nu \geqq \nu_0 \text{ and } \mu \geqq 0 \qquad (0.13,1)$$

(cf. Theorem (3.16), §3.) Similarly, given an integer $\alpha \geqq 0$, there exists ν_0 (possibly depending upon α) such that

$$\tilde{\boldsymbol{H}}(\infty)^{\gamma}\boldsymbol{G}^X_{\nu,\nu+\alpha} = \boldsymbol{G}^X_{\nu+\gamma,\nu+\alpha+\gamma} \qquad \text{for all } \nu \geqq \nu_0 \text{ and } \gamma \geqq 0. \quad (0.13,2)$$

For instance, to prove (0.13,2), it suffices to observe that $\oplus_{\gamma=0}^{\infty} \tilde{\boldsymbol{H}}(\infty)^{\gamma}$ is a quasicoherent sheaf of $\boldsymbol{O}_{\tilde{Z}(\infty)}$–algebras of finite type, and that $\oplus_{\nu=0}^{\infty}\boldsymbol{G}^X_{\nu,\nu+\alpha}$ is the kernel of the homomorphism of $[\oplus_{\gamma=0}^{\infty}\tilde{\boldsymbol{H}}(\infty)^{\gamma}]$–modules of finite type:

$$\bigoplus_{\nu=0}^{\infty} \boldsymbol{G}_{\nu} \to \bigoplus_{\nu=0}^{\infty}\left(\prod^{m} \frac{\tilde{\boldsymbol{H}}(\infty)^{\nu+1} + \tilde{\boldsymbol{K}}(\infty)}{\tilde{\boldsymbol{H}}(\infty)^{\nu+\alpha+1} + \tilde{\boldsymbol{K}}(\infty)}\right)$$

which is the direct sum of the homomorphisms induced by τ.

Remark (0.14). Note that if ideals E and H on Z satisfy the condition (1), (2), (3), and (4), then so does E and EH. In fact, as for the condition (4), it suffices to notice that the EH-adic topology is the same as the H-adic one. However, after replacing H by EH, we can be sure that the following is true.

5. For every coherent sheaf of $\boldsymbol{O}_{\tilde{Z}(\infty)}$–modules, say $\boldsymbol{G}$, there exists an integer $\bar{\nu} \geqq 0$ such that

$$H^q(\tilde{Z}(\infty), \tilde{\boldsymbol{H}}(\infty)^{\nu+1}\boldsymbol{G}) = (0)$$

for all $\nu \geqq \bar{\nu}$ and $q > 0$.

We are now ready to obtain an H-adic TR-index (t, r) of the scheme X at the point x_0.

a. *Let s be the chosen integer in* (0.7), *and let* $t_1 = \max\{s + 2, 2s\}$. A lemma analogous to Lemma (0.3) will be applicable to each of the H-adic completions $\tilde{A}_i(\infty)$ of $\tilde{A}_i$, $1 \leqq i \leqq e$ [cf. (0.5)]. Here we need the fact that, for $\nu \geqq 2$, every element $\xi = (\xi_1, \ldots, \xi_N) \in \Pi^N H^{\nu+1}\tilde{A}_i(\infty)$ gives rise to a unique automorphism of $\tilde{A}_i(\infty)$ which maps x_j to $x_j + \xi_j$ for $1 \leqq j \leqq N$, where $(x) = (x_1, \ldots, x_N)$ is the chosen regular system of parameters of Z at x_0 (viewed as a system of elements of $\tilde{A}_i(\infty)$ in a canonical way), [cf. Lemma (3.4), §3]. As a matter of fact, this is the way in which a local automorphism of $\tilde{Z}(\infty)$ is associated with each local section of $\boldsymbol{G}_{\nu}$. Let $\tilde{\lambda} : \Pi^N\tilde{\boldsymbol{H}}(\infty)^3 \to \mathrm{Aut}(\tilde{Z}(\infty))$ (= the sheaf of groups of automorphisms of $\tilde{Z}(\infty)$) be the map so obtained [cf. Theorem (3.16) together with Lemma (3.4), §3 for its precise definition]. Following the analogy to Lemma (0.3), we get (in view of the inclusion $G_\nu \supseteqq \Pi^N \tilde{H}(\infty)^{\nu+2}$):

Lemma (0.15). Let $\tilde{X}'(\infty)$ be a formal subscheme of $\tilde{Z}(\infty)$, or even, such within an open subset of $\tilde{Z}(\infty)$. Let $\tilde{Z}(\infty) = \cup_{i=1}^{e} \tilde{Z}(\infty)_i$ be the covering by the formal affine schemes $\tilde{Z}(\infty)_i = \mathrm{Spf}(\tilde{A}_i(\infty))$, which corresponds to the covering of $\tilde{Z}$ in (0.5). Let $\nu \geqq t_1 + 1$, and suppose that $\tilde{X}(\nu)$ coincides with the subscheme $\tilde{X}'(\nu)$ of $\tilde{Z}(\nu)$ induced by $\tilde{X}'(\infty)$, say within $\tilde{Z}(\infty)_i$ for some i. Then there exists $\xi \in \Gamma(\tilde{Z}(\infty)_i, G_{\nu-s-1})$ such that

$$\lambda(\xi)(\tilde{X}'(\infty) \cap \tilde{Z}(\infty)_i) \subseteqq \tilde{X}(\infty) \cap \tilde{Z}(\infty)_i.$$

b. Let $\tilde{K}(\infty)$ denote the ideal sheaf of $\tilde{X}(\infty)$ on $\tilde{Z}(\infty)$, which is generated by the ideal sheaf of X on Z. Let $\tilde{K}_0(\infty) = \cup_{a=1}^{\infty} (\tilde{K}(\infty) : \tilde{H}(\infty)^a)$, which is the ideal sheaf of the smallest subscheme of $\tilde{Z}(\infty)$ that induces the same subscheme of $\tilde{Z}(\infty) - \tilde{Z}(0)$ as $\tilde{X}(\infty)$. Then *there exists an integer t_2 ($\geqq 0$) such that*

$$\tilde{K}_0(\infty) \cap (\tilde{K}(\infty) + \tilde{H}(\infty)^{\nu+1}) = \tilde{K}(\infty) \qquad \textit{for every } \nu \geqq t_2. \tag{0.16}$$

We can then easily prove

Lemma (0.17). Let $\tilde{X}'(\infty)_i$ be a subscheme (closed) of $\tilde{Z}(\infty)_i$ for an index i ($1 \leqq i \leqq e$). Suppose $\tilde{X}'(\infty)_i \cap (\tilde{Z}(\infty)_i - \tilde{Z}(0)) = \tilde{X}(\infty) \cap (\tilde{Z}(\infty)_i - \tilde{Z}(0))$, $X'(\infty)_i \subseteqq \tilde{X}(\infty) \cap \tilde{Z}(\infty)_i$, and that $\tilde{X}'(\infty)_i$ and $\tilde{X}(\infty)$ induce the same subscheme of $\tilde{Z}(\nu)_i$ ($= \tilde{Z}(\nu) \cap \tilde{Z}(\infty)_i$) for at least one integer $\nu \geqq t_2$. Then $\tilde{X}'(\infty)_i = \tilde{X}(\infty) \cap \tilde{Z}(\infty)_i$. (The inclusion of subschemes is by definition the reverse of the inclusion of ideals.)

In the applications of this lemma, the assumption (4) plays an important role. Namely, by (4), $\tilde{X}'(\infty)_i \subseteqq \tilde{X}(\infty) \cap \tilde{Z}(\infty)_i$ implies $\tilde{X}'(\infty)_i \cap (\tilde{Z}(\infty)_i - \tilde{Z}(0)) = \tilde{X}(\infty) \cap (\tilde{Z}(\infty)_i - \tilde{Z}(0))$ locally at every closed point of $\tilde{Z}(\infty)_i$ where $\tilde{X}'(\infty)_i$ has at least one irreducible component of dimension $\geqq n$ which is not contained in $\tilde{Z}(\nu)$ for any integer ν, provided a subscheme of $\tilde{Z}(\infty)$ induces $\tilde{X}'(\infty)_i$ in $\tilde{Z}(\infty)_i$. The same is trivially true at every point of $\tilde{Z}(\infty)_i$ where $\tilde{X}(\infty)$ is locally contained in $\tilde{Z}(\nu)$ for some integer ν.

c. Choose and fix an integer $\alpha > s + 1$ (say, $\alpha = s + 2$). *Let t_3 be an integer (say, the smallest one) such that* $\nu - s - 1 \geqq 2$, $2(\nu - s - 2)$

$\geqq \nu + \alpha - s - 1$ *and*

$$H^1(\tilde{Z}(\infty), \mathbf{G}^X_{\nu-s-1,\nu+\alpha-s-1}) = (0) \qquad (0.18)$$

for all integers $\nu \geqq t_3$.

The significance of this integer t_3 is as follows. Let $\nu \geqq t_3$ as above. The situation being the same as in Lemma (0.15), suppose there exists $\xi_a \in \Gamma(\tilde{Z}(\infty)_a, \mathbf{G}_{\nu-s-1})$ such that $\tilde{\lambda}(\xi_a)(\tilde{X}'(\infty) \cap \tilde{Z}(\infty)_a) = \tilde{X}(\infty) \cap \tilde{Z}(\infty)_a$, say for $a = i$ and j. Then $\tilde{\lambda}(\xi_i) \circ \tilde{\lambda}(\xi_j)^{-1}$ is an automorphism of $\tilde{Z}(\infty)_i \cap \tilde{Z}(\infty)_j$ which maps $\tilde{X}(\infty)$ to itself. Since $\nu - s - 1 \geqq 2$ and $2(\nu - s - 2) \geqq \nu + \alpha - s - 1$, $\tilde{\lambda}(\xi_i - \xi_j)$ is an automorphism of $\tilde{Z}(\infty)_i \cap \tilde{Z}(\infty)_j$ which, when induced to $\tilde{Z}(\nu + \alpha - s - 1)$, maps $\tilde{X}(\nu + \alpha - s - 1)$ to itself [cf. Theorem (3.16), (e), §3]. Thus $\xi_i - \xi_j$ belongs to $\Gamma(\tilde{Z}(\infty)_i \cap \tilde{Z}(\infty)_j, \mathbf{G}^X_{\nu-s-1,\nu+\alpha-s-1})$. Suppose we can find $\eta_a \in \Gamma(\tilde{Z}(\infty)_a, \mathbf{G}^X_{\nu-s-1,\nu+\alpha-s-1})$, $a = i$ and j, such that $\xi_i - \xi_j = \eta_i - \eta_j$. This means that there exists $\xi \in \Gamma(\tilde{Z}(\infty)_i \cup \tilde{Z}(\infty)_j, \mathbf{G}_{\nu-s-1})$ such that, for $\mu = \nu + \alpha - s - 1 > \nu$, $\tilde{\lambda}(\xi)$ transforms $\tilde{X}'(\mu)$ to $\tilde{X}(\mu)$ within $\tilde{Z}(\infty)_i \cup \tilde{Z}(\infty)_j$. We see clearly that the first cohomology in (0.18) is the space of obstructions to extending a given isomorphism (or the identity) between $\tilde{X}'(\nu)$ and $\tilde{X}(\nu)$ to an isomorphism between $\tilde{X}'(\nu + \alpha - s - 1)$ and $\tilde{X}(\nu + \alpha - s - 1)$ (through automorphisms of the ambient scheme $\tilde{Z}(\infty)$), provided such an extension of isomorphisms is locally possible. To be precise, if $\tilde{X}'(\infty)$ is any subscheme of $\tilde{Z}(\infty)$ then $\tilde{X}'_0(\infty)$ will denote the smallest (closed) subscheme of $\tilde{X}'(\infty)$ that induces the same restriction to $\tilde{Z}(\infty) - \tilde{Z}(0)$ as $\tilde{X}'(\infty)$. For instance, $\tilde{X}_0(\infty)$ is the subscheme of $\tilde{Z}(\infty)$ defined by the ideal sheaf $\tilde{\boldsymbol{K}}_0(\infty)$ of (b). Recall that, by (4), every *connected* component of $\tilde{X}_0(\infty)$ is an *irreducible* component. But the formal scheme $\tilde{X}_0(\infty)$ is not in general locally irreducible. Let s' be any nonnegative integer (say, the smallest one) such that if $\nu \geqq s'$ and if U is any open subset of $\tilde{Z}(\infty)$, then any two different subschemes of $\tilde{X}_0(\infty) \cap U$ do not induce the same subscheme in $\tilde{Z}(\nu - s - 1) \cap U$, provided they are reduced, equidimensional, and of the same dimension as $\tilde{X}_0(\infty)$.

Lemma (0.19). Let $\tilde{X}'(\infty)$ be a formal subscheme of $\tilde{Z}(\infty)$ such that every irreducible component of $\tilde{X}'_0(\infty)$ is of dimension $\geqq n$. Let $\nu \geqq \max\{t_1 + 1, t_2, t_3, s'\}$ and suppose $\tilde{X}'(\nu)$ coincides with $\tilde{X}(\nu)$. Then there exists a subscheme $\tilde{X}^*(\infty)$ of $\tilde{Z}(\infty)$ such that if Δ is the union of those irreducible components of $\tilde{X}_0(\infty)$ which do not meet with $\tilde{X}'_0(\infty)$, then $\tilde{X}^*(\infty)$ coincides with $\tilde{X}'(\infty)$ in $\tilde{Z}(\infty) - \Delta$ and with $\tilde{X}(\infty)$ in a neighborhood of Δ in $\tilde{Z}(\infty)$. Moreover, there exists $\xi \in \mathbf{G}_{\nu-s-1}$ such that

$$\tilde{\lambda}(\xi)(\tilde{X}^*(\nu + \alpha - s - 1)) = \tilde{X}(\nu + \alpha - s - 1).$$

Replacing $\tilde{X}'(\infty)$ by the image of $\tilde{X}^*(\infty)$ under $\tilde{\lambda}(\xi)$ and the integer ν by $\nu + \alpha - s - 1(> \nu)$, we can apply the lemma again and repeatedly. Therefore:

Corollary (0.20). The notation and the assumption being the same as above, there exists $\xi \in \mathbf{G}_{\nu-s-1}$ such that $\tilde{\lambda}(\xi)(\tilde{X}^*(\infty)) = \tilde{X}(\infty)$.

d. Let $X(\infty)$ be the H-adic completion of X, and $Z(\nu)$ the subscheme of Z defined by $H^{\nu+1}$. Let t_4 be an integer such that if $X'(\infty)$ is any subscheme of $X(\infty)$ which is reduced, equidimensional of dimension n, then $X'(\infty)$ and $X(\infty)$ induce different subschemes of $Z(\nu)$ for every $\nu \geqq t_4$ unless $X'(\infty) = X(\infty)$.
e. Finally, let t_5 be an integer (say, the smallest) $\geqq 0$ such that the direct image $p_*(\tilde{\boldsymbol{H}}(\infty)^{\nu+t_5})$ by the morphism $p : \tilde{Z}(\infty) \to Z(\infty)$ (or the one induced by the blowing-up $p : \tilde{Z} \to Z$) is contained in $\boldsymbol{H}(\infty)^\nu$ for all integers $\nu \geqq 0$, where $\tilde{\boldsymbol{H}}(\infty)$ [resp. $\boldsymbol{H}(\infty)$] denotes the ideal sheaf on $\tilde{Z}(\infty)$ [resp. $Z(\infty)$] generated by H. Such an integer t_5 exists for the reason that H is contained in E and $p : \tilde{Z} \to Z$ is the birational blowing-up of E. [This existence can be also proven by (5).]

Theorem D. Let X be an algebraic scheme over an algebraically closed field k, which is reduced and equidimensional. Let x_0 be a closed point of X. Pick a nonsingular ambient scheme Z of X, say locally at x_0, and a pair of ideals E and H satisfying the 5 conditions (1)–(5). With reference to these, choose the integers s, s', and $t_j (1 \leqq j \leqq 5)$ according to the procedures described in (a)–(e). Let $t = \max\{t_1 + 1, t_2, t_3, s', t_4 + s + 1 + t_5\}$ and $r = s + 1 + t_5$. Then (t, r) is an H-adic TR-index of the scheme X at x_0.

This assertion is easily proven by virtue of the preceding lemmas, and also by observing that every algebraic scheme over k, say X', with H'-adic truncations $X'(\nu)$, admits an imbedding of its completion $X'(\infty)$ into the same $Z(\infty)$ as above, so as to induce any given isomorphism of $X'(\mu)$ to $X(\mu)$ with $\mu \geqq 2$, provided this isomorphism induces an isomorphism of $X'(\gamma)$ to $X(\gamma)$ for every nonnegative integer $\gamma < \nu$.

I have claimed the existence of TR-index in a much more general situation than Theorem D, and I have stated this as Main Theorem I. The basic ideas in the proof of Main Theorem I are the same as that of Theorem D. However, the generalization requires some further preparations about rather foundational materials concerning blowing-ups and formalizations. Main Theorem I has an obvious *complex-analytic analogue*, in which case the TR-index has a stronger property that, in Definition (0.2), $\hat{\phi}$ can be required to be the formalization of a holomorphic map. In the algebraic case, as is stated in Main Theorem I, the corresponding $\hat{\phi}$ cannot be required to be an isomorphism of the given schemes X and X' (or their localizations) but *to be the formalization of an isomorphism between suitable étale coverings of X and X'* (or between their Henselizations in a suitable sense). The complex-analytic case can be also formulated in the language of schemes, because the problem is local at a point. The point in the analytic case is that the local rings of a complex-analytic space is itself Henselian.

Thus we can formulate a generalization of Main Theorem I, within the language of schemes, which includes the complex-analytic analogue. Such a generalization requires some algebraic preliminaries on certain special kinds of algebras which appear in algebraic schemes and complex spaces. The following two sections are designed for this purpose. The final section concerns the structure of groups of local automorphisms of certain formal schemes, which play the most important role in a proof of Main Theorem I or its further generalizations. A complete proof of Main Theorem I will be given elsewhere.

§1. ALGEBRAS WITH CONDITION (T)

Let Λ be a noetherian ring.

Definition (1.1). Let A be a noetherian Λ-algebra, and T an ideal in A. Then the condition (T) on the pair (A, T) means the following three:

(T.1). The structural homomorphism $\Lambda \rightarrow A$ induces an isomorphism $\Lambda \stackrel{\approx}{\rightarrow} A/T$.

(T.2). The T-adic topology in A is separated, that is $\bigcap_{i=1}^{\infty} T^i = (0)$.

(T.3). There exists a base $(x_1, \ldots, x_N)$ of the ideal T, and a Λ-homomorphism

$$\lambda = \lambda_{(x,t)} : A \rightarrow A[[t_1, \ldots, t_N]]$$

such that $\lambda(x_i) = x_i + t_i$ for $1 \leqq i \leqq N$, where $A[[t_1, \ldots, t_N]]$ is the formal power series ring of N variables with coefficients in A.

Remark (1.2). The condition (T.2) is seen to be equivalent to that the canonical homomorphism $A \rightarrow A_\infty$ is injective, where A_∞ denotes the T-adic completion of A. We can show, by examples, that (T.2) does not follow from the other two.

Remark (1.3). The condition (T) implies that the Λ-algebra, topologized T-adically, is formally smooth. In fact, the *T-adic completion A_∞ of A is isomorphic to a formal power series ring $\Lambda[[x_1, \ldots, x_N]]$ of N variables with coefficients in Λ.*

Proof. Consider the $(T, (t))$-adic topology of $A[[t_1, \ldots, t_N]]$. Then $\lambda : A \rightarrow A[[t_1, \ldots, t_N]]$ is continuous and extends to a Λ-homomorphism $\lambda_\infty : A_\infty \rightarrow A_\infty[[t_1, \ldots, t_N]]$. The Λ-homomorphism $A_\infty \rightarrow \Lambda[[t_1, \ldots, t_N]]$ is then obtained by composing λ_∞ and the natural homomorphism $A_\infty[[t_1, \ldots, t_N]] \rightarrow \Lambda[[t_1, \ldots, t_N]]$ whose kernel is generated by T. This homomorphism can be easily proven bijective.

Q.E.D.

Corollary (1.4). The Λ-module T/T^2 is free and of rank N, if the condition (T) is satisfied.

Remark (1.5). Under the condition (T), λ induces the identity endomorphism of A when followed by the natural homomorphism $A[[t_1, \ldots, t_N]] \rightarrow A$ which annihilates the t_j $(1 \leqq j \leqq N)$. [Check it first when A is T-adically complete. Then reduce the proof in the general case to the complete case by means of (T.2).]

Remark (1.6). Suppose (A, T) satisfies the conditions (T.1) and (T.2). If the condition (T.3) is satisfied for a base $(x_1, \ldots, x_N)$ of T, then it is so for any other base $(y_1, \ldots, y_N)$ of T with the same N, which is obtained by an invertible A-linear transformation.

Proof. Write $y_i = \Sigma_{j=1}^N a_{ij}x_j$ with $a_{ij} \in A$ such that $\det(a_{ij})$ is a unit in A. Now, let $s_i = \lambda_{(x,t)}(y_i) - y_i \in A[[t_1, \ldots, t_N]]$ for $1 \leqq i \leqq N$. Let $a_{ij}^* = \lambda_{(x,t)}(a_{ij}) \in A[[t_1, \ldots, t_N]]$. Then $\det(a_{ij}^*)$ is a unit, because $\det(a_{ij})$ is such. Moreover,

$$s_i = \Sigma_{j=1}^N a_{ij}^*(x_j + t_j) - \Sigma_{j=1}^N a_{ij}x_j = \Sigma_{j=1}^N a_{ij}^* t_j + \Sigma_{j=1}^N (a_{ij}^* - a_{ij})x_j,$$

where $a_{ij}^* - a_{ij} \in (t)A[[t_1, \ldots, t_N]]$ by (1.5). These facts show that $(x, t)A[[t_1, \ldots, t_N]] = (x, s)A[[t_1, \ldots, t_N]]$ and $s_i \in (t)A[[t_1, \ldots, t_N]]$ for all i. Now it is clear that the natural homomorphism $A[[s_1, \ldots, s_N]] \to A[[t_1, \ldots, t_N]]$ is bijective. Identifying these two power series rings we find $\lambda_{(x, t)} = \lambda_{(y, s)}$. Q.E.D.

Let us recall the following.

Definition (1.7). Let A be a Λ-algebra. Then a Hasse differentiation of A is an infinite sequence $d = \{d_i\}_{i=0, 1, 2, \ldots}$ of endomorphisms d_i of A viewed as Λ-module, such that

(D.1) $d_0(x) = x,$

(D.2) $d_\nu(xy) = \sum_{\alpha+\beta=\nu} d_\alpha(x) d_\beta(y),$ and

(D.3) $d_\alpha(d_\beta(x)) = \binom{\alpha+\beta}{\alpha} d_{\alpha+\beta}(x),$ for all x and y in A.

Note that d_1 is a derivation of A into itself, that if A contains the field of rational numbers then d_1 determines all the other d_ν by (D.3), and that in general (e.g., in positive-characteristic cases) d_1 does not.

Remark (1.8). Let $d = \{d_i\}_{i=0, 1, 2, \ldots}$ be a Hasse differentiation of a Λ-algebra A. Then we get a homomorphism of Λ-algebras

$$\delta = \delta_{(d, t)} : A \to A[[t]]$$

where $A[[t]]$ is a formal power series ring of one variable, as follows. For $y \in A$, $\delta(y) = \sum_{i=0}^{\infty} d_i(y) t^i \in A[[t]]$. A homomorphism δ so obtained has the following properties:

(D*.1) We get the identity of A into itself by composing δ and the natural homomorphism $A[[t]] \to A$ which annihilates t.

(D*.2) Let $\delta^{(x)} : A \to A[[x]]$ be the homomorphism obtained from $\delta : A \to A[[t]]$ by replacing t by x. Then for two indeterminates t and u, we get a commutative diagram

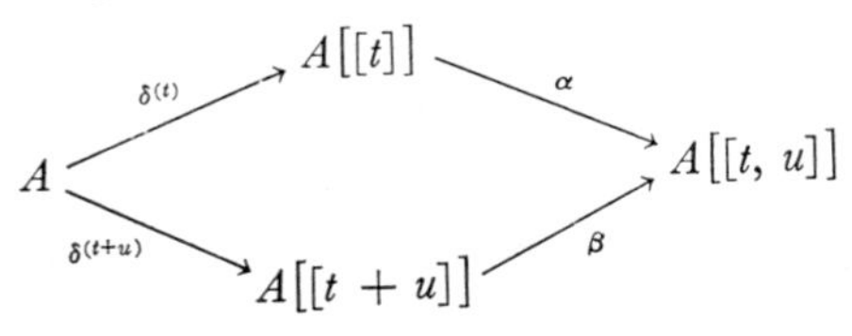

where α is the extension of $\delta^{(u)} : A \to A[[u]]$ by $\alpha(t) = t$, and β is the obvious inclusion.

Conversely, if a homomorphism of Λ-algebras $\delta : A \to A[[t]]$ with an indeterminate t satisfies the conditions (D*.1) and (D*.2), then we get a Hasse differentiation d of the Λ-algebra A such that $\delta = \delta_{(d,t)}$.

Remark (1.9). We say that two Hasse differentiations $d^{(1)}$ and $d^{(2)}$ of a Λ-algebra A *commute* (and write $d^{(1)}d^{(2)} = d^{(2)}d^{(1)}$ in symbol) if $d_\alpha^{(1)}(d_\beta^{(2)}(x)) = d_\beta^{(2)}(d_\alpha^{(1)}(x))$ for all (α, β) and $y \in A$. If A contains the field of rational numbers, $d^{(1)}$ and $d^{(2)}$ commute if and only if $d_1^{(1)}$ and $d_1^{(2)}$ do. This is false in general (e.g., A contains a finite field).

Remark (1.10). Let Λ be a noetherian ring, and A a noetherian Λ-algebra. Let T be an ideal in A which satisfies the conditions (T.1) and (T.2) of Definition (1.1). Then Λ can be viewed as A-module by means of the isomorphism $\Lambda \overset{\approx}{\to} A/T$. In this manner, we can speak of Λ-derivations of A with values in Λ. These form a Λ-module in a natural manner, and this will be denoted by $\mathrm{Der}_\Lambda(A, \Lambda)$. Every Λ-derivation d of A into itself induces an element of $\mathrm{Der}_\Lambda(A, \Lambda)$ by composing with the natural homomorphism $A \to A/T \cong \Lambda$. Namely, we have a homomorphism $\gamma : \mathrm{Der}_\Lambda(A, A) \to \mathrm{Der}_\Lambda(A, \Lambda)$ (which is actually a homomorphism of A-modules, as the second one is viewed as A-module by $\Lambda \cong A/T$). In general, γ is not surjective even when A is formally smooth with respect to the T-adic topology. Now, I claim:

If (A, T) satisfies the condition (T.3) of Definition (1.1), then there exists a system of Hasse differentiations $(d^{(1)}, d^{(2)}, \ldots, d^{(N)})$ of the Λ-algebra A such that

a. They commute one another.
b. And $(\gamma(d_1^{(1)}), \gamma(d_1^{(2)}), \ldots, \gamma(d_1^{(N)}))$ is a free base of the Λ-module $\mathrm{Der}_\Lambda(A, \Lambda)$.

Proof. Let $\lambda = \lambda_{(x,t)} : A \to A[[t_1, \ldots, t_N]]$ be the homomorphism of (T.3), where $T = (x_1, \ldots, x_N)A$. Let $\delta^{(i)}$ be the homomorphism $A \to A[[t]]$ (the formal power series ring of one variable t) obtained by composing λ with the natural A-homomorphism $A[[t_1, \ldots, t_N]] \to A[[t]]$ which maps t_j to $\delta_{ij}t$ with Kronecker symbol δ_{ij}. Then the claim is that those $\delta^{(i)}$ satisfy the conditions (D*.1) and (D*.2) of (1.8), and that if $\delta^{(i)} = \delta_{(d^{(i)}, t)}$ with Hasse differentiations $d^{(i)}$, then those $d^{(i)}$ satisfy the conditions (a) and (b). The proof of these facts can be easily done by reducing it to the case in which A is T-adically complete and hence is canonically isomorphic to the formal power series ring $\Lambda[[x_1, x_2, \ldots, x_N]]$.

Q.E.D.

Remark (1.11). Suppose (A, T) satisfies the condition (T.1) of Definition (1.1), (A and Λ are noetherian.) Let $1 + T$ denote the multiplicatively closed subset of A consisting of those elements of the form $1 + x$ with $x \in T$. Let A' be the localization of A by $1 + T$, and $T' = TA'$. Then we can show that the natural homomorphism $A \rightarrow A'$ induces an isomorphism $A_\infty \overset{\approx}{\rightarrow} A'_\infty$ where A_∞ (resp. A'_∞) denotes the T-adic (resp. T'-adic) completion of A (resp. A'), and that (A', T') satisfies the condition (T.2) of Definition (1.1). In fact, A being neotherian, the kernel of $A \rightarrow A_\infty$ is annihilated by an element of the form $1 + x$ with $x \in T$. Moreover, it can be shown that (A', T') has the property that an element of A' is a unit in A' if and only if its image in A'_∞ is such.

Remark (1.12). Suppose (A, T) satisfies (T.1). Then an element y of A is mapped to a unit in A_∞ if and only if y can be written in the form $a + x$ with a unit a in Λ and $x \in T$. Let U be any multiplicatively closed subset of A consisting of such elements as above. Let A' be the localization of A by U, and $T' = TA'$. Then I claim that if (A, T) *satisfies* (T.3) *then* (A', T') *does the same.*

Proof. Let λ be a homomorphism of Λ-algebras, $A \rightarrow A[[t_1, \ldots, t_N]]$, such that $\lambda(x_i) = x_i + t_i$ for $1 \leqq i \leqq N$, where $T = (x_i, \ldots, x_N)A$. Let $y \in U$. Then $\lambda(y) = y + s$ with $s \in (t_1, \ldots, t_N)$. Hence the natural image of $\lambda(y)$ in $A'[[t_1, \ldots, t_N]]$ is a unit. This shows that λ extends (uniquely) to a homomorphism $\lambda' : A' \rightarrow A'[[t_1, \ldots, t_N]]$. The condition (T.3) on (A', T') is now immediate.

Remark (1.13). Suppose (A, T) satisfies the conditions (T.1) and (T.2) of Definition (1.1). Suppose there exists a system of Hasse differentiations $(d^{(1)}, d^{(2)}, \ldots, d^{(N)})$ of the Λ-algebra A such that the conditions (a) and (b) of Remark (1.10) are satisfied. Suppose, in addition,

c. The Λ-module T/T^2 is free.

Under these assumptions, we cannot conclude in general that (A, T) satisfies the condition (T.3) of Definition (1.1). However, *if A' is the localization of A by $1 + T$ and $T' = TA'$, then (A', T') satisfies the condition* (T.3) (*in addition to* (T.1) *and* (T.2)).

Proof. Define a map $\lambda : A \to A[[t_1, \ldots, t_N]]$

by $$\lambda(y) = \Sigma d_{i_1}^{(1)} d_{i_2}^{(2)} \ldots d_{i_N}^{(N)}(y) t_1^{i_1} t_2^{i_2}, \ldots, t_N^{i_N}$$

where the summation extends to all the N-tuples of nonnegative integers $(i_1, \ldots, t_N)$. Then we can see that λ is a homomorphism of Λ-algebras, in view of the properties of Hasse differentiation and the commutativity assumption (a) of Remark (1.10). On the other hand, we have a canonical isomorphism

$$\theta : \mathrm{Der}_\Lambda(A, \Lambda) \xrightarrow{\sim} \mathrm{Hom}_\Lambda(T/T^2, \Lambda)$$

(In fact, every element of $\mathrm{Der}_\Lambda(A, \Lambda)$ annihilates T^2, because T annihilates Λ, and A/T^2 is the trivial extension of $\Lambda \cong A/T$ by the Λ-module T/T^2.) In view of (b) of Remark (1.10) and (c), we can choose $y_i \in T$, $1 \leqq i \leqq N$, such that if $\bar{y}_i$ denotes the class of y_i in T/T^2, then

$$\theta(\gamma(d_1^{(i)}))(\bar{y}_j) = \delta_{ij} \qquad \text{(Kronecker symbol)}$$

for $1 \leqq i, j \leqq N$. Obviously, $(\bar{y}_1, \bar{y}_2, \ldots, \bar{y}_N)$ form a free base of the Λ-module T/T^2, so that $T' = TA'$ is generated by $(y_1, \ldots, y_N)$. (Note that T itself may not be generated by $(y_1, \ldots, y_N)$.) Moreover, we can write $\lambda(y_i) = y_i + \Sigma y_{ij} t_j + \epsilon_i$, where $y_{ij} = d_1^{(j)}(y_i) \equiv \delta_{ij} \pmod T$ and $\epsilon_i \in (t_1, \ldots, t_N)^2 A[[t_1, \ldots, t_N]]$. Let $s_i = \lambda(y_i) - y_i$. Since $\det(y_{ij}) \in 1 + T$ and $A' = (1 + T)^{-1}A$, we get $(t_1, \ldots, t_N)A'[[t_1, \ldots, t_N]] = (s_1, \ldots, s_N)A'[[t_1, \ldots, t_N]]$, and therefore a canonical isomorphism $A'[[s_1, \ldots, s_N]] \xrightarrow{\approx} A'[[t_1, \ldots, t_N]]$. Thus, the homomorphism λ defined above can be so extended as to be identified with the homomorphism of Λ-algebras

$$\lambda_{(y,s)} : A' \to A'[[s_1, \ldots, s_N]]$$

which maps y_i to $y_i + s_i$ for $1 \leqq i \leqq N$. Q.E.D.

Remark (1.14). In the previous Remark, it was shown that the assumptions (T.1), (T.2), (a), (b), and (c) implies (T.3). However, the relation is *indirect* between the given Hasse differentiations $(d^{(1)}, d^{(2)}, \ldots, d^{(N)})$ in (a) and (b), and the derived ideal base $(x_1, \ldots, x_N)$ of T' with $\lambda' : A' \to A'[[t_1, \ldots, t_N]]$ as in (T.3). In other words, *we cannot choose in general the ideal base* $(x_1, \ldots, x_N)$

of T' so that the Λ-homomorphism $\delta_{(d^{(i)},t)} : A' \to A'[[t]]$ *associated with* $d^{(i)}$ *as in Remark* (1.8) *is the one which maps* x_j *to* $x_j + \delta_{ij}t$ *for* $1 \leqq i, j \leqq N$. (δ_{ij}: Kronecker symbol.) Note that this last condition is equivalent to saying that $d_\nu^{(i)}(x_j) = \delta_{ij}\delta_{\nu 1}$ for all (i, j, ν) with $\nu \geqq 1$.

Remark (1.14). The following facts will help the reader to understand the previous remark better. Let A be a noetherian Λ-algebra which, together with an ideal T in A, satisfies the conditions (T.1), (T.2), and (T.3). Let us, moreover, assume that every element of $1 + T$ is a unit in A so that every minimal base of T induces a free base of the Λ-module T/T^2. (In particular, all the minimal bases of T have the same length.) Let A_∞ be the T-adic completion of A, and $T_\infty = TA_\infty$. Let $N = \text{rank}(T/T^2)$, and let $\lambda_{(x,t)} : A_\infty \to A_\infty[[t_1, t_2, \ldots, t_N]]$ be the homomorphism of Λ-algebras such that $\lambda_{(x,t)}(x_j) = x_j + t_j$ for $1 \leqq j \leqq N$, where $(x) = (x_1, x_2, \ldots, x_N)$ is a minimal base of T_∞ and $(t_1, \ldots, t_N)$ is a system of N indeterminates. Then we can prove that:

A. There exists a one to one correspondence between the set of systems of Hasse differentiations $(d^{(1)}, d^{(2)}, \ldots, d^{(N)})$ of A_∞ satisfying (a) and (b) of Remark (1.10), and the set of minimal bases $(x_1, x_2, \ldots, x_N)$ of T_∞, in such a fashion that $\lambda_{(x,t)}(y) = \Sigma_{(i)} d_{i_1}^{(1)} d_{i_2}^{(2)} \ldots d_{i_N}^{(N)}(y) t_1^{i_1} t_2^{i_2} \ldots t_N^{i_N}$ for all $y \in A_\infty$.

B. Let $(x_1, x_2, \ldots, x_N)$ be a minimal base of T_∞ (where x_j may and may not be contained in A, A being canonically imbedded in A_∞). Let $(d^{(1)}, \ldots, d^{(N)})$ be the corresponding system of Hasse differentiations of A_∞. Then the following conditions are equivalent to one another:

1. $d_\nu^{(i)}$ maps A into itself for all (i, ν).
2. $\lambda_{(x,t)} : A_\infty \to A_\infty[[t_1, t_2, \ldots, t_N]]$ maps A into $A[[t_1, t_2, \ldots, t_N]]$.
3. There exists a minimal base $(y_1, \ldots, y_N)$ of T_∞ such that $\lambda_{(y,t)}$ maps A into $A[[t_1, \ldots, t_N]]$ and $\lambda_{(y,t)}(x_j) - x_j \in A[[t_1, \ldots, t_N]]$ for all j.
4. There exists a system of Hasse differentiations $(e^{(1)}, e^{(2)}, \ldots, e^{(N)})$ of A_∞ satisfying (a) and (b) of Remark (1.10), such that $e_\nu^{(i)}$ maps A into itself for all (i, ν) and $e_{\bar\nu}^{(i)}(x_j) \in A$ for all $(i, j, \bar\nu)$ with $\bar\nu \geqq 1$.

Suppose Λ contains a field of characteristic p. For each positive integer a, let $A_\infty^{(a)}$ be the closure in A_∞ of the Λ-subalgebra of A_∞

generated by the elements of the form h^q with $q = p^a$ and $h \in A_\infty$. Note that if $A_\infty = \Lambda[[y_1, y_2, \ldots, y_N]]$ then $A_\infty^{(a)} = \Lambda[[y_1^q, y_2^q, \ldots, y_N^q]]$ with $q = p^a$. Now, I claim that the conditions (1)–(4) are implied by (but not in general equivalent to) the following:

5. For every positive integer a, x_j is written in the form $x_j' + x_j''$ with $x_j' \in A$ and $x_j'' \in A_\infty^{(a)}$ for all j $(1 \leqq j \leqq N)$.

Proof of (A). It suffices to show that, given $(d^{(1)}, \ldots, d^{(N)})$ satisfying (a) and (b) of Remark (1.10), there exists a minimal base $(x_1, \ldots, x_N)$ of T_∞ for which $\lambda_{(x,t)}$ can be written in the form given in (a). To prove this, first define a map $\lambda : A_\infty \to A_\infty[[t_1, \ldots, t_N]]$ by $\lambda(y) = \Sigma_{(i)} d_{i_1}^{(1)} d_{i_2}^{(2)} \ldots d_{i_N}^{(N)}(y) t_1^{i_1} t_2^{i_2} \ldots t_N^{i_N}$. The assumptions (a) and (b) of Remark (1.10) implies not only that λ is a homomorphism of Λ-algebras but also that, by the completeness of A_∞, λ induces an isomorphism $\rho : A_\infty \to \Lambda[[t_1, \ldots, t_N]]$ when followed by the natural homomorphism $A_\infty[[t_1, \ldots, t_N]] \to \Lambda[[t_1, \ldots, t_N]]$ whose kernel is generated by T_∞. Now, let $x_i = \rho^{-1}(t_i)$ for $1 \leqq i \leqq N$. Obviously, $T_\infty = (x_1, \ldots, x_N)A_\infty$ by the isomorphism ρ. I want to prove that $\lambda = \lambda_{(x,t)}$. Let $\lambda' = \lambda_{(x,t)}$. If $(u) = (u_1, \ldots, u_N)$ is any system of N indeterminates, then I shall write $\lambda_{(u)}$ (resp. $\lambda'_{(u)}$) for the homomorphism $A_\infty \to A_\infty[[u_1, u_2, \ldots, u_N]]$ obtained by composing λ (resp. λ') with the homomorphism of A_∞-algebras $A_\infty[[t_1, \ldots, t_N]] \to A_\infty[[u_1, u_2, \ldots, u_N]]$ which maps t_i into u_i for $1 \leqq i \leqq N$. I shall also write $\lambda_{(u)t}$ (resp. $\lambda'_{(u)t}$) for the trivial extension of $\lambda_{(u)}$ (resp. $\lambda'_{(u)}$) to $A_\infty[[t_1, \ldots, t_N]] \to A_\infty[[u_1, \ldots, u_N, t_1, \ldots, t_N]]$ which maps t_i into itself for $1 \leqq i \leqq N$. Then, by the properties of Hasse differentiations, we get

$$\lambda_{(u)t} \circ \lambda_{(t)} = \lambda_{(u+t)}$$

and

$$\lambda'_{(u)t} \circ \lambda'_{(t)} = \lambda'_{(u+t)},$$

where $(u + t) = (u_1 + t_1, u_2 + t_2, \ldots, u_N + t_N)$. By the selection of those x_j, we have $\lambda_{(u+t)}(z) \equiv \lambda'_{(u+t)}(z)$ modulo the ideal in $A_\infty[[u_1, \ldots, u_N, t_1, \ldots, t_N]]$ generated by T for all $z \in A_\infty$. [This follows from the same statement for (t) instead of $(u + t)$.] However, $\lambda_{(u)t}$ and $\lambda'_{(u)t}$ induce the same isomorphism of $A_\infty[[t_1, \ldots, t_N]]$ into $A_\infty[[u_1, \ldots, u_N, t_1, \ldots, t_N]]/(T)$, where (T) denotes the ideal generated by T. Therefore, we should get $\lambda_{(t)} = \lambda'_{(t)}$ or $\lambda = \lambda_{(x,t)}$.

Q.E.D.

Proof of (B). The equivalences are immediately seen between (1) and (2) and also between (3) and (4). The implication (2) $\Rightarrow$ (3) is trivial, as we may take $(y) = (x)$. I shall prove that (3) $\Rightarrow$ (2). Let ρ be the homomorphism of A_∞-algebras $A_\infty[[s_1, \ldots, s_N]] \rightarrow A_\infty[[t_1, \ldots, t_N]]$ such that $\rho(s_i) = \lambda_{(y,t)}(x_i) - x_i$, where $(s) = (s_1, \ldots, s_N)$ is another system of indeterminates. To see that ρ exists, it is enough that $(y_1, \ldots, y_N)A_\infty = (x_1, \ldots, x_N)A_\infty = T_\infty$ implies

$$(y_1 + t_1, \ldots, y_N + t_N)A_\infty[[t_1, \ldots, t_N]]$$
$$= (x_1 + \rho(s_1), \ldots, x_N + \rho(s_N)A_\infty[[t_1, \ldots, t_N]]$$

and that $\rho(s_i) \in (t_1, \ldots, t_N)A_\infty[[t_1, \ldots, t_N]]$. As a matter of fact, we can see immediately that ρ is an isomorphism. Moreover, we get $\lambda_{(y,t)} = \rho \circ \lambda_{(x,s)}$ by checking it only for each x_i $(1 \leqq i \leqq N)$, because any homomorphism of Λ-algebras $A_\infty \rightarrow A_\infty[[t_1, \ldots, t_N]]$ is determined by the image of any ideal base of T_∞. Now, the last assumption in (3) implies that the isomorphism ρ maps $A[[s_1, \ldots, s_N]]$ (subalgebra of $A_\infty[[s_1, \ldots, s_N]]$) into $A[[t_1, \ldots, t_N]]$. Then, clearly, ρ induces an isomorphism of $A[[s_1, \ldots, s_N]]$ to $A[[t_1, \ldots, t_N]]$. The equality $\lambda_{(y,t)} = \rho \circ \lambda_{(x,s)}$ then implies that $\lambda_{(y,t)}$ maps A into $A[[t_1, \ldots, t_N]]$ if and only if so does $\lambda_{(x,t)}$. Thus (2) $\Rightarrow$ (3). Finally, it is easy to see that (5) $\Rightarrow$ (4). Q.E.D.

NOTE. Let $\mathbf{C}$ be the complex number field, $A = \mathbf{C}[y](1 + (y)\mathbf{C}[y])^{-1}$ and $T = (y)A$. The T-adic completion of A is $\mathbf{C}[[y]]$, the formal power series of one variable. Let x be the Taylor expansion of $\log(1+y)$, which is an element of $\mathbf{C}[[y]]$, but not of A. Check that the homomorphism of $\mathbf{C}$-algebras $\lambda_{(x,t)}$ $\mathbf{C}[[y]] \rightarrow \mathbf{C}[[y, t]]$ maps A into $A[[t]]$, and hence there corresponds a differentiation of A into itself, which may be written as d/dx (and its iterations with suitable binomial coefficients).

§2. EXTENSIONS OF ALGEBRAS WITH CONDITION (T)

Proposition (2.1). Let A be a noetherian Λ-algebra with an ideal T such that (A, T) satisfies the condition (T) [cf. Definition (1.1)]. Let J be any ideal in A which is contained in T, $\hat{A}$ the J-adic completion of A, and $\hat{T} = T\hat{A}$. Let $\hat{N} = \bigcap_{i=1}^{\infty} \hat{T}^i$, $\hat{A}' = \hat{A}/\hat{N}$, and $\hat{T}' = \hat{T}\hat{A}'$. Then $(\hat{A}', \hat{T}')$ satisfies the condition (T).

Proof. There exists a homomorphism of Λ-algebra $\lambda = \lambda_{(x,t)}$: $A \to A[[t_1, \ldots, t_N]]$ such that $\lambda(x_i) = x_i + t_i$ for $1 \leqq i \leqq N$, where $T = (x_1, \ldots, x_N)A$. By Remark (1.5), $\lambda(z) - z \in (t)$ for all $z \in A$, where $(t) = (t_1, \ldots, t_N)A[[t_1, \ldots, t_N]]$. Hence $\lambda(J) \subset (J, t)$. Therefore, λ can be extended to a homomorphism of Λ-algebras $\hat{\lambda} : \hat{A} \to$ the (J, t)-adic completion of $A[[t_1, \ldots, t_N]]$. This last Λ-algebra is canonically isomorphic to $\hat{A}[[t_1, \ldots, t_N]]$. Clearly, $\hat{\lambda}$ maps $\hat{N}$ into the intersection of all powers $(\hat{T}, t)^\nu$ for positive integers ν. But this intersection is nothing but the ideal generated by $\hat{N}$. Hence $\hat{\lambda}$ induces a homomorphism $\hat{\lambda}' : \hat{A}' \to \hat{A}'[[t_1, \ldots, t_N]]$. It is clear that $\hat{T}' = (x_1, \ldots, x_N)\hat{A}'$ and $\hat{\lambda}'(x_j) = x_j + t_j$ for all j. Finally, the $\hat{T}'$-adic topology in $\hat{A}'$ is separated (although in general, the $\hat{T}$-adic topology in $\hat{A}$ is not separated).

Q.E.D.

Proposition (2.2). Let A be a noetherian Λ-algebra, and assume that (A, T) satisfies the condition (T) for an ideal T in A. Let y be an indeterminate over A. Then $(A[y], (T, y))$ satisfies the condition (T), where the polynomial ring $A[y]$ is canonically viewed as Λ-algebra.

Proof. Let $A' = A[y]$ and $T' = (T, y)A'$. It is easy to check the conditions (T.1) and (T.2) on (A', T'). Take a homomorphism of Λ-algebras $\lambda = \lambda_{(x,t)} : A \to A[[t_1, \ldots, t_N]]$, where $T = (x_1, x_2, \ldots, x_N)A$. Then λ extends to a homomorphism (uniquely)

$$\lambda_0' : A[y] \to A[[t_1, \ldots, t_N]][y, t_{N+1}]$$

by setting $\lambda_0'(y) = y + t_{N+1}$, where t_{N+1} is an indeterminate over $A[[t_1, \ldots, t_N]][y]$. Note that the $(t_1, \ldots, t_N, t_{N+1})$-adic completion of $A[[t_1, \ldots, t_N]][y, t_{N+1}]$ is canonically isomorphic to $A[y][[t_1, \ldots, t_{N+1}]]$. Thus λ_0' followed by this completion produces a homomorphism $\lambda' : A' \to A'[[t_1, \ldots, t_{N+1}]]$, such that $\lambda'(x_j) = x_j + t_j$ and $\lambda'(y) = y + t_{N+1}$.

Q.E.D.

Proposition (2.3). Let A be a noetherian Λ-algebra, and let T be an ideal in A. Suppose (A, T) satisfies the condition (T) and $(x_1, \ldots, x_N)$ is a base of T for which the condition (T.3) holds. Let n be an integer $1 \leqq n < N$, and assume that there exists a Λ-subalgebra A_0 of A such that $T \cap A_0 = (x_1, \ldots, x_n)A_0$ and the canonical homomorphism $A_0 \to A/(x_{n+1}, \ldots, x_N)A$ is bijective. Then (A_0, T_0) with $T_0 = T \cap A_0$ satisfies the condition (T), and if A is viewed as A_0-algebra, then (A, T_1) with $T_1 = (x_{n+1}, \ldots, x_N)A$ satisfies the condition (T).

Proof. The T-adic completion A_∞ of A is canonically isomorphic to $\Lambda[[x_1, \ldots, x_N]]$. The assumptions on A_0 imply that A_0 is the preimage of $\Lambda[[x_1, \ldots, x_n]]$ by the canonical homomorphism $A \to \Lambda[[x_1, \ldots, x_N]]$. In fact, $T \cap A_0 = (x_1, \ldots, x_n)A_0$ implies that the image of A_0 in A_∞ is contained in $\Lambda[[x_1, \ldots, x_n]]$, and the bijectivity of $A_0 \to A/(x_{n+1}, \ldots, x_n)A$ implies that A_0 is the maximal one with that property. Now, the conditions (T.1) and (T.2) are obviously satisfied by the pairs (A_0, T_0) and (A, T_1). To prove the condition (T.3), let $\lambda = \lambda_{(x,t)} : A \to A[[t_1, \ldots, t_N]]$ be the Λ-homomorphism in the condition (T.3) for (A, T). Then λ extends uniquely to a homomorphism of Λ-algebras $\lambda_\infty : A_\infty \to A_\infty[[t_1, \ldots, t_N]]$. This λ_∞ obviously maps $\Lambda[[x_1, \ldots, x_n]]$ into $\Lambda[[x_1, \ldots, x_n]][[t_1, \ldots, t_n]]$. Therefore, it maps A_0 into $\Lambda[[x_1, \ldots, x_n]][[t_1, \ldots, t_n]] \cap A[[t_1, \ldots, t_N]]$ which is $A_0[[t_1, \ldots, t_n]]$. Thus (A_0, T_0) satisfies (T.3). Next, consider the natural homomorphism $A[[t_1, \ldots, t_N]] \to A[[t_{n+1}, \ldots, t_N]]$ which annihilates the t_j for $1 \leqq j \leqq n$. Let $\lambda_1 : A \to A[[t_{n+1}, \ldots, t_N]]$ be the composition of $\lambda_{(x,t)}$ and this natural homomorphism. Clearly, $\lambda_1(x_j) = x_j$ for $1 \leqq j \leqq n$, and $\lambda_1(x_j) = x_j + t_j$ for $n + 1 \leqq j \leqq N$. Moreover, λ_1 extends to a homomorphism $A_\infty \to A_\infty[[t_{n+1}, \ldots, t_N]]$ which induces the identity in $\Lambda[[x_1, x_2, \ldots, x_n]]$. It follows that λ_1 induces the identity in A_0, that is, λ_1 is a homomorphism of A_0-algebras. Q.E.D.

Proposition (2.4). Let A be a noetherian Λ-algebra and assume that (A, T) with an ideal T satisfies the condition (T). Let $p : \Lambda \to \Lambda'$ be a homomorphism of rings, both noetherian. Let A' be the canonical image of $\Lambda' \otimes_\Lambda A$ into $\Lambda' \otimes_\Lambda A_\infty$ where A_∞ is the T-adic completion of A. Let $T' = TA'$. Then, when A' is viewed as Λ'-algebra, (A', T') satisfies the condition (T).

Remark. If $1 + T$ consists of units in A, then A' is isomorphic to $\Lambda' \otimes_\Lambda A$, but certainly not in general.

Proof. The canonical homomorphism $\Lambda' \otimes_\Lambda A \to \Lambda' \otimes_\Lambda A_\infty$ induces an isomorphism $\Lambda' \otimes_\Lambda (A/T) \to \Lambda' \otimes_\Lambda (A_\infty/TA_\infty)$ which is isomorphic to Λ' in a natural way. It follows that A'/T' is canonically isomorphic to Λ'. Similarly, $\Lambda' \otimes_\Lambda A \to \Lambda' \otimes_\Lambda A_\infty$ induces an isomorphism of $\Lambda' \otimes_\Lambda (A/T^\nu) \to \Lambda' \otimes_\Lambda (A_\infty/T^\nu A_\infty)$ for all positive integers ν, and therefore we can conclude that the T'-adic completion A'_∞ of A' is canonically isomorphic to the $T(\Lambda' \otimes_\Lambda A_\infty)$-adic completion of $\Lambda' \otimes_\Lambda A_\infty$. This last completion is $\Lambda'[[x_1, \ldots, x_N]]$ if $(x_1, \ldots, x_N)$ is a base of the ideal T which appears in the condition (T.3), or, $A_\infty = \Lambda[[x_1, \ldots, x_N]]$. Clearly, the natural homomorphism $\Lambda' \otimes_\Lambda \Lambda[[x_1, \ldots, x_N]] \to \Lambda'[[x_1, \ldots, x_N]]$ is injective. (Here, of course, the noetherian assumption on Λ is essential.) Therefore, it follows that the canonical homomorphism $A' \to A'_\infty$ is injective. Now, the condition (T.3) on (A', T') is the only fact to be established. Take a base $(x_1, \ldots, x_N)$ of T as above. Then $T' = (x_1, \ldots, x_N)A'$. There is a homomorphism of Λ-algebras $\lambda = \lambda_{(x,t)} : A \to A[[t_1, \ldots, t_N]]$ such that $\lambda(x_j) = x_j + t_j$ for $1 \leqq j \leqq N$. This naturally extends to a homomorphism of Λ'-algebras $\lambda' : \Lambda' \otimes_\Lambda A \to \Lambda' \otimes_\Lambda A[[t_1, \ldots, t_N]]$. On the other hand, λ extends to $A_\infty \to A_\infty[[t_1, \ldots, t_N]]$ and then to $\Lambda' \otimes_\Lambda A_\infty \to \Lambda' \otimes_\Lambda A_\infty[[t_1, \ldots, t_N]]$. Call this homomorphism of Λ'-algebras λ'_∞. Then λ' and λ'_∞ are compatible with each other in reference to the canonical homomorphism $A \to A_\infty$. It follows that λ' induces a homomorphism of Λ'-algebras $A' \to A'[[t_1, \ldots, t_N]]$ which obviously maps each x_j into $x_j + t_j$ for $1 \leqq j \leqq N$. Thus the condition (T.3) is verified on (A', T').

Q.E.D.

Proposition (2.5). Let A and B be noetherian Λ-algebras. Suppose (A, T) with an ideal T in A and (B, S) with an ideal S in B satisfy the condition (T). Let A_∞ (resp. B_∞) be the T-adic (resp. S-adic) completion of A(resp. B). Let C be the canonical image of $A \otimes_\Lambda B$ into $A_\infty \otimes_\Lambda B_\infty$, and let $R = (T, S)C$. Then (C, R) satisfies the condition (T).

Proof. Clearly, C/R is canonically isomorphic to Λ. Let $R' = (T, S)A \otimes_\Lambda B$ and $R'' = (T, S)A_\infty \otimes_\Lambda B_\infty$. Then we get a canonical isomorphism of Λ-algebras from the R'-adic completion of $A \otimes_\Lambda B$ to the R''-adic completion of $A_\infty \otimes_\Lambda B_\infty$ and, therefore, a canonical isomorphism from the R-adic completion C_∞ of C to the R''-adic completion of $A_\infty \otimes_\Lambda B_\infty$. This last completion is canonically isomorphic to $\Lambda[[x_1, \ldots, x_N, y_1, \ldots, y_M]]$, where $(x_1, \ldots, x_N)$ is a base of T and $(y_1, \ldots, y_M)$ is a base of S, which appear in the condition (T.3) for (A, T) and (B, S). Now the homomorphism

$\Lambda[[x_1, \ldots, x_N]] \otimes_\Lambda \Lambda[[y_1, \ldots, y_M]](= A_\infty \otimes_\Lambda B_\infty) \to \Lambda[[x_1, \ldots, x_N, y_1, \ldots, y_M]]$ is obviously injective. It follows that $C \to C_\infty$ is injective. Now, let us pass to the condition (T.3) on (C, R). We have $\lambda = \lambda_{(x,t)} : A \to A[[t_1, \ldots, t_N]]$, and $\mu = \lambda_{(y,u)} : B \to B[[u_1, \ldots, u_M]]$. Canonically λ and μ gives rise to a homomorphism of Λ-algebras

$$\nu : A \otimes_\Lambda B \to (A \otimes_\Lambda B)[[t_1, \ldots, t_N, u, \ldots, u_M]]$$

and also

$$\nu_\infty : A_\infty \otimes_\Lambda B_\infty \to (A_\infty \otimes_\Lambda B_\infty)[[t_1, \ldots, t_N, u_1, \ldots, u_M]],$$

where ν and ν_∞ are compatible with each other. It follows that ν induces a homomorphism of Λ-algebras: $C \to C[[t_1, \ldots, t_N, u_1, \ldots, u_M]]$, which sends each x_j to $x_j + t_j$ and each y_i to $y_i + u_i$.

Q.E.D.

Definition (2.6). Let A be a noetherian ring, T an ideal in A, A' an A-algebra, and T' an ideal in A'. Then I say that (A', T') is étale over (A, T) (or, an étale extension of (A, T)) if the following conditions are satisfied:

a. The A' is of finite type as an A-algebra, and
b. The canonical homomorphism $A \to A'$ induces an isomorphism $A/T^\nu \xrightarrow{\approx} A'/T'^\nu$ for all positive integers ν.

The condition (b) is equivalent to saying that if A_∞ (resp. A'_∞) denotes the T-adic (resp. T'-adic) completion of A (resp. A'), then

b*. There exists a canonical isomorphism $A_\infty \xrightarrow{\approx} A'_\infty$, which maps TA_∞ to $T'A'_\infty$.

Lemma (2.7). Let A be a noetherian ring, and T an ideal in A. Let $A' = A[y]/(f)A[y]$ where $A[y] = A[y_1, \ldots, y_n]$ with n indeterminates $y_j (1 \leqq j \leqq n)$ and $(f) = (f_1, \ldots, f_m)$ with $f_i \in A[y]$ $(1 \leqq i \leqq m)$. Let T' be an ideal in A' such that the canonical homomorphism $A \to A'$ induces a surjective homomorphism $A/T \to A'/T'$. Then the following two conditions are equivalent to each other:

1. The canonical homomorphisms

$$A/T^\nu \to A'/T'^\nu$$

is surjective for all integers $\nu \geqq 1$.
2. The $n \times n$-minors of the Jacobian $\partial(f_1, \ldots, f_m)/\partial(y_1, \ldots, y_n)$ generate the unit ideal in A'/T'.

Proof. We may strengthen the assumption on $A/T \to A'/T'$ by replacing T by the preimage of T' (which contains T). Namely, we shall assume that $A/T \to A'/T'$ is *bijective*. Note that, by this replacement of T, the conditions (1) and (2) remain equivalent, respectively. Moreover, the conditions remain equivalent if each y_j is replaced by $y_j - a_j$ with $a_j \in A (1 \leqq j \leqq n)$. Such a_j may be so chosen, by the bijection $A/T \to A'/T'$, that the preimage S in $A[y]$ of T' contains all the y_i. Then $S = (T, y_1, \ldots, y_n)A[y]$ by the isomorphism $A/T \overset{\approx}{\to} A'/T'$. Let A_∞(resp. A'_∞) be the T-adic (resp. T'-adic) completion of A(resp. A'). Then the S-adic completion of $A[y]$ is canonically isomorphic to $A_\infty[[y]]$ and A'_∞ to $A_\infty[[y]]/(f)A_\infty[[y]]$, where $(f) = (f_1, \ldots, f_m)$. It is clear that the condition (1) is equivalent to saying that the canonical homomorphism $A_\infty \to A'_\infty$ is surjective. (The bijectivity of $A/T \to A'/T'$ is here essential.) This surjectivity is then equivalent to the existence of $\xi_i \in TA_\infty$ for $1 \leqq i \leqq n$ such that $y_i - \xi_i \in (f)A_\infty[[y]]$ for all i. Since $\partial(y_1 - \xi_1, \ldots, y_n - \xi_n)/\partial(y_1, \ldots, y_n)$ is the unit $n \times n$-matrix, this condition implies that the $f_j (1 \leqq j \leqq m)$ and the $n \times n$-minors of $\partial(f_1, \ldots, f_m)/\partial(y_1, \ldots, y_n)$ generate the unit ideal in $A_\infty[[y]]$. Then the condition (2) follows immediately.

Conversely, let us assume (2). I shall prove that the subalgebra $A_\infty[[f]] = A_\infty[[f_1, \ldots, f_m]]$ of $A_\infty[[y]]$ is actually the full algebra. (Note that since $f_j \in S$ for all j, every power series in the f_j may be canonically identified as an element of $A_\infty[[y]]$.) This suffices for the condition (1), because then the homomorphism $A_\infty \to A'_\infty$ may be decomposed into $A_\infty \to A_\infty[[f]]/(f)A_\infty[[f]] \to A_\infty[[y]]/(f)A_\infty[[y]] = A'_\infty$. Now, to prove $A_\infty[[f]] = A_\infty[[y]]$, it suffices to show that, if R denotes the ideal $(T, f_1, \ldots, f_m)A[f]$, then the canonical homomorphism $A[f]/R^\nu \to A[y]S^\nu$ is surjective for all $\nu \geqq 1$. For each ν, this surjectivity is equivalent to the same of $A_P[f]/R^\nu A_P[f] \to A_P[y]/S^\nu A_P[y]$ for all prime ideals P in A containing T. This condition for a fixed P but for all $\nu \geqq 1$ is equivalent to saying that if

$B =$ the TA_P-adic completion of A_P, then the subalgebra $B[[f]]$ of $B[[y]]$ is the full subalgebra. Thus, in the proof of $A_\infty[[y]] = A_\infty[[f]]$, A may be assumed to be local, without any loss of generality. Thus assume A is local. The assumption (2) says that the $n \times n$-minors of $\partial(f_1, \ldots, f_m)/\partial(y_1, \ldots, y_n)$ generate the unit ideal in $A[y]$ modulo S, hence, the same in $A_\infty[[y]]$ modulo $SA_\infty[[y]] = (T, y_1, \ldots, y_n)A_\infty[[y]]$. Since $A_\infty[[y]]$ is local, one of the $n \times n$-minors must be a unit in $A_\infty[[y]]$, say $\partial(f_1, \ldots, f_n)/\partial(y_1, \ldots, y_n)$. (Here, necessarily, $n \leqq m$.) We have inclusions $A_\infty[[f_1, \ldots, f_n]] \subseteqq A_\infty[[f]] \subseteqq A_\infty[[y]]$. It suffices to show $A_\infty[[f_1, \ldots, f_n]] = A_\infty[[y]]$. This is a consequence of the fact that $\partial(f_1, \ldots, f_n)/\partial(y_1, \ldots, y_n)$ has unit determinant. In fact, take $\zeta_i \in A_\infty$ such that $f_i - \zeta_i \in (y)A_\infty[[y]]$, for $1 \leqq i \leqq n$, where necessarily $\zeta_i \in TA_\infty$. Then $A_\infty[[f_1, \ldots, f_n]] = A_\infty[[g_1, \ldots, g_n]]$ with $g_i = f_i - \zeta_i (1 \leqq i \leqq n)$, and $\partial(g_1, \ldots, g_n)/\partial(y_1, \ldots, y_n) = \partial(f_1, \ldots, f_n)/\partial(y_1, \ldots, y_n)$ which has unit determinant. This last fact implies that $g_i - \sum_j c_{ij} y_j \in (y)^2 A_\infty[[y]]$ with $c_{ij} \in A_\infty$ and $\det(c_{ij})$ is a unit in A_∞. Then directly seen is the equality $A_\infty[[g]] = A_\infty][[y]]$. Q.E.D.

Proposition (2.8). Let A be a noetherian Λ-algebra and T an ideal in A such that (A, T) satisfies the condition (T). Let (A', T') be an étale extension of (A, T). Then there exists an element $\xi' \in T'$ such that if A'' is the localization of A' by the powers of $1 + \xi'$ and if $T'' = T'A''$, then (A'', T'') is again an étale extension of (A, T) and it satisfies the condition (T).

Proof. The fact that (A'', T'') is an étale extension of (A, T) is clear by the definition, because $1 + \xi'$ with any $\xi' \in T'$ is a unit in the T'-adic completion A'_∞ of A'. We shall choose ξ' so that:

1. $TA'' = T''$.
2. The canonical homomorphism $A'' \to A''_\infty$ is injective, where A''_∞ denotes the T''-adic completion of A'' (which is isomorphic to the T-adic completion A_∞ of A).
3. If $A'' = A[y]/(f)A[y]$ where $(y) = (y_1, \ldots, y_n)$ and $(f) = (f_1, \ldots, f_m)$, then the $n \times n$-minors of $\partial(f_1, \ldots, f_m)/\partial(y_1, \ldots, y_n)$ generate the unit ideal in A''.

As is easily seen, it suffices to check the existence of such ξ' for each one of the three conditions (1)–(3). For (1), note that $A_\infty \to A'_\infty$ is bijective and hence $TA'_\infty = T'A'_\infty$, or, $TA' + T'^2 = T' + T'^2$.

Similarly, for (2). For (3), it suffices to note that, expressing A' in the form $A[z]/(g)A[z]$ with $(z) = (z_1, \ldots, z_n)$ and $(g) = (g_1, \ldots, g_m)$, the $n \times n$-minors of the Jacobian $\partial(g_1, \ldots, g_m)/\partial(z_1, \ldots, z_n)$ generate the unit ideal in A'/T'. But this is seen by Lemma (2.7). Now, under the additional assumptions (1)–(3), I shall prove that (A'', T'') satisfies the condition (T). For this, we have only to check (T.3). Let $\lambda = \lambda_{(x,t)}$ be the homomorphism of Λ-algebras $A \rightarrow A[[t]]$ in the condition (T.3) for (A, T), where $(x) = (x_1, \ldots, x_N)$ is a base of T and $(t) = (t_1, \ldots, t_N)$ is a system of N indeterminates. It extends uniquely to a homomorphism $\lambda_\infty : A_\infty \rightarrow A_\infty[[t]]$, where $A_\infty =$ the T-adic completion of A. By the assumptions, we shall identify A'' with a subalgebra of A_∞ in a canonical manner. Now, the lemma will be established if $\lambda_\infty(A'')$ is contained in $A''[[t]]$. Let us take an expression $A'' = A[y]/(f)A[y]$ as in (3). Let η_i be the image of y_i in A'' for $1 \leqq i \leqq n$. Let $\eta_i^* = \lambda_\infty(\eta_i)$, and I shall prove that $\eta_i^* \in A''[[t]]$ for all i $(1 \leqq i \leqq n)$. Let $f_j^*(y)$ be the image of f_j by $\lambda : A \rightarrow A[[t]]$, for $1 \leqq j \leqq m$. Then $f_j^*(\eta^*) = 0$ for $1 \leqq j \leqq n$, where $(\eta^*) = (\eta_1^*, \ldots, \eta_n^*)$. By the definition of λ_∞, $\eta_i^* - \eta_i \in (t)A_\infty[[t]]$. Since the $n \times n$-minors of $\partial(f_1, \ldots, f_m)/\partial(y_1, \ldots, y_n)$ generate the unit ideal in A'' by (3), the $n \times n$-minors of $\partial(f_1^*, \ldots, f_m^*)/\partial(y_1, \ldots, y_n)$ for $(y) = (\eta^*)$ generate the unit ideal in $A''[[t]][\eta^*]$. Let $S'' = (t_1, \ldots, t_N, \eta_1^* - \eta_1, \ldots, \eta_n^* - \eta_n)A''[[t]][\eta^*]$. Then, by Lemma (2.7), the canonical homomorphism from $A''[[t]]$ to the S''-adic completion of $A''[[t]][\eta^*]$ is surjective. (Check that $(t)A''[[t]] = S'' \cap A''[[t]]$.) By means of the canonical map from this completion to $A_\infty[[t]]$, it follows that the homomorphism from $A''[[t]]$ to the completion is bijective. Since $A''[[t]][\eta^*]$ is a subring of $A_\infty[[t]]$ and $S''A_\infty[[t]] = (t)A_\infty[[t]]$, the S''-adic topology is separated and then the above result shows that $A''[[t]] \rightarrow A''[[t]][\eta^*]$ is bijective. Namely, $\eta_j^* \in A''[[t]]$ for all i, which shows that $\lambda_\infty(A'') \subset A''[[t]]$. Thus the condition (T.3) is verified for (A'', T'').

Q.E.D.

Lemma (2.9). Let A be a noetherian ring and T an ideal in A. Let (A', T') and (A'', T'') be two étale extensions of (A, T). Then $(A' \otimes_A A'', (T' + T''))$ is an étale extension of (A, T), where $(T' + T'')$ denotes the ideal in $A' \otimes_A A''$ generated by the image of T' and of T'' by the canonical homomorphisms $A' \rightarrow A' \otimes_A A''$ and $A'' \rightarrow A' \otimes_A A''$.

Proof. We have a canonical isomorphism $A/T^{\nu} \xrightarrow{\approx} (A'/T'^{\nu}) \otimes_A (A''/T''^{\nu})$ by the assumptions. Consider the natural homomorphism $\rho_{\nu} : A' \otimes_A A'' \to (A'/T'^{\nu}) \otimes_A (A''/T''^{\nu})$ for each $\nu \geqq 1$. I want to prove $\mathrm{Ker}(\rho_{\nu}) = (T' + T'')^{\nu}$ for every ν. It is clear that $\mathrm{Ker}(\rho_{\nu})$ contains the canonical images in $A' \otimes_A A''$ of $T'^{\nu} \otimes_A A''$ and of $A' \otimes_A T''^{\nu}$. Therefore, it contains the canonical images in $A' \otimes_A A''$ of $T'^{\alpha} \otimes_A T''^{\beta}$ if $\max(\alpha, \beta) \geqq \nu$. Let (p, q) be any pair of integers $\geqq 0$ such that $p + q = \nu$. Then $T'^{p} \otimes_A T''^{q} = (T^{p}A' + T'^{\nu}) \otimes_A (T^{q}A'' + T''^{\nu})$. However, $T^{p}A' \otimes_A T^{q}A''$ has the same image in $A' \otimes_A A''$ as $T^{p+q}A' \otimes_A A'' = T^{\nu}A' \otimes_A A''$. Therefore, we conclude that $\mathrm{Ker}(\rho_{\nu})$ contains the canonical image of $T'^{p} \otimes_A T''^{q}$ for all $p + q = \nu$, $p \geqq 0$ and $q \geqq 0$. This is the same as saying $\mathrm{Ker}(\rho_{\nu})$ contains $(T' + T'')^{\nu}$. Since $(A'/T'^{\nu}) \otimes_A (A''/T''^{\nu})$ is canonically isomorphic to $(A/T^{\nu}) \otimes_A (A/T^{\nu})$ which is isomorphic to A/T^{ν}, we get a canonical homomorphism, induced by ρ_{ν},

$$\bar{\rho}_{\nu} : A' \otimes_A A''/(T' + T'')^{\nu} \to A/T^{\nu}.$$

This homomorphism composed with the canonical homomorphism

$$A/T^{\nu} \to A' \otimes_A A''/(T' + T'')^{\nu}$$

is the identity of A/T^{ν}. Since this last homomorphism is surjective, we conclude that $\mathrm{Ker}(\rho_{\nu}) = (T' + T'')^{\nu}$. Namely, $\bar{\rho}_{\nu}$ is bijective for all $\nu \geqq 1$. Q.E.D.

Definition (2.10). A noetherian ring A with an ideal T in A, that is, the pair (A, T), is said to be Henselian if for any étale extension (A', T') of (A, T) there exists a unique homomorphism of A-algebras $A' \to A$.

Remark (2.11). If (A, T) is Henselian then the canonical homomorphism $A \to A_{\infty}$ is injective, where A_{∞} denotes the T-adic completion of A. In fact, let A' be the image of A in A_{∞}, and $T' = TA'$. Then it is clear that (A', T') is an étale extension of (A, T). Hence there exists a homomorphism of A-algebras: $A' \to A$. Hence $A \to A'$ must be injective, and therefore it is bijective. Moreover, *if* (A, T) *is Henselian, then every element of the form* $1 + x$ *with* $x \in T$ *must be a unit in* A.

Lemma (2.12). Given a noetherian ring A with an ideal T in A, there exists an A-algebra $\tilde{A}$ such that:

a. If (A', T') is any étale extension of (A, T), then there exists a unique homomorphism of A-algebras $A' \to \tilde{A}$ such that T' is the preimage of $T\tilde{A}$,
b. Every element of $\tilde{A}$ is in the image of the homomorphism $A' \to \tilde{A}$ for some étale extension (A', T') of (A, T), and
c. $(\tilde{A}, T\tilde{A})$ is Henselian.

Proof. Note that if (A', T') is any étale extension of (A, T), then the canonical homomorphism $A \to A'$ induces an isomorphism $A_\infty \to A'_\infty$, where A_∞ (resp. A'_∞) denotes the T (resp. T')-adic completion of A (resp. A'). By this means, we get a canonical homomorphism of A-algebras $A' \to A_\infty$. It is easy to see that this is the only homomorphism of A-algebras such that T' is the preimage of TA_∞. If (A'', T'') is another étale extension of (A, T), then $(A' \otimes_A A'', (T' + T''))$ is also an étale extension of (A, T) by Lemma (2.9), and the canonical homomorphism $A' \otimes_A A'' \to A_\infty$ is induced by the canonical homomorphisms $A' \to A_\infty$ and $A'' \to A_\infty$. Therefore, if $\tilde{A}$ is the union of the canonical images in A_∞ of A' for all étale extensions (A', T') of (A, T), then $\tilde{A}$ is a subring of A_∞. Here, in the definition of $\tilde{A}$, I can take only those étale extensions (A', T') of (A, T) such that the canonical homomorphism $A' \to A_\infty$ is injective. Moreover, we can then prove that $\tilde{A}$ is then the union of all the localizations $A^* = A'(1 + T')^{-1}$ for such (A', T') and that A_∞ is faithfully flat over A^*. Or equivalently, $\mathfrak{a}^*A_\infty \cap A^* = \mathfrak{a}^*$ for every ideal $\mathfrak{a}^*$ in A^*. (All that must be checked is that the additional condition implies that T' is contained in the Jacobson radical of A^*.) Since A_∞ is noetherian, it follows that $\tilde{A}$ is noetherian and that A_∞ is faithfully flat over $\tilde{A}$. It follows that $T\tilde{A} = TA_\infty \cap \tilde{A}$ and that the $T\tilde{A}$-adic completion of $\tilde{A}$ is canonically isomorphic to A_∞. The properties (a)–(c) of this $(\tilde{A}, T\tilde{A})$ can be easily derived from the above results.

Q.E.D.

Remark (2.13). In view of Remark (2.11), we can see the uniqueness of $(\tilde{A}, T\tilde{A})$, for a given (A, T), under the properties (a), (b) and (c) in Lemma (2.12).

Definition (2.14). The pair $(\tilde{A}, \tilde{T})$ with $T\tilde{A} = \tilde{T}$ in Lemma (2.12) is called the Henselization of (A, T).

Proposition (2.15). Let A be a noetherian Λ-algebra, and T an ideal in A. Let $(\widetilde{A}, \widetilde{T})$ be the Henselization of (A, T). If (A, T) satisfies the condition (T), then so does $(\widetilde{A}, \widetilde{T})$.

Proof. The conditions (T.1) and (T.2) are immediate for $(\widetilde{A}, \widetilde{T})$. [See Remark (2.11).] To prove (T.3) for $(\widetilde{A}, \widetilde{T})$, let $\lambda = \lambda_{(x,t)} : A \rightarrow A[[t]]$ be the homomorphism in (T.3) for (A, T), where $(x) = (x_1, \ldots, x_N)$ is a base of T and $(t) = (t_1, \ldots, t_N)$ is a system of N indeterminates. Let (A', T') be any étale extension of (A, T) such that $A' \rightarrow A_\infty$ is injective and let us identify A' with its canonical image in the T-adic completion A_∞ of A. Let $\lambda_\infty : A_\infty \rightarrow A_\infty[[t]]$ be the extension of λ. Then, by the proof of Proposition (2.8), $\lambda_\infty(A')$ is contained in $A''[[t]]$, where A'' is the localization of A' by the powers of $1 + \xi'$ with a suitable $\xi' \in T'$. $\widetilde{A}$ being obtained as the union of such A'' (and also of such A'), $\lambda_\infty(\widetilde{A})$ is contained in $\widetilde{A}[[t]]$. Hence, we get the condition (T.3) for $(\widetilde{A}, \widetilde{T})$. Q.E.D.

§3. AUTOMORPHISMS OF A CERTAIN FORMAL SCHEME

Let Λ be a noetherian ring, A a noetherian Λ-algebra and T an ideal in A. Throughout this section, I shall assume that

$$(A, T) \textit{ satisfies the condition } (T). \tag{3.1}$$

Thus we have a homomorphism of Λ-algebras $\lambda = \lambda_{(x,t)} : A \rightarrow A[[t]]$ such that $\lambda(x_j) = x_j + t_j$ for $1 \leqq j \leqq N$, where $(x) = (x_1, \ldots, x_N)$ is a base of T and $(t) = (t_1, \ldots, t_N)$ is a system of N indeterminates. I choose and fix, once and for all, such (x) and λ. Let $Y = \mathrm{Spec}(\Lambda)$ and $Z = \mathrm{Spec}(A)$. Let $\epsilon : Y \rightarrow Z$ (resp. $\pi : Z \rightarrow Y$) be the canonical morphism associated with $A \rightarrow A/T \cong \Lambda$ (resp. with $\Lambda \rightarrow A$). Then we have $\pi \circ \epsilon = id_Y$.

Let us then pick, once and for all, *an ideal E in A which is contained in T*. Consider the ideal sheaf (coherent) on Z generated by E, say $\mathbf{E}$, and the birational blowing-up of $\mathbf{E}$, say $p : \tilde{Z} \rightarrow Z$, where $\tilde{Z} = \mathrm{Proj}(S_A(E))$ with the graded A-algebra $S_A(E) = \oplus_{\nu=0}^{\infty} E^\nu$. ($E^\circ = A$ and $E^\nu =$ the νth power of the ideal E in A.) Then:

$$\tilde{Z} = \bigcup_{i=0}^{\alpha} \mathrm{Spec}(\widetilde{A}_i), \tag{3.2}$$

where $\tilde{A}_i = A[e_0/e_i, e_1/e_i, \ldots, e_\alpha/e_i]$ *with an ideal base* $(e_0, e_1, \ldots, e_\alpha)$ *of* E. Here $\tilde{A}_i$ with the expression should be understood as a subring of the ring of fractions of A by the positive powers of e_i.

Let $\mathbf{E}$ (resp. $\tilde{\mathbf{E}}$) be the ideal sheaf on Z (resp. $\tilde{Z}$) generated by E by the canonical morphism π (resp. p). I shall now choose, once for all, *a coherent ideal sheaf* $\tilde{\mathbf{H}}$ *on* $\tilde{Z}$ *which is contained in* $\tilde{\mathbf{E}}$. Let $\tilde{Z}(\nu)$ be the subscheme of $\tilde{Z}$ defined by $\tilde{\mathbf{H}}^{\nu+1}$ for each $\nu \geqq 0$, and $\tilde{Z}(\infty)$ the $\tilde{\mathbf{H}}$-adic completion of $\tilde{Z}$ which is a formal scheme with the same underlying topological space as all the $\tilde{Z}(\nu)$. Let $\tilde{\mathbf{H}}(\infty)$ be the ideal sheaf on $\tilde{Z}(\infty)$ generated by $\tilde{\mathbf{H}}$, so that $\tilde{Z}(\nu)$ may be canonically identified with the subscheme of $\tilde{Z}(\infty)$ defined by $\tilde{\mathbf{H}}(\infty)^{\nu+1}$.

Let us now investigate the structure of the sheaf of those automorphisms of $\tilde{Z}(\infty)$ over Y which induce the identity in $\tilde{Z}(\nu)$ for a given integer $\nu \geqq 1$. I shall choose an ideal base $(e_0, e_1, \ldots, e_\alpha)$ of E, so that $\tilde{Z}$ is expressed as in (3.2). The ideal sheaf $\tilde{\mathbf{H}}$ on $\tilde{Z}$ is generated by an ideal $\tilde{H}_i$ in $\tilde{A}_i$ within the open subscheme $\mathrm{Spec}(\tilde{A}_i)$. Let $\tilde{A}_i(\nu) = \tilde{A}_i/\tilde{H}_i^{\nu+1}$ for each $\nu \geqq 0$, and $\tilde{A}_i(\infty)$ the $\tilde{H}_i$-adic completion of $\tilde{A}_i$. Let $\tilde{H}_i(\infty) = \tilde{H}_i\tilde{A}_i(\infty)$. I shall first examine the group of automorphisms of $\tilde{A}_i(\infty)$ which induce the identity in $\tilde{A}_i(\nu)$ for each positive integer ν. I take, in what follows, a slightly more general situation in which $\tilde{A}_i$ is replaced by its ring of fractions by the positive powers of an arbitrary element d of $\tilde{A}_i$. *Let us pick and fix* $d \in \tilde{A}_i$, *and let* $\tilde{A}'_i$ *denote the ring of fractions of* $\tilde{A}_i$ *by the powers of* d. Let $\tilde{H}'_i = \tilde{H}_i\tilde{A}'_i$ and $\tilde{A}'_i(\nu) = \tilde{A}'_i/\tilde{H}'^{\nu+1}_i$ for $\nu \geqq 0$. Let $\tilde{A}'_i(\infty)$ be the $\tilde{H}'_i$-adic completion of $\tilde{A}'_i$ and $\tilde{H}'_i(\infty) = \tilde{H}'_i\tilde{A}'_i(\infty) = \tilde{H}_i\tilde{A}'_i(\infty) = \tilde{H}_i(\infty)\tilde{A}'_i(\infty)$. In this last equality, I refer to the canonical homomorphism $\tilde{A}_i(\infty) \to \tilde{A}'_i(\infty)$ induced by $\tilde{A}_i \to \tilde{A}'_i$. In what follows, *I shall exclude those cases in which* $\tilde{A}'_i(\infty)$ *is the zero ring.*

Recall the homomorphism $\lambda : A \to A[[t]]$. By means of the canonical homomorphisms $A \to \tilde{A}'_i \to \tilde{A}'_i(\infty)$, λ gives rise to a homomorphism $A \to \tilde{A}'_i(\infty)[[t]]$. Let $(\xi) = (\xi_1, \xi_2, \ldots, \xi_N) \in \Pi^N \tilde{H}'_i(\infty)$. Then, by the completeness of $\tilde{A}'_i(\infty)$, there exists a unique homomorphism $\tilde{A}'_i(\infty)[[t]] \to \tilde{A}'_i(\infty)$ which induces the identity in $\tilde{A}'_i(\infty)$ and maps t_j to ξ_j for all $j (1 \leqq j \leqq N)$. By composing this homomorphism with the preceding one, I get a homomorphism $A \to \tilde{A}'_i(\infty)$. *This homomorphism associated with each* $(\xi) \in \Pi^N \tilde{H}'_i(\infty)$ *will be denoted by* $\lambda'_i(\xi)$.

Lemma (3.3). Let B be a noetherian ring, and I an ideal in B. Suppose B is I-adically complete. Let σ be a homomorphism of B

into itself which induces automorphisms of B/I^2 and B/I. Then σ is an automorphism.

Proof. Let $\bar{B} = B/I$ and $X = I/I^2$. Then σ induces an automorphism of the ring $\bar{B}$ and an automorphism of the $\bar{B}$-module X. Let X_ν be the νth symmetric tensor power of X, for every positive integer ν. Then we have a canonical surjective homomorphism of $\bar{B}$-modules $\beta_\nu : X_\nu \to I^\nu/I^{\nu+1}$. We have an endomorphism of $I^\nu/I^{\nu+1}$, say δ_ν, which is induced by σ. The automorphism δ_1 in X canonically extends to an automorphism of X_ν, and this extension, say δ_ν^*, induces δ_ν, in a natural manner. I shall first show that δ_ν is an automorphism. For this, it suffices that $\delta_\nu^*(\mathrm{Ker}(\beta_\nu)) = \mathrm{Ker}(\beta_\nu)$. Clearly, $\delta_\nu^*(\mathrm{Ker}(\beta_\nu)) \subset \mathrm{Ker}(\beta_\nu)$ because δ_ν^* induces δ_ν, or equivalently, $\mathrm{Ker}(\beta_\nu) \subset \delta_\nu^{*-1}(\mathrm{Ker}(\beta_\nu))$. By applying δ_ν^{*-1} repeatedly, we get a monotone increasing sequence of $\bar{B}$-submodules of X_ν. Since X_ν is noetherian, this sequence must be stationary. Then the equality $\mathrm{Ker}(\beta_\nu) = \delta_\nu^*(\mathrm{Ker}(\beta_\nu))$ follows immediately. Thus σ induces an automorphism of $I^\nu/I^{\nu+1}$ for all $\nu \geqq 0$. By the I-adic completeness of B, it is now easy to show that σ is bijective. Q.E.D.

Lemma (3.4). If $(\xi) \in \Pi^N \tilde{H}_i'(\infty)^{\nu+1}$ with $\nu \geqq 2$, then the homomorphism $\lambda_i'(\xi) : A \to \tilde{A}_i'(\infty)$ extends uniquely to an automorphism $\tilde{\lambda}_i'(\xi)$ of $\tilde{A}_i'(\infty)$, which induces the identity in $\tilde{A}_i'(\nu-1)$. Moreover, the automorphism $\tilde{\lambda}_i'(\xi)$ induces the identity in $\tilde{A}_i'(\nu)$ if and only if

$$\sum_{j=1}^{N} \Delta_{p,q}^{(j)} \xi_j \equiv 0 \bmod E^2 \tilde{H}_i'(\infty)^{\nu+1} \tag{3.5}$$

for all (p, q), where

$$\Delta_{p,q}^{(j)} = e_q\left(\frac{\partial e_p}{\partial x_j}\right) - e_p\left(\frac{\partial e_q}{\partial x_j}\right) \qquad \text{for } 0 \leqq p,\, q \leqq \alpha$$

with the ideal base (x) of T and $(e_0, e_1, \ldots, e_\alpha)$ of E.

Proof. Recall that the derivations $\partial/\partial x_j (1 \leqq j \leqq N)$ of A are such that, for each $a \in A$, $\lambda(a) = a + \sum_{j=1}^N (\partial a/\partial x_j)t_j + \delta(a)$ with $\delta(a) \in (t)^2 A[[t]]$. Hence, by the definition of $\lambda_i'(\xi)$,

$$\lambda_i'(\xi)(a) \equiv a + \sum_{j=1}^{N} \left(\frac{\partial a}{\partial x_j}\right) \xi_j \bmod \tilde{H}_i'(\infty)^{2(\nu+1)}$$

for every $a \in A$. In particular, for $0 \leqq p \leqq \alpha$,

$$\lambda_i'(\xi)(e_p) \equiv e_p + \sum_{j=1}^{N} \left(\frac{\partial e_p}{\partial x_j}\right) \xi_j \bmod \tilde{H}_i'(\infty)^{2(\nu+1)}.$$

Now, e_i is not a zero-divisor in $\tilde{A}_i = A[e_0/e_i, \ldots, e_\alpha/e_i]$. Since $\tilde{A}_i'(\infty)$ is obtained from $\tilde{A}_i$ by localization and completion, *e_i is not a zero-divisor of $\tilde{A}_i'(\infty)$*. (Note that I have excluded once for all the cases in which $\tilde{A}_i'(\infty)$ is the zero ring.) Therefore, the above congruence is equivalent to:

$$\frac{\lambda_i'(\xi)(e_p)}{e_i} \equiv \frac{e_p}{e_i} + \sum_{j=1}^{N} \left(\frac{\partial e_p}{\partial x_j}\right)\left(\frac{\xi_j}{e_i}\right) \bmod e_i^{-1}\tilde{H}_i'(\infty)^{2(\nu+1)}$$

In particular, if $p = i$, the right-hand side is a unit in $\tilde{A}_i'(\infty)$. Hence, by taking the reciprocal, I get

$$\frac{e_i}{\lambda_i'(\xi)(e_i)} \equiv 1 - \sum_{j=1}^{N} \left(\frac{\partial e_i}{\partial x_j}\right)\left(\frac{\xi_j}{e_i}\right) \bmod e_i^{-2}\tilde{H}_i'(\infty)^{2(\nu+1)}$$

By multiplying the above two congruences,

$$\frac{\lambda_i'(\xi)(e_p)}{\lambda_i'(\xi)(e_i)} - \frac{e_p}{e_i} \equiv \sum_{j=1}^{N} \left(\frac{\partial e_p}{\partial x_j}\right)\left(\frac{\xi_j}{e_i}\right)$$
$$- \frac{e_p}{e_i} \sum_{j=1}^{N} \left(\frac{\partial e_i}{\partial x_j}\right)\left(\frac{\xi_j}{e_i}\right) \bmod [\{e_i^{-1}\tilde{H}_i'(\infty)^{\nu+1}\}^2 + e_i^{-1}\tilde{H}_i'(\infty)^{2(\nu+1)}]. \quad (3.6)$$

Since $\nu \geqq 2$, the ideal in [ ] is contained in $\tilde{H}_i'(\infty)^{\nu+2}$. Moreover, the right-hand side of (3.6) is zero $\bmod e_i^{-1}\tilde{H}_i'(\infty)^{\nu+1}$, hence, $\bmod \tilde{H}_i'(\infty)^{\nu}$. Thus we see that the homomorphism $\lambda_i'(\xi)$ can be extended to a homomorphism $\tilde{A}_i = A[e_0/e_i, \ldots, e_\alpha/e_i] \rightarrow \tilde{A}_i'(\infty)$ in a unique way, and that this extension induces the identity of $\tilde{A}_i$ modulo $\tilde{H}_i'(\infty)^{\nu}$. This last fact is enough to prove that the image of the element d of $\tilde{A}_i$ by the extension is a unit (unless $\tilde{A}_i'(\infty)$ is the zero ring), so that it extends further to a homomorphism $\tilde{A}_i' \rightarrow \tilde{A}_i'(\infty)$. Moreover, since d and its image are both units in $\tilde{A}_i'(\infty)$, I get:

(3.7) The extension $\tilde{A}_i \rightarrow \tilde{A}_i'(\infty)$ of $\lambda_i'(\xi)$ induces the identity in $\tilde{A}_i \bmod \tilde{H}_i'(\nu^*)$, if and only if the same remains true when $\tilde{A}_i$ is replaced by $\tilde{A}_i'$, where ν^* is either ν or $\nu + 1$.

Take the case of $\nu^* = \nu$, then we can conclude that the extension $\tilde{A}'_i \to \tilde{A}'_i(\infty)$ is continuous with respect to $\tilde{H}'_i(\infty)$-adic topology. Therefore, it extends, again uniquely, to a homomorphism $\tilde{A}'_i(\infty) \to \tilde{A}'_i(\infty)$ which induces the identity in $\tilde{A}'_i(\infty)/\tilde{H}'_i(\infty)^\nu$ where $\nu \geqq 2$. By Lemma (3.3), this must be an automorphism of $\tilde{A}'_i(\infty)$. Denote this by $\tilde{\lambda}'_i(\xi)$. The first half of the Lemma (3.4) is now established. To prove the second half, observe the congruence (3.6). In view of (3.7), $\tilde{\lambda}'_i(\xi)$ induces the identity in $\tilde{A}'_i(\nu)$ if and only if the second side of (3.6) is zero modulo $\tilde{H}'_i(\infty)^{\nu+1}$ for all $p (0 \leqq p \leqq \alpha)$. By multiplying this congruence by e_i^2, we get (3.5). The converse is obtained by the fact that $e_i\tilde{A}'_i(\alpha) = E\tilde{A}'_i(\infty) \supseteq \tilde{H}'_i(\infty)$ and that e_i is not a zero divisor in $\tilde{A}'_i(\infty)$. Q.E.D.

Lemma (3.8). Let (ξ) and (η) be two elements in $\Pi^N\tilde{H}'_i(\infty)^{\nu+1}$, with $\nu \geqq 2$. Then $\tilde{\lambda}'_i(\eta) \circ \tilde{\lambda}'_i(\xi) = \tilde{\lambda}'_i(\eta + \tilde{\lambda}'_i(\eta)(\xi))$ *where* $\tilde{\lambda}'_i(\eta)(\xi) = (\tilde{\lambda}'_i(\eta)(\xi_1), \tilde{\lambda}'_i(\eta)(\xi_2), \ldots, \tilde{\lambda}'_i(\eta)(\xi_N)) \in \Pi^N\tilde{H}'_i(\infty)^{\nu+1}$.

Proof. Since $\tilde{\lambda}'_i(\eta)$ induces the identity in $\tilde{A}'_i(1)$ at least, $\tilde{\lambda}'_i(\eta)(\tilde{H}'_i(\infty)) = \tilde{H}'_i(\infty)$ and hence $\tilde{\lambda}'_i(\eta)(\xi) \in \Pi^N\tilde{H}'_i(\infty)^{\nu+1}$ is clear. To prove the equality of the lemma, it suffices, by Lemma (3.4), that the composition of $\lambda'_i(\xi) : A \to \tilde{A}'_i(\infty)$ and the automorphism $\tilde{\lambda}'_i(\eta) : \tilde{A}'_i(\infty) \to \tilde{A}'_i(\infty)$ is equal to $\lambda'_i(\eta + \tilde{\lambda}'_i(\eta)(\xi)) : A \to \tilde{A}'_i(\infty)$. Take any element $y \in A$. Let us recall $\lambda = \lambda_{(x,t)} : A \to A[[t]]$, by means of which λ'_i and $\tilde{\lambda}'_i$ are defined, and let us write $\lambda(y) = \Sigma_I y_I t^I$, where I runs through the set of all N-tuples I of nonnegative integers and t^I means $t_1^{i_1}t_2^{i_2} \ldots t_N^{i_N}$ if $I = (i_1, i_2, \ldots, i_N)$. Then $\lambda'_i(\xi)(y)$ can then be written as a convergent series $\Sigma_I y_I \xi^I$ in $\tilde{A}'_i(\infty)$ with respect to $\tilde{H}'_i(\infty)$-adic topology. Let us write $\lambda(y_I) = \Sigma_J y_{IJ} t^J$ where, again, J runs through the same set as I did. Then $\lambda'_i(\eta)(y_I) = \Sigma_J y_{IJ}\eta^J$ which is a convergent series in $\tilde{A}'_i(\infty)$. By the continuity of $\tilde{\lambda}'_i(\eta)$ and in view of the convergence,

$$\tilde{\lambda}'_i(\eta)(\lambda'_i(\xi)(y)) = \Sigma_I \tilde{\lambda}'_i(\eta)(y_I)(\tilde{\lambda}'_i(\eta)(\xi))^I = \Sigma_{I,J} y_{IJ}\eta^J(\tilde{\lambda}'_i(\eta)(\xi))^I$$

We know that $\Sigma_{I,J} y_{IJ} t^I u^J = \Sigma_I y_I (t+u)^I$ if $(u) = (u_1, \ldots, u_N)$ is another system of N indeterminates. Therefore, $\tilde{\lambda}'_i(\eta)(\tilde{\lambda}'_i(\xi)(y)) = \Sigma_I y_I(\eta + \tilde{\lambda}'_i(\eta)(\xi))^I = \lambda'_i(\eta + \tilde{\lambda}'_i(\eta)(\xi))(y)$. Q.E.D.

Lemma (3.9). Let $(\eta) \in \Pi^N\tilde{H}'_i(\infty)^{\nu+1}$ with $\nu \geqq 2$. Then for every $\zeta \in \tilde{H}'_i(\infty)^{\mu+1}$ with $\mu \geqq 0$, we have $\tilde{\lambda}'_i(\eta)(\zeta) \equiv \zeta \bmod \tilde{H}'_i(\infty)^{\nu+\mu}$.

Proof. Since ζ is a sum of elements of the form $\zeta_1\zeta_2 \ldots \zeta_{\mu+1}$ with $\zeta_p \in \tilde{H}'_i(\infty)$ for $1 \leqq p \leqq \mu + 1$, it suffices to prove the congruence for the case $\zeta = \zeta_1\zeta_2 \cdots \zeta_{\mu+1}$ with $\zeta_p \in \tilde{H}'_i(\infty)$. Then, by Lemma (3.4), $\tilde{\lambda}'_i(\eta)(\zeta_p) \equiv \zeta_p \bmod \tilde{H}'_i(\infty)^\nu$ for all p. It follows immediately, $\tilde{\lambda}'_i(\eta)(\Pi_p\zeta_p) \equiv \Pi_p\zeta_p \bmod \tilde{H}'_i(\infty)^\mu\tilde{H}'_i(\infty)^\nu$. Q.E.D.

Lemma (3.10). Let $(\xi) \in \Pi^N\tilde{H}'_i(\infty)^{\nu+1}$ with $\nu \geqq 2$. Then there exists $(\eta) \in \Pi^N\tilde{H}'_i(\infty)^{\nu+1}$ such that $\tilde{\lambda}'_i(\xi) \circ \tilde{\lambda}'_i(\eta)$ = the identity automorphism of $\tilde{A}'_i(\infty)$.

Proof. By Lemma (3.8), the last equality is equivalent to $\tilde{\lambda}'_i(\xi)(\eta) = -\xi$. If we are given (ξ), the existence of (η) with this property is asserted. However, this is clear because $\tilde{\lambda}'_i(\xi)$ is an automorphism of $\tilde{A}'_i(\infty)$ which maps $\tilde{H}'_i(\infty)$ surjectively to itself. Q.E.D.

Proposition (3.11). Let $\mathrm{Aut}_\nu = \mathrm{Aut}_\nu(\tilde{A}'_i(\infty))$ be the group of those automorphisms of the Λ-algebra $\tilde{A}'_i(\infty)$ which induce the identity in $\tilde{A}'_i(\nu)$, where $\nu \geqq 2$. Let $G_\nu = G_\nu(\tilde{A}'_i(\infty))$ be the set of those $(\xi) \in \Pi^N\tilde{H}'_i(\infty)^3$ such that $\tilde{\lambda}'_i(\xi) \in \mathrm{Aut}_\nu$. Then we have:

a. G_ν is an $\tilde{A}'_i(\infty)$-submodule of $\Pi^N\tilde{H}'_i(\infty)^{\nu+1}$ containing $\Pi^N\tilde{H}'_i(\infty)^{\nu+2}$ and
b. $\tilde{\lambda}'_i : G_\nu \to \mathrm{Aut}_\nu$, which sends (ξ) to $\tilde{\lambda}'_i(\xi)$, is injective and the image is a subgroup.
c. Let $G^*_\nu = \tilde{\lambda}'_i(G_\nu)$. Then, for every $\mu > \nu \geqq 2$, G^*_μ is a normal subgroup of G^*_ν.

Proof. Take $(\xi) \in \Pi^N\tilde{H}'_i(\infty)^3$. Let $x'_j \in \tilde{A}'_i(\infty)$ be the canonical image of x_j for $1 \leqq j \leqq N$, where $(x) = (x_1, \ldots, x_N)$ is the chosen base of the ideal T in A. Then $\tilde{\lambda}'_i(\xi)(x'_j) = x'_j + \xi_j$ for $1 \leqq j \leqq N$. Therefore, if $\tilde{\lambda}'_i(\xi) \in \mathrm{Aut}_\nu$, then $\xi_j \in \tilde{H}'_i(\infty)^{\nu+1}$ (at least) for all j $(1 \leqq j \leqq N)$. Thus, in proving the proposition, it suffices to consider $(\xi) \in \Pi^N\tilde{H}'_i(\infty)^{\nu+1}$. For such (ξ), $\tilde{\lambda}'_i(\xi) \in \mathrm{Aut}_\nu$ if and only if (ξ) satisfies the linear congruence equations (3.5), by Lemma (3.4). It follows immediately that G_ν is *an* $\tilde{A}'_i(\infty)$*-submodule* of $\Pi^N\tilde{H}'_i(\infty)^{\nu+1}$. The fact that it contains $\Pi^N\tilde{H}'_i(\infty)^{\nu+2}$ is a consequence of the first part of Lemma (3.4). It is clear by $\tilde{\lambda}'_i(\xi)(x'_j) = x'_j + \xi_j (1 \leqq j \leqq N)$, that $\tilde{\lambda}'_i$ is injective. The fact that $\tilde{\lambda}'_i(G_\nu)$ is a subgroup is an immediate consequence of the Lemmas (3.8), (3.9) and (3.10). (c) is clear from $G^*_\mu = G^*_\nu \cap \mathrm{Aut}_\mu$, because Aut_ν is obviously a normal subgroup of Aut_ν.
Q.E.D.

Proposition (3.12). View G_ν as an additive group as it is a submodule of $\Pi^N \tilde{H}'_i(\infty)^{\nu+1}$, and let $G^*_\nu = \tilde{\lambda}'_i(G_\nu)$ be the subgroup (multiplicative) of Aut_ν. Then we have:

A. For $\xi \in G_\nu$ and $\eta \in G_\mu$ with $\nu \geqq 2$ and $\mu \geqq 2$, $\tilde{\lambda}'_i(\xi + \eta)^{-1} \circ \tilde{\lambda}'_i(\eta) \circ \tilde{\lambda}'_i(\xi) \in G^*_{\nu+\mu-2}$.
B. $\tilde{\lambda}'_i$ induces a set-theoretical map from the factor group G_ν/G_μ to the factor group G^*_ν/G^*_μ for every $\mu \geqq \nu \geqq 2$ (not necessarily a group homomorphism), which sends the identity and the only identity into the identity.
C. The map of (B) is bijective for $\mu \geqq \nu \geqq 3$.
D. The map of (B) is an isomorphism of groups for $2(\nu - 1) \geqq \mu \geqq \nu \geqq 2$.

Proof. By Lemma (3.9), $\tilde{\lambda}'_i(\eta)(\xi) \equiv \xi \mod \Pi^N \tilde{H}'_i(\infty)^{\nu+\mu}$. Let $\beta = \tilde{\lambda}'_i(\eta)(\xi) - \xi$. Then $\tilde{\lambda}'_i(\xi + \eta)$ is an automorphism of $\tilde{A}'_i(\infty)$ which induces the identity in $\tilde{A}'_i(\infty)/\tilde{H}'_i(\infty)$, so that it maps $\tilde{H}'_i(\infty)^{\nu+\mu}$ onto itself. Hence there exists $\gamma \in \Pi^N \tilde{H}'_i(\infty)^{\nu+\mu}$ such that $\beta = \tilde{\lambda}'_i(\xi + \eta)(\gamma)$. In view of Lemma (3.8), $\tilde{\lambda}'_i(\eta) \circ \tilde{\lambda}'_i(\xi) = \tilde{\lambda}'_i(\eta + \tilde{\lambda}'_i(\eta)(\xi)) = \tilde{\lambda}'_i(\eta + \xi + \beta) = \tilde{\lambda}'_i(\eta + \xi + \tilde{\lambda}'_i(\eta + \xi)(\gamma)) = \tilde{\lambda}'_i(\xi + \eta) \circ \tilde{\lambda}'_i(\gamma)$. Hence $\tilde{\lambda}'_i(\xi + \eta)^{-1} \circ \tilde{\lambda}'_i(\eta) \circ \tilde{\lambda}'_i(\xi) = \tilde{\lambda}'_i(\gamma) \in G^*_{\nu+\mu-2}$, because $\gamma \in \Pi^N \tilde{H}'_i(\infty)^{\mu+\nu} \subset G_{\nu+\mu-2}$. Hence (A). Since G^*_μ is a normal subgroup of G^*_ν and it contains $G^*_{\nu+\mu-2}$, we get $\tilde{\lambda}'_i(\xi + \eta)^{-1} \circ \tilde{\lambda}'_i(\xi) \in G^*_\mu$ for every $\xi \in G_\nu$ and $\eta \in G_\mu$ as above. Hence $\tilde{\lambda}'_i$ maps each coset modulo G_μ into a coset modulo G^*_μ, so that (B). To prove (C), take any $\xi \in G_\nu$ and $\eta \in G_\nu$. Let $\zeta = \xi - \eta \in G_\nu$. Let a be the largest integer such that $\zeta \in G_a$. I want to prove that if $\tilde{\lambda}'_i(\xi) \equiv \tilde{\lambda}'_i(\eta) \mod G^*_\mu$ then $\xi \equiv \eta \mod G_\mu$, that is, $a \geqq \mu$. Suppose $a < \mu$. $\tilde{\lambda}'_i(\xi)^{-1} \circ \tilde{\lambda}'_i(\eta) \circ \tilde{\lambda}'_i(\zeta) \equiv \tilde{\lambda}'_i(\zeta) \mod G^*_\mu$, by assumption, and also $\equiv$ the identity $\mod G^*_{\nu+a-2}$ by the preceding result. Since $\nu \geqq 3$, $\nu + a - 2 \geqq a + 1$. Hence $\tilde{\lambda}'_i(\zeta) \in G^*_{a+1}$. But $\tilde{\lambda}'_i$ is bijective as $G_\mu \to G^*_\nu$ and $G^*_{a+1} = \tilde{\lambda}'_i(G_{a+1})$. Hence $\zeta \in G_{a+1}$, which contradicts the choice of a. (D) is immediate from the congruence of (A) and the bijectivity of (C). Q.E.D.

Lemma (3.12). Let $\bar{A}$ be any Λ-algebra and $\bar{T}$ an ideal in $\bar{A}$ such that $\bigcap_{\nu=1}^{\infty} \bar{T}^\nu = (0)$. Let ρ and ρ' be two homomorphisms of Λ-algebras from A to $\bar{A}$ which map the ideal T into $\bar{T}$. If ρ and ρ' induce the same homomorphism from $\Lambda[x]$ to $\bar{A}$, where (x) is the chosen base of T, then $\rho = \rho'$.

Proof. For every $\xi \in A$ and for every positive integer ν, there exists $\xi_\nu \in \Lambda[x]$ such that $\xi - \xi_\nu \in T^\nu$. Therefore, $\rho(\xi) - \rho'(\xi) =$

$\rho(\xi - \xi_\nu) + \rho(\xi_\nu) - \rho'(\xi - \xi_\nu) - \rho'(\xi_\nu) = \rho(\xi - \xi_\nu) - \rho'(\xi - \xi_\nu) \in \bar{T}^\nu$. Hence $\rho(\xi) - \rho'(\xi) \in \bigcap_{\nu=1}^{\infty} \bar{T}^\nu = (0)$. Hence $\rho(\xi) = \rho'(\xi)$.

Q.E.D.

Remark (3.13). Let us recall that $\tilde{A}_i'(\infty)$ is obtained as the $\tilde{H}_i'$-adic completion of $\tilde{A}_i'$ and that $\tilde{A}_i'$ is obtained as the localization of $\tilde{A}_i = A[e_0/e_i, \ldots, e_\alpha/e_i]$ by the powers of an element $d \in \tilde{A}_i$, where $(e_0, \ldots, e_\alpha)$ is a base of the given ideal E in A. Let $\bar{T}_i'(\infty) = T\tilde{A}_i'(\infty)$. In general, $\bigcap_{\nu=1}^{\infty} \bar{T}_i'(\infty)^\nu$ is not a zero ideal. However, I claim that *there exists an element* $\delta \in T\tilde{A}_i'$ *such that if* $\tilde{A}_i''$ *is the localization of* $\tilde{A}_i'$ *by the powers of* $1 + \delta$, *if* $\tilde{A}_i''(\infty)$ *is the* $(\tilde{H}_i'\tilde{A}_i'')$-*adic completion of* $\tilde{A}_i''$ *and if* $\bar{T}_i''(\infty) = T\tilde{A}_i''(\infty)$, *then* $\bigcap_{\nu=1}^{\infty} \bar{T}_i''(\infty)^\nu = (0)$. This fact follows easily from the following two lemmas; namely, I apply the first lemma to $B = \tilde{A}_i'$ and $I = \tilde{H}_i'$, and the second lemma to $B = \tilde{A}_i''$, $S = T\tilde{A}_i''$ and $I = \tilde{H}_i'\tilde{A}_i''$.

Lemma (3.13,1). Let B be a noetherian ring, and I an ideal in B. Then there exists only a finite number of prime ideals which are associated prime ideals of some positive power of I.

Proof. It suffices to show that if $L = B/I \oplus I/I^2 \oplus \ldots$ (the associated graded algebra of B with respect to the powers of I), then for every associated prime ideal P of a positive power I^ν there exists at least one associated prime ideal of zero in L whose homogeneous part of degree zero is equal to P/I. In fact, the finiteness of the Lemma (3.13,1) follows from the noetherian property of the ring L. Now, to prove the fact above, take any such prime ideal P in B. Let $\Delta = B - P$. By then replacing B by $\Delta^{-1}B$ and accordingly the others, I may assume that P is the maximal ideal of B. Then the assumption on P implies that every element of P is a zero divisor in L. Namely, every element of the ideal PL is a zero divisor in L. Hence there exists an associated prime ideal of zero in L which contains PL. Clearly, $P(B/I)$ $(= P/I)$ is the homogeneous part of degree zero of this prime ideal in L. Q.E.D.

Lemma (3.13,2). Let B be a noetherian ring, S an ideal in B, and I an ideal in B which is contained in S. If any associated prime ideal of any positive power of I does not contain any element of $1 + S$, then for the I-adic completion $B(\infty)$ of B, $\bigcap_{\nu=1}^{\infty} S^\nu B(\infty) = (0)$.

Proof. Let $B' = (1 + S)^{-1}B$, and $I' = IB'$. Then the assumption on the powers of I implies that $I'^\nu \cap B = I^\nu$ for all positive integers ν.

Therefore, the canonical homomorphism $B(\infty) \to B'(\infty)$ is injective, where $B'(\infty)$ = the I'-adic completion of B'. It is easy to prove that $(1 + SB')^{-1} \subseteqq B'$, and then that $(1 + SB'(\infty))^{-1} \subseteqq B'(\infty)$. Since $B'(\infty)$ is noetherian, this implies that $\bigcap_{\nu=1}^{\infty} S^{\nu}B'(\infty) = (0)$. Since $S^{\nu}B(\infty) \subset S^{\nu}B'(\infty)$ as $B(\infty)$ may be identified with its isomorphic image in $B'(\infty)$, we get $\bigcap_{\nu=1}^{\infty} S^{\nu}B(\infty) = (0)$. Q.E.D.

Finally, let me point out that, for the proof of Remark (3.13), I choose $\delta_{\alpha} \in T\tilde{A}_i'$ such that $1 + \delta_{\alpha} \in P_{\alpha}$, for each prime ideal P_{α} in $\tilde{A}_i'$ which is an associated prime ideal of some positive power of $\tilde{H}_i'$ and which has nonempty intersection with the set $1 + T\tilde{A}_i'$. Then let $\delta = \Pi_{\alpha}(1 + \delta_{\alpha}) - 1$. It is then easy to see that this δ has the required property in the assertion of Remark (3.13).

Lemma (3.14). Assume that $\bigcap_{\mu=1}^{\infty} \tilde{T}_i'(\infty)^{\mu} = (0)$ for $\tilde{T}_i'(\infty) = T\tilde{A}_i'(\infty)$. Then we have $G_{\nu}^* = \mathrm{Aut}_{\nu}$, or equivalently, $\tilde{\lambda}_i' : G_{\nu}(\tilde{A}_i'(\infty)) \to \mathrm{Aut}_{\nu}(\tilde{A}_i'(\infty))$ is bijective, where $\nu \geqq 2$ [cf. Proposition (3.11)].

Proof. We know that $\tilde{\lambda}_i'$ is injective. We want to prove that if $\rho \in \mathrm{Aut}_{\nu}(\tilde{A}_i'(\infty))$ then there exists $(\xi) \in G_{\nu}(\tilde{A}_i'(\infty))$ such that $\rho = \tilde{\lambda}_i'(\xi)$. In fact, define $(\xi) = (\xi_1, \ldots, \xi_N)$ by $\rho(x_j') = x_j' + \xi_j$ for $1 \leqq j \leqq N$, where (x) is the chosen base of T and x_j' denotes the canonical image of x_j in $\tilde{A}_i'(\infty)$. Then ρ and $\tilde{\lambda}_i'(\xi)$ induce the same homomorphism of Λ-algebras $\Lambda[x] \to \tilde{A}_i'(\infty)$. Hence, by Lemma (3.12), the assumption on $\tilde{T}_i'(\infty)$ implies that P and $\tilde{\lambda}_i'(\xi)$ induce the same $A \to \tilde{A}_i'(\infty)$, so that by Lemma (3.4), they must coincide. $(\xi) \in G_{\nu}(\tilde{A}_i'(\infty))$ is automatic. Q.E.D.

Lemma (3.15). Let G_{ν} be the $\tilde{A}_i'(\infty)$-submodule of $\Pi^N \tilde{H}_i'(\infty)^{\nu+1}$ defined in Proposition (3.11) for all $\nu \geqq 2$. Then there exists an integer ν_0 such that $\tilde{H}_i'(\infty)^{\mu} G_{\nu} = G_{\nu+\mu}$ for all $\nu \geqq \nu_0$ and $\mu \geqq 0$.

Proof. Let $D = \oplus_{\nu=0}^{\infty} \tilde{H}_i'(\infty)^{\nu}$, the graded $\tilde{A}_i'(\infty)$-algebra. ($\tilde{H}_i'(\infty)^0 = \tilde{A}_i'(\infty)$.) Then D is noetherian. Let $\Delta_{p,q}^{(j)} \in A (1 \leqq j \leqq N, 1 \leqq p, q \leqq \alpha)$ be the same as in Lemma (3.4), and define the homomorphism of D-modules $\Delta : \Pi^N D \to \Pi^{(\alpha+1)^2} D$ by sending $d = (d_1, \ldots, d_N) \in \Pi^N D$ into $\Delta(d)_{p,q} = \Sigma_{j=1}^{N} \Delta_{p,q}^{(j)} d_j$, where $0 \leqq p, q \leqq \alpha$. View $\Pi^{(\alpha+1)^2} D$ as D-module in an obvious manner, and consider the submodule $E^2 \Pi^{(\alpha+1)^2} D$ of $\Pi^{(\alpha+1)^2} D$. Then clearly $\Delta^{-1}(E^2 \Pi^{(\alpha+1)^2} D)$ is a D-submodule of $\Pi^N D$, which is *of finite type*. Then G_{ν} is the homogeneous part of degree ν of this D-module $\Delta^{-1}(E^2 \Pi^{(\alpha+1)^2} D)$ by Lemma (3.4) and Proposition (3.11). Lemma (3.15) follows. Q.E.D.

Let us now recall the notations $\pi : Z \to Y$, $\epsilon : Y \to Z$, $p : \tilde{Z} \to Z$, $\tilde{\boldsymbol{H}} \subset \boldsymbol{O}_{\tilde{Z}}$, $\tilde{Z}(\nu)$, $\tilde{Z}(\infty)$, $\tilde{\boldsymbol{H}}(\infty) \subset \boldsymbol{O}_{\tilde{Z}(\infty)}$, which are defined in the beginning of this section. (Recall the assumption (3.1) and the selections of E and $\tilde{\boldsymbol{H}}$.) Let $c : \tilde{Z}(\infty) \to \tilde{Z}$ be the canonical morphism of the $\tilde{\boldsymbol{H}}$-adic completion. Let $q : \tilde{Z}(\infty) \to Z$ be the composition $p \circ c$. I shall denote by $\mathrm{Aut}_\nu(\tilde{Z}(\infty))$ the sheaf of those automorphism of $\tilde{Z}(\infty)$ which induce the identity automorphism in $\tilde{Z}(\nu)$, where ν is any nonnegative integer. Let $\tilde{Y} = q^{-1}(\epsilon(Y))$, a subscheme of $\tilde{Z}(\infty)$, which is canonically isomorphic to the subscheme $p^{-1}(\epsilon(Y))$ of $\tilde{Z}$. We are now ready to state (and prove) the following:

Theorem (3.16). The notation and the assumption being as above, there exists an injective map of sheaves of sets $\tilde{\lambda} : \Pi^N \tilde{\boldsymbol{H}}(\infty)^3 \to \mathrm{Aut}_0(\tilde{Z}(\infty))$ such that:

a. Let $\boldsymbol{G}_\nu = \tilde{\lambda}^{-1}(\mathrm{Aut}_\nu(\tilde{Z}(\infty))$ for each integer $\nu \geqq 2$; then $\boldsymbol{G}_\nu$ is a coherent subsheaf of $O_{\tilde{Z}(\infty)}$-modules of $\Pi^N \tilde{\boldsymbol{H}}(\infty)^{\nu+1}$ and contains $\Pi^N \tilde{\boldsymbol{H}}(\infty)^{\nu+2}$.

b. $\tilde{\boldsymbol{H}}(\infty)^\mu \boldsymbol{G}_\nu \subseteqq \boldsymbol{G}_{\mu+\nu}$ for all (ν, μ) with $\nu \geqq 2$ and $\mu \geqq 0$, and the equality holds for all μ if ν is greater than a certain number.

c. Let $\boldsymbol{G}_\nu^* = \tilde{\lambda}(\boldsymbol{G}_\nu)$; then $\boldsymbol{G}_\nu^*$ is a sheaf of subgroups of $\mathrm{Aut}_\nu(\tilde{Z}(\infty))$ for every $\nu \geqq 2$, and $\boldsymbol{G}_\mu^*$ is a sheaf of normal subgroups of $\boldsymbol{G}_\nu^*$ for every $\mu \geqq \nu \geqq 2$.

d. For each $\nu \geqq 2$, let us view $\boldsymbol{G}_\nu$ (resp. $\boldsymbol{G}_\nu^*$) as sheaves of topological groups by means of the sheaves of normal subgroups $\{\boldsymbol{G}_{\nu+\mu}\}$ (resp. $\boldsymbol{G}_{\nu+\mu}^*$) for all nonnegative integers μ; then $\tilde{\lambda} : \boldsymbol{G}_\nu \to \boldsymbol{G}_\nu^*$ is an isomorphism of sheaves of topological sets (not as topological groups).

e. $\tilde{\lambda}$ induces a homomorphism of sheaves of sets: $\boldsymbol{G}_\nu / \boldsymbol{G}_\mu \to \boldsymbol{G}_\nu^* / \boldsymbol{G}_\mu^*$ for all $\mu \geqq \nu \geqq 2$, which is bijective for $\mu \geqq \nu \geqq 3$ and which is an isomorphism of sheaves of groups for $\nu \leqq \mu \leqq 2(\nu - 1)$; here the group structure (additive) in $\boldsymbol{G}_\nu / \boldsymbol{G}_\mu$ is induced from $\Pi^N \tilde{\boldsymbol{H}}(\infty)^{\nu+1}$ and the one (multiplicative) in $\boldsymbol{G}_\nu^* / \boldsymbol{G}_\mu^*$ from $\mathrm{Aut}_\nu(\tilde{Z}(\infty))$.

f. $\boldsymbol{G}_\nu^*$ and $\mathrm{Aut}_\nu(\tilde{Z}(\infty))$ have the same restriction to the closed subspace $\tilde{Y}$ of $\tilde{Z}(\infty)$, or equivalently, $\tilde{\lambda}$ induces a bijective map from the stalk of $\boldsymbol{G}_\nu$ to that of $\mathrm{Aut}_\nu(\tilde{Z}(\infty))$ at every point of the subscheme $\tilde{Y}$ of $\tilde{Z}(\infty)$.

Proof. Recall those elements $\Delta_{p,q}^{(j)} \in A$ for $1 \leqq j \leqq N$ and $0 \leqq p$, $q \leqq \alpha$ in (3.5) [or, Lemma (3.4)]. Get a homomorphism of $\boldsymbol{O}_{\tilde{Z}(\infty)}$-

modules $\Delta : \Pi^N \tilde{\boldsymbol{H}}(\infty)^{\nu+1} \to \Pi^{(\alpha+1)^2}\tilde{\boldsymbol{H}}(\infty)^{\nu+1}$, defined by $\Delta(\xi) = (\ldots, \Sigma_j \Delta^{(j)}_{p,q}\xi_j, \ldots)$. Then $\boldsymbol{G}_\nu = \Delta^{-1}(\Pi^{(\alpha+1)^2}\tilde{E}(\infty)^2\tilde{\boldsymbol{H}}(\infty)^{\nu+1})$, where $\tilde{E}(\infty)$ is the ideal sheaf on $\tilde{Z}(\infty)$ generated by the ideal E in A. Clearly, $\boldsymbol{G}_\nu$ is a coherent subsheaf of $\boldsymbol{O}_{\tilde{Z}(\infty)}$-modules of $\Pi^N\tilde{\boldsymbol{H}}(\infty)^{\nu+1}$. (Check that only coherent sheaves are involved in the construction.) Over the formal affine subscheme $\mathrm{Spf}(\tilde{A}'_i(\infty))$ of $\tilde{Z}(\infty)$, the $\tilde{A}'_i(\infty)$-module of sections of $\boldsymbol{G}_\nu$ is equal to $G_\nu(\tilde{A}'_i(\infty))$ of Propositions (3.11) and (3.12). Note that $\{\mathrm{Spf}(\tilde{A}'_i(\infty))\}$ for all possible choices of $\tilde{A}'_i$ form a base of topology in $\tilde{Z}(\infty)$. Hence the injective mappings $\tilde{\lambda}'_i : G_\nu(\tilde{A}'_i(\infty)) \to \mathrm{Aut}_\nu(\tilde{A}'_i(\infty))$ in Proposition (3.11) defines an injective mapping of the sheaves: $\boldsymbol{G}_\nu \to \mathrm{Aut}_\nu(\tilde{Z}(\infty))$, which are viewed as sheaves of sets in a canonical manner [(b) of Proposition (3.11)]. Then (c), (d) and (e) of Theorem 3.16 follow by Propositions (3.11) and (3.12); also (b) of this theorem follows by Lemma (3.15); finally, (f) of the theorem is proven as follows. As was seen in Remark (3.13), for each $\tilde{A}'_i$, we can choose $\delta \in T\tilde{A}'_i$ so that if d is replaced by $d^n(1 + \delta)$ in the definition of $\tilde{A}'_i$ (here, n is a positive integer so large that $d^n(1 + \delta)$ is the canonical image of some element of $\tilde{A}_i$) then $\bigcap_{\mu=1}^{\infty} \tilde{T}'_i(\infty)^\mu = (0)$. Notice that $\tilde{Y}$ is the subscheme of $\tilde{Z}(\infty)$ defined by the ideals $\tilde{T}'_i(\infty)$ (or, the ideal sheaf generated by T). Therefore, the above replacement of d by $d^n(1 + \delta)$ does not change the intersection $\tilde{Y} \cap \mathrm{Spf}(\tilde{A}'_i(\infty))$. It is now easily seen that Lemma (3.14) suffices for (f) of the Theorem 3.16.

Q.E.D.

Remark (3.17). The sheaf $\boldsymbol{G}_\nu$ and the mapping $\tilde{\lambda} : \boldsymbol{G}_\nu \to \mathrm{Aut}_\nu(\tilde{Z}(\infty))$ are not canonical. They depend upon the choice of the base $(x) = (x_1, \ldots, x_N)$ of the ideal T in A. We know that (x) gives rise to a system of N Hasse differentiations $d = (d^{(1)}, \ldots, d^{(N)})$ of the Λ-algebra A in the sense of Remark (1.10) and its proof. *We can prove that* $\boldsymbol{G}_\nu$ and $\tilde{\lambda}$ *are canonical up to the choice of such d; namely, for every open subset* $\tilde{U}$ *of* $\tilde{Z}(\infty)$, *say affine, the system* $d = (d^{(1)}, \ldots, d^{(N)})$ *extends, when multiplied by elements of* $\Gamma(\tilde{U}, \tilde{\boldsymbol{H}}(\infty)^3)$, *canonically to a system of N (continuous) differentiations of the* Λ*-algebra* $\Gamma(\tilde{U}, \boldsymbol{O}_{\tilde{Z}(\infty)})$ *and the mapping* $\tilde{\lambda}$ *is such that for*

$$\xi = (\xi_1, \ldots, \xi_N) \in \Gamma(\tilde{U}, \Pi^N\tilde{\boldsymbol{H}}(\infty)^{\nu+1}),$$

say $\nu \geqq 2$, *the automorphism* $\tilde{\lambda}(\xi)$ *transforms* $h \in \Gamma(\tilde{U}, \boldsymbol{O}_{\tilde{Z}(\infty)})$ *to* $\Sigma_{(i)} d^{(1)}_{i_1} d^{(2)}_{i_2} \ldots d^{(N)}_{i_N}(h)\xi_1^{i_1}\xi_2^{i_2} \ldots \xi_N^{i_N}$, *where* (i) *runs through the set of all N-tuples of non-negative integers and each Hasse differentiation* $d^{(p)}$ *is expressed as a sequence* $(d_0^{(p)}, d_1^{(p)}, d_2^{(p)}, \ldots)$ [cf. Remark (1.14), §1].

Remark (1.15). Let (A', T') be a pair of a noetherian Λ'-algebra and an ideal T' in A' which satisfies the condition (T). Suppose (A', T') is an extension of (A, T) in the sense *that there are given homomorphisms of rings* $\alpha : \Lambda \to \Lambda'$ and $\beta : A \to A'$, *which are compatible with the algebra structures of* A *and* A' *over* Λ *and* Λ', *respectively, and such that* $T' = \beta(T)A'$. Let us also assume *that the base* $(x) = (x_1, \ldots, x_N)$ *of* T *is transformed by* β *into a base* $(x') = (x'_1, \ldots, x'_N)$ *of the ideal* T' *which has the property* (T.3) *of Definition* (1.1), §1, *and that* A' *is* A*-flat.*

Then, E being the chosen ideal in A as above, let us take $E' = EA'$. By this E', let us define a birational blowing-up $p' : \tilde{Z}' \to Z' = \mathrm{Spec}(A')$ in the same way as we did $p : \tilde{Z} \to Z = \mathrm{Spec}(A)$ by E. Then there exists a canonical morphism $\gamma : \tilde{Z}' \to \tilde{Z}$, compatible with the morphism $Z' \to Z$ induced by β. By means of this γ, $\tilde{\boldsymbol{H}}$ generates an ideal sheaf $\tilde{\boldsymbol{H}}'$ on $\tilde{Z}'$. Let $\tilde{Z}'(\infty)$ be the $\tilde{\boldsymbol{H}}'$-adic completion of $\tilde{Z}'$ and $\gamma(\infty) : \tilde{Z}'(\infty) \to \tilde{Z}(\infty)$ be the completion of the morphism γ. The theorem (3.16) applies to $(\tilde{Z}'(\infty), \tilde{\boldsymbol{H}}'(\infty)$, etc.) in the same way as to $(\tilde{Z}(\infty), \tilde{\boldsymbol{H}}(\infty)$, etc.), and the base (x') gives rise to a bijective map $\tilde{\lambda}' : \Pi^N \tilde{\boldsymbol{H}}'(\infty)^3 \to \mathrm{Aut}_0(\tilde{Z}'(\infty))$ in the same way as (x) did to $\tilde{\lambda} : \Pi^N \tilde{\boldsymbol{H}}(\infty)^3 \to \mathrm{Aut}_0(\tilde{Z}(\infty))$. Let us define the coherent subsheaf $\boldsymbol{G}'_\nu$ of $\Pi^N \tilde{\boldsymbol{H}}'(\infty)^{\nu+1}$ by $\tilde{\lambda}'$, in the same way as we did $\boldsymbol{G}_\nu$ of $\Pi^N \tilde{\boldsymbol{H}}(\infty)^{\nu+1}$ by $\tilde{\lambda}$. *Then I claim that* $\boldsymbol{G}'_\nu$ *is the sheaf of* $\boldsymbol{O}_{\tilde{Z}'(\infty)}$*-submodules of* $\Pi^N \tilde{\boldsymbol{H}}'(\infty)^{\nu+1}$ *generated by the image of* $\boldsymbol{G}_\nu$ *by the canonical homomorphism* $\Pi^N \tilde{\boldsymbol{H}}(\infty)^{\nu+1} \to \Pi^N \tilde{\boldsymbol{H}}'(\infty)^{\nu+1}$. In fact, since A' is flat over A, the graded A'-algebra $\oplus_{\nu=0}^{\infty} E'^{\nu}$ is canonically isomorphic to $(\oplus_{\nu=0}^{\infty} E^{\nu}) \otimes_A A'$ which is flat over the graded A-algebra $\oplus_{\nu=0}^{\infty} E^{\nu}$. Hence the morphism $\gamma : \tilde{Z}' \to \tilde{Z}$ is flat. Moreover, the completion being always flat, it follows that $\gamma(\infty) : \tilde{Z}'(\infty) \to \tilde{Z}(\infty)$ is flat.

Now, let us recall the way in which $\boldsymbol{G}_\nu$ (resp. $\boldsymbol{G}'_\nu$) is obtained. Namely, let $(e_0, e_1, \ldots, e_\alpha)$ be a base of the ideal E [and hence its image $(e'_0, e'_1, \ldots, e'_\alpha)$ is such of E']. Let us fix an arbitrary $\nu \geqq 2$. Consider $\Delta : \Pi^N \tilde{\boldsymbol{H}}(\infty)^{\nu+1} \to \Pi^{(\alpha+1)^2} \tilde{\boldsymbol{H}}(\infty)^{\nu+1}$ defined by $\Delta(\xi) = (\ldots, \Sigma_j \Delta_{p,q}^{(j)} \xi_j, \ldots)$, where $\Delta_{p,q}^{(j)} = e_q \left(\frac{\partial e_p}{\partial x_j}\right) - e_p \left(\frac{\partial e_q}{\partial x_j}\right)$. Similarly, define $\Delta' : \Pi^N \tilde{\boldsymbol{H}}'(\infty)^{\nu+1} \to \Pi^{(\alpha+1)^2} \tilde{\boldsymbol{H}}'(\infty)^{\nu+1}$ by replacing e_p by $e'_p (0 \leqq p \leqq \alpha)$ and x_j by $x'_j (1 \leqq j \leqq N)$. By the flatness of $\boldsymbol{O}_{\tilde{Z}'(\infty)}$ over $\boldsymbol{O}_{\tilde{Z}(\infty)}$, we get $\Delta' = \Delta \otimes \boldsymbol{O}_{\tilde{Z}'(\infty)}$ with the tensor product taken over $O_{\tilde{Z}(\infty)}$. Moreover, the same flatness implies that

$$(E')^2\tilde{H}'(\infty)^{\nu+1} \cong \{E^2\tilde{H}(\infty)^{\nu+1}\} \otimes O_{\tilde{Z}'(\infty)}$$

and that

$$\Delta'^{-1}\big(\Pi^{(\alpha+1)^2}(E')^2\tilde{H}'(\infty)^{\nu+1}\big)(=G'_\nu)$$
$$\cong \Delta^{-1}\big(\Pi^{(\alpha+1)^2}E^2\tilde{H}(\infty)^{\nu+1}\big) \otimes O_{\tilde{Z}'(\infty)}\big(=G_\nu \otimes O_{\tilde{Z}'(\infty)}\big),$$

where all the tensor products are taken over $O_{\tilde{Z}(\infty)}$ and the isomorphisms are canonical. The assertion on the relation between G_ν and G'_ν is now clear.

REFERENCES

I. The following references are for the purpose of helping the reader to understand the introductory paragraphs of this article well, especially Theorems A and B. For a quick account on the classical theory of singularities of plane curves, sections 2 and 4, Ch. I, of Zariski [6] are handy.The first of those two sections provides a brief survey of the detailed studies on the effects of successive quadratic transformations applied to a plane curve singularity in terms of characteristic pairs and of multiplicities of infinitely near points, which are due to Enriques and Chisini [1] (Book IV, Chs. I and II). There we find an explicit formula which relates the characteristic pairs of a singularity to the multiplicities of all infinitely near singularities. The second of the cited sections of Zariski [6] summarizes the main theorems on the topology of a singularity of an irreducible plane curve (or, to be precise, the topology of the local imbedding of a complex curve in a complex 2-space), which is completely described by the characteristic pairs. Reeve [10] contains a more extensive summary of this topic. For its details, refer to the original works: Brauner [2] and Kähler [3], which gives an explicit description of the knot and its fundamental group attached to a singularity in terms of the characteristic pairs; Burau [4] and Zariski [5], show that the characteristic pairs are extractible from the Alexander polynomial of such a knot. Zariski [5] includes the above result of Brauner and Kähler.

Chapter IV of Serre [15] is an excellent exposition of the orders of singularities of an algebraic curve in terms of their effects upon Riemann-Roch theorems. This is based upon the idea of Rosenlicht [8]. There is an explicit formula, due to Italian geometers (see Enriques-Chisini [1]), which expresses the order of singularity of a plane curve singularity in terms of the multiplicities of all the infinitely near singular points. For this, Northcott [11] and [12] are available. One may also refer to Hironaka [14]. As for the explicit relation between the order of singularity and the order of the conductor in the normalization, known as Gorenstein's formula, refer to Samuel [7], Gorenstein [9], and also Rosenlicht [8].

II. Let us now come to the main theme of this paper, that is the formal (or analytic) equivalence of singularities in higher dimensions. It was proven by Samuel [13] that every algebroid hypersurface with an isolated singularity is obtained by completion (or formalization) from an algebraic hypersurface. Theorem C and Remark (0.4) of this article generalizes the idea of Samuel [13] from hypersurfaces to complete intersections. Then a further generalization of the equivalence theorem (not including the algebraicity theorem), shown as Theorem D (and the Main Theorem), is established by creating a situation similar to that of complete intersections by means of birational blowing-ups. I presented this idea in the Zariski Seminar at Harvard during the academic year 1963–1964 before the Conference on Arithmetic Algebraic Geometry. There was another source which initiated this theory of equivalences, namely the idea of Grauert [16] which proved an equivalence theorem for complex manifolds along submanifolds with negative normal bundles. This result of Grauert can be interpreted as an equivalence theorem for isolated singularities of certain special kind, and it inspired us to propose its generalization to arbitrary isolated singularities by means of Hironaka [17]. This generalization was worked out jointly by Hironaka and Rossi [18].

1. Enriques, F., and O. Chisini, *Lezioni sulla teoria geometrica delle equazioni e delle funzioni algebriche*, Vol. II, Bologna (1918); Book IV, *Le singolarità delle curve algebriche;* Ch. I, *Le singolarità e gli sviluppi in serie de Puiseux*, and Ch. II, *Le singolarità rispetto alle transformazioni quadratiche.*
2. Brauner, K., Zur Geometrie der Funktionen zweier Veranderlichen, *Abh. math. Semin. Hamburg Univ.*, **6**(1928), 1–55; II, Das Verhalten der Functionen in der Umgebung ihrer Verzweigungsstellen; III, Klassifikationen der Singularitäten algebroider Kurven; IV, Die Verzweigungsgruppen.
3. Kähler, E., Uber die Verzweigung einer algebraischen Funktion zweier Veränderlichen in der Umgebung einer singulären Stelle, *Math. Zeit.*, **30**(1929), 188–204.
4. Burau, W., Kennzeichnung der Schlauchknotten, *Abh. math. Semin. Hamburg Univ.*, **9**(1932), 125–133.
5. Zariski, O., On the topology of algebroid singularities, *Amer. J. Math.*, **51**(1932), 453–470.

6. Zariski, O., Algebraic surfaces, *Ergeb. der Math.* Springer (1932) and also Chelsea (1948).
7. Samuel, P., Singularités des variétés algébriques, *Bull. Soc. Math. de France*, **79**(1951), 121–129.
8. Rosenlicht, M., Equivalence relations on algebraic curves, *Ann. Math.*, **56**(1952), 169–191.
9. Gorenstein, D., An arithmetic theory of adjoint plane curves, *Trans. Amer. Math. Soc.*, **72**(1952), 414–436.
10. Reeve, J. E., A summary of results in the topological classification of plane algebroid singularities, *Rend. Sem. Mat. Torino*, **14**(1954–5), 159–187.
11. Northcott, D., The neighborhoods of a local ring, *J. London Math. Soc.*, **30**(1955), 360–375.
12. Northcott, D., A note on the genus formula for plane curves, *J. London Math. Soc.*, **30**(1955), 376–382.
13. Samuel, P., Algebricité de certains points singuliers algebröides, *J. Math. Pures Appl.*, **35**(1956), 1–6.
14. Hironaka, H., On the arithmetic genera and the effective genera of algebraic curves, *Mem. Kyoto*, **30**(1957), 177–195.
15. Serre, J.-P., *Groupes algébriques et corps de classes*, Hermann, Paris (1959).
16. Grauert, H., Uber Modifikationen und exceptionelle analytische Mengen, *Math. Ann.*, **146**(1962), 331–368.
17. Hironaka, H., Resolution of singularities of an algebraic variety over a field of characteristic zero, *Ann. Math.*, **79**(1964), 109–326.
18. Hironaka, H., and H. Rossi, On the equivalence of imbeddings of exceptional complex spaces, *Math. Ann.*, **156**(1964), 313–333.